GLENCOE

EARTH SCIENCE
Geology, the Environment, and the Universe

Laboratory Manual

Teacher Edition

**Glencoe
McGraw-Hill**

New York, New York   Columbus, Ohio   Woodland Hills, California   Peoria, Illinois

A Glencoe Program

Earth Science: Geology, the Environment, and the Universe

Laboratory Manual, SE and TE

GeoLab and MiniLab Worksheets

Exploring Environmental Problems, SE and TE

Study Guide for Content Mastery, SE and TE

Chapter Assessment

Performance Assessment in Earth Science

ExamView™ Pro CD-ROM Windows/Macintosh

Cooperative Learning in the Science Classroom

Performance Assessment in the Science Classroom

Alternate Assessment in the Science Classroom

Lesson Plans

Block Scheduling Lesson Plans

Section Focus Transparencies and Masters

Teaching Transparencies and Masters

MindJogger Videoquizzes, VHS/DVD

Puzzlemaker Software, Windows/Macintosh

Guided Reading Audio Program

Interactive Teacher Edition CD-ROM

Interactive Lesson Planner CD-ROM

Using the Internet in the Science Classroom

Glencoe Science Web Site: science.glencoe.com

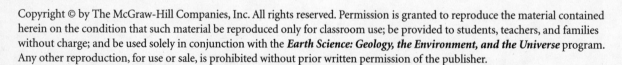

Glencoe/McGraw-Hill
A Division of The McGraw·Hill Companies

Send all inquiries to:
Glencoe/McGraw-Hill
8787 Orion Place
Columbus, OH 43240

ISBN 0-07-824568-0
Printed in the United States of America.
1 2 3 4 5 6 7 8 9 10   045   08 07 06 05 04 03 02 01

Teacher Edition

Contents

To the Teacher

Earth Science: Geology, the Environment, and the Universe, Laboratory
Manual follows the chapter sequence and reinforces concepts presented in
that text. In this Teacher Edition, the chapters of *Earth Science: Geology, the
Environment, and the Universe* that correspond to each laboratory activity
are listed in the table of contents. However, the 62 activities in the manual
are designed to be used with any high school Earth science text.

Scientific literacy, scientific principles, and scientific inquiry are developed.
Students increase their science vocabulary, learn how to handle laboratory
equipment, use modern laboratory techniques, and acquire skill in working
with tables and graphs. Scientific methods become most important
as students perform each activity, collect and record data, and form conclusions based on analysis and interpretation of experimental results. Skills
requiring proper and careful reading of experimental procedures, accurate
data collection, data interpretation, and graphing are utilized throughout
the manual.

The activities in this laboratory manual are of three types: Investigation,
Mapping, and Design Your Own. In an Investigation, students are presented
with a problem. Then, through use of scientific methods, they seek answers.
In a Mapping activity, students will use existing maps or create maps of
their own to help them solve and understand various topics in Earth science. In the Design Your Own labs, students will design their own experiments to find answers to geologic problems. These labs are similar to the
Design Your Own labs in the *Earth Science: Geology, the Environment, and
the Universe* textbook. For laboratory activities that are Calculator-Based
(CBL labs) or that utilize the Global Positioning System (GPS),
please refer to the *Exploring Environmental Problems* lab manual.

The Teacher Edition for *Earth Science: Geology, the Environment, and the
Universe,* Laboratory Manual provides general information designed to aid
you in the laboratory. Helpful teaching strategies and safety and chemical
storage and disposal guidelines are outlined. A lab-by-lab materials list has
also been included to aid you in preparing for laboratory activities.

The Teacher Edition provides a variety of helpful information about each
activity in the form of a Teacher Guide section. Teaching tips, helpful comments and suggestions, objectives, process skills, and time allotments,
as well as answers to all questions, are to be found in this section.

Safety in the Laboratory

The activities in the *Earth Science: Geology, the Environment, and the Universe,* Laboratory Manual are designed to minimize dangers in the laboratory. Careful planning and preparation as well as being aware of hazards can keep accidents to a minimum. Practice good laboratory housekeeping and management by observing these guidelines.

Personal Protection

The use of personal protection equipment is required when potentially hazardous material is present. Personal protection equipment includes eyewear, laboratory aprons, laboratory coats, and protective gloves.

Eyewear

Eyewear should meet the ANSI Standard Z87.1-*Practice for Occupational and Educational Eye and Face Protection.* Eyewear meeting this standard will bear markings such as "Z87.1" on the frames, and the lens will be marked with the manufacturer's trademark.

Safety goggles are required for science laboratory and field activities involving any hazardous chemical, which could damage the eye if the chemical splashed into the eye or rubbed onto the eye. Goggles provide eye protection from fine dusts, liquids, splashes, mists, and sprays. They also prevent splashes and sprays from body fluids or dangerous chemicals.

Safety goggles should be large enough to protect and form a seal around the eyes. If not able to seal, goggles should contain side shields to prevent contamination to the eyes.

Eye protection may also be provided with safety glasses. Safety glasses with side shields will not provide adequate protection for chemical splashes. These are designed primarily to protect the eyes from flying objects.

Protective Gloves

Gloves protect hands from heat, absorb perspiration, and provide a shield from corrosive chemicals, body fluids, and prevent the transmission of microorganisms from person to person. Always check gloves to be sure that there are no tears, punctures, or holes. When removing gloves, peel the gloves off your hand, starting at the wrists and working toward the fingers. Keep the working surface of the gloves from contact with the skin during removal.

Laboratory Aprons and Coats

Laboratory aprons and coats are designed to protect clothing and skin from splashed and spilled chemicals and biological materials. They should fit the wearer properly to provide maximum protection. A laboratory coat or apron should be worn at all times in the laboratory.

Aprons are usually listed as "bib type," which are suitable for laboratory use. Aprons should be worn over clothing that covers the arms and body.

Laboratory coats are usually fire retardant and made of cotton or paper. They are good for protection against flying objects, sharp or rough edges, splashes and spills, and fire.

Fire Protection

Fire is one of the most frequent mishaps in the science laboratory. The first line of defense from a fire is fire prevention. Effective fire prevention centers on thorough understanding of combustion and the required ingredients. As long as air is present, oxygen will be available for combustion to take place. The areas where prevention measures are best exercised are the fuel and ignition sources.

Fires are classified by the chemical properties of the fuel.

The basic classifications are grouped as follows:
- Class A – Ordinary combustible (i.e., paper, wood, etc.)
- Class B – Organic solvents (i.e., acetone, alcohols, ethers)
- Class C – Electrical wiring or static charges
- Class D – Active metals (i.e., sodium, potassium, magnesium)

These symbols are accepted for the different classifications of fire. They are applied to fire extinguishers and extinguisher locations to indicate their suitability in extinguishing the different types of fires.

Safety in the Laboratory, *continued*

The following precautions should be taken to prevent fires from occurring in the science classroom, laboratory, storage room, and preparation area.

- Be aware of ignition sources in your laboratory area (open flames, heat, and electrical equipment).
- Purchase and store flammable reagents in the smallest quantities possible.
- Do not store flammable liquids in standard refrigerators (an explosion-proof refrigerator should be used).
- Store flammable liquids in appropriate safety cabinets and/or safety cans.
- Make sure that all electrical cords are in good condition. All electrical outlets should be grounded and should accommodate a 3-pronged plug.

Each science classroom, laboratory, storage room, and preparation area should have a fire blanket and an appropriate fire extinguisher.

Fire Extinguishers

In most school environments, handheld, portable fire extinguishers are the first fire-extinguishing agent used. Therefore, a multipurpose ABC fire extinguisher must be located in each science classroom, laboratory, storage room, and preparation area. Extinguishers must be:

- Located to be easily seen and the area around them kept clear
- Inspected on a regular basis
- Used by well-trained teachers and students

Fire extinguishers are labeled in accordance with NFPA standards.

Fire Blankets

Actual fire control revolves around proper types of control devices such as a fire blanket. Fire blankets are made of specially treated fabric and should be located at strategic areas for all science laboratories where hazardous chemicals are stored and used. Fire blankets can be used if one is unable to reach the safety shower.

Safety in the Laboratory material used with permission from Texas Safety Standards, produced by the Texas Education Agency.

Chemical Storage and Disposal

General Guidelines

Be sure to store all chemicals properly. The following are guidelines commonly used. Your school, city, county, or state may have additional requirements for handling chemicals. It is the responsibility of each teacher to become informed as to what rules or guidelines are in effect in his or her area.

1. Separate chemicals by reaction type. Strong acids should be stored together. Likewise, strong bases should be stored together and should be separated from acids. Oxidants should be stored away from easily oxidized materials, and so on.

2. Be sure all chemicals are stored in labeled containers indicating contents, concentration, source, date purchased (or prepared), any precautions for handling and storage, and expiration date.

3. Dispose of any outdated or waste chemicals properly according to accepted disposal procedures.

4. Do not store chemicals above eye level.

5. Wood shelving is preferable to metal. All shelving should be firmly attached to the wall and should have antiroll edges.

6. Store only those chemicals that you plan to use.

7. Hazardous chemicals require special storage containers and conditions. Be sure to know what those chemicals are and the accepted practices for your area. Some substances must even be stored outside the building.

8. When working with chemicals or preparing solutions, observe the same general safety precautions that you would expect from students. These include wearing an apron and goggles. Wear gloves and use the fume hood when necessary. Students will want to do as you do whether they admit it or not.

9. If you are a new teacher in a particular laboratory, it is your responsibility to survey the chemicals stored there to be sure they are stored properly, or they should be disposed of. Consult the rules and laws in your area concerning what chemicals can be kept in your classroom. For disposal, consult up-to-date disposal information from the state and federal governments.

Disposal of Chemicals

Local, state, and federal laws regulate the proper disposal of chemicals. These laws should be consulted before chemical disposal is attempted. Although most substances encountered in high school laboratories can be flushed down the drain with plenty of water, it is not safe to assume that this is always true. It is recommended that teachers who use chemicals consult the following book from the National Research Council:

Prudent Practices in the Laboratory. Washington, DC: National Academy Press, 1995.

This book is useful and was revised in 1995. Current laws in your area would, of course, supersede the information in these books.

DISCLAIMER Glencoe Publishing Company makes no claims to the completeness of this discussion of laboratory safety and chemical storage. The material presented is not all-inclusive, nor does it address all of the hazards associated with handling, storage, and disposal of chemicals, or with laboratory management.

Materials List per Lab

(quanties needed for a class of 30 students)

Lab	Non-consumables	Consumables	Chemicals	Standard Equipment
1.1	Figures 2–7 in lab manual	pens or pencils (30)		
1.2	small objects (35) magnets (5) measuring tapes (5)	boxes (5) string (1 spool) bubble wrap (1 roll) newspapers (5) transparent tape (5 rolls)	modeling clay (1 container)	balances or scales (5) scissors (5)
2.1	5-gallon aquarium tanks (10) turkey basters (10) black yarn (2 skeins)	black waterproof markers (10) masking tape (1 roll) grease pencils (10) transparency paper (30 sheets) tap water	modeling clay (10 containers)	metric rulers or metersticks (10) aprons (30) safety goggles (30)
2.2		pencils (30)		calculators (30)
3.1	clear plastic tubing or distillation apparatus	tap water carnauba wax graph paper (30 sheets)		hot plates (10) ring stands (10) test-tube clamps (10) beakers (10) flasks (10) test-tube corks or stoppers (20) test tubes (20) alcohol-based thermometers (10) aprons (30) safety goggles (30) thermal mitts (30 pairs)
3.2		glass markers (10) tap water	granulated zinc, large pieces (60) granulated zinc, small pieces (240) HCl solution A (2 moles/liter) HCl solution B (1 mole/liter)	forceps (10) test tubes (60) test-tube racks (10) alcohol-based thermometers (10) beakers (10) hot plates (10) aprons (30) safety goggles (30) thermal mitts (30 pairs)
4.1	metal spatulas (10) lighters (10) table lamps (10)	glass markers (10)	solutions A–D (20 test tubes full of each solution) solutes A–D (50 grams of each solute)	test tubes (40) test-tube racks (10) small petri dishes (40) Bunsen burners (10) test-tube tongs (10) pipettes (10) microscope slides (40) compound microscopes (30) aprons (30) safety goggles (30) gloves (30 pairs) thermal mitts (30 pairs)

Materials List per Lab, *continued*

Lab	Non-consumables	Consumables	Chemicals	Standard Equipment
4.2	resources on local geology small backpacks (30) chisel-edged hammers (30) short pry bars (30) cloth or leather gloves (30 pairs) field guide to rocks and minerals porcelain tiles (30) hardness testing kit long-sleeved shirts or jackets (30)	newspapers (several) brown paper lunch bags (30) notebooks (30) masking tape (2 rolls) markers, assorted colors (30) food tap water sunscreen (1 bottle)	dilute hydrochloric acid	hand lenses (30)
5.1	igneous-rock key pictures of lunar rocks (several)		igneous rock samples (60)	
5.2			igneous rock samples (135)	
6.1		tap water (5.7 L)	chemical sedimentary rocks (45; 15 samples of each of 3 rock types) sodium chloride solution (30 test tubes) silver nitrate solution (1 test tube)	test tubes (30) test-tube racks (15) test-tube holders (30) 500-mL beakers (15) hot plates (15) droppers (15) aprons (30) safety goggles (30) gloves (30 pairs) thermal mitts (30 pairs)
6.2		colored pencils, assorted colors (300)		
7.1	plastic spoons (30)	paper towels (2 rolls) glass markers (15) ice aluminum foil (1 roll) hot water	pea-sized limestone chips (1500 grams) vinegar (6 L)	balances (15) 200-mL beakers (30) 500-mL beakers (30) 100-mL graduated cylinders (15) alcohol-based thermometers (15) gloves (30 pairs) aprons (30) safety goggles (30)
7.2				metric rulers (30)
8.1	hair dryer with cool heat setting	cardboard boxes (30 cm $\times$ 60 cm $\times$ 10 cm) (10) cardboard strips (15 cm $\times$ 5 cm) (10) twigs (40) candles (10) matches (1 box) string (1 spool)	sand (1 bag) gravel (1 bag)	400-mL beakers (10) rubber stoppers, assorted sizes (30) protractors (10) aprons (30) safety goggles (30) gloves (30 pairs) thermal mitts (30 pairs)

(continued on next page)

Materials List per Lab, *continued*

Lab	Non-consumables	Consumables	Chemicals	Standard Equipment
8.1 *(cont.)*		paper clips (10) transparent tape (1 roll)		
8.2	pan sets (10) screening sieves, sets of 4 (10 sets)	glacial till or outwash filter paper (10 filters)		balances (10) beakers (10)
9.1		markers, assorted colors (60)		metric rulers (30)
9.2				metric rulers (30)
10.1	rubber bands (40) cheesecloth (40 squares)	tap water	sand (1 bag) pebbles (several) potter's clay (5 containers) unsorted soil (1 bag)	hand lenses (10) 100-mL graduated cylinders (10) stopwatches (10) large funnels (40) 500–1000-mL beakers (40) aprons (30) safety goggles (30)
10.2	computer	white unlined paper (60 sheets)		
11.1				metric rulers (30) calculators (30)
11.2	rubber bands (5) outdoor thermometer vacuum cleaner with intake hose outdoor extension cord	coffee filters (5) masking tape (1 roll)	petroleum jelly (1 container)	microscopes (5) microscope slides (25) petri dishes with lids (25) aprons (30) safety goggles (30)
12.1	globes (15) blue chalk (15 pieces) green chalk (15 pieces) red chalk (15 pieces) yellow chalk (15 pieces)			
12.2	weather maps (10) barometer anemometer wind vane rain gauge			alcohol-based thermometers (5)
13.1	stream table water source hose large plastic sheet	wooden stick	sand (1 bag)	metric ruler aprons (30) safety goggles (30)
13.2	electric fans, each with variable speeds and a grounded/polarized plug (15)	wooden sticks (60) toothpicks (3 boxes) cardboard (15 sets of squares, assorted sizes) marshmallows (5 bags) transparent tape (15 rolls)	modeling clay (10 containers) glue (15 bottles)	scissors (15) aprons (30) safety goggles (30)

Materials List per Lab, *continued*

Lab	Non-consumables	Consumables	Chemicals	Standard Equipment

14.1	clear plastic boxes (10)
	 overhead lights with
	    reflectors (5)
		masking tape (1 roll)
		 tap water
		 colored pencils, assorted
		    colors (20; 5 sets of 4
		    different colors)
			soil (1 bag)	alcohol-based thermometers
				    (20)
				 ring stands (5)
				 stopwatches (5)
				 metric rulers (30)
				 thermal mitts (30 pairs)
				 aprons (30)
				 safety goggles (30)

14.2	world map or globe			
15.1	globe			

15.2	electric fan with
	    variable speed and a
	    grounded/polarized plug
	 overhead light with reflectors
	 clear, shallow, rectangular
	    containers (30)
		white unlined paper
		    (30 sheets)
		 tap water
				ring stands (30)
				 timers (30)
				 metric rulers (30)
				 safety goggles (30)

16.1		string (1 spool)		metric rulers (30)

16.2	stirring rods (20)	glass markers (5)
		 tap water, room temperature
		    (12 L)
		 wooden sticks (5)
		 brine-shrimp eggs (60)
		 plastic wrap (1 roll)
			noniodized salt (450 grams)	metric rulers (30)
				 100-mL graduated cylinders
				    (5)
				 alcohol-based thermometers
				    (5)
				 balances (15)
				 droppers (20)
				 petri dishes (20)
				 microscopes (5)
				 safety goggles (30)

17.1	bar magnets (10) plotting compasses (10)		iron filings	test tubes (10) test-tube stoppers (10) metersticks (10) safety goggles (30)
17.2		graph paper (60 sheets)		calculators (30)

18.1	buckets with pouring spouts
	    (6)
	 wire whisks (6)
	 coffee tins, each with a 2-cm
	    circular hole in the bot-
	    tom (6)
	 large spatulas (6)
	 wooden boards
	    (1 m × 2 m) (6)
	 wooden shims (24)
	 wooden wedges (24)
	 plumb lines (6)
		dry cake mix (6 boxes)
		 tap water
		 white unlined paper
		    (30 sheets)
		 plastic wrap (1 roll)
		 toothpicks (1 box)
		 masking tape (1 roll)
				protractors (6)
				 stopwatches (6)
				 metric rulers (6)
				 aprons (30)
				 safety goggles (30)

Materials List per Lab, *continued*

Lab	Non-consumables	Consumables	Chemicals	Standard Equipment
18.2	Tables 1 and 2			calculators (30)
19.1	computer with internet access	fine-point pens, assorted colors (90; 15 each of 6 different colors)		
19.2	research resources about earthquakes overhead projector	poster boards (6) drawing supplies printer paper		
20.1		blue markers (30) orange markers (30) red markers (30)		
20.2	map D from Lab 20.1	markers, assorted colors (240; 30 each of 8 different colors)		
21.1	seashells (10) plastic spoons (20) paper cups (40) freezer	plaster of paris (1 bag) tap water (2 gallons) food coloring (1 bottle) grapes (20) marking pens (10) dead, hard-bodied insects (such as beetles or ants) (10) waxed paper (10 pieces)	petroleum jelly (1 jar) glue (1 bottle)	aprons (30) safety goggles (30) gloves (30 pairs)
21.2	microfossil samples (representations from the present to 160 000 years ago) (10 sets)			calculators (30)
22.1		pencils (30) paper roll (75 m)		calculators (30) metersticks (30)
22.2	geologic time scale event cards (30)			
23.1	fossil cards or models (30)	blue pencils (30) yellow pencils (30) green pencils (30)		
23.2		colored pencils, assorted colors (60; 30 pairs of 2 different colors)		
24.1	political map of North America	colored pencils or fine-point colored markers, assorted colors (300; 30 each of 10 different colors)		
24.2	index-fossil chart	colored pencils, assorted colors (60)		

Materials List per Lab, *continued*

Lab	Non-consumables	Consumables	Chemicals	Standard Equipment
25.1	stirring rods (30) measuring spoons (30) pH color charts (15)	distilled water (8 L) marking pens (15) plastic wrap (1 roll) pH paper (75 strips)	powdered limestone (1 bottle) white vinegar (1 bottle) baking soda (1 box)	250-mL beakers (30) droppers (15) aprons (30) safety goggles (30) gloves (30 pairs)
25.2				calculators (30)
26.1	black plastic tubing (18 m) clothespins (6)	tap water shallow cardboard boxes (30 cm × 40 cm) (6) black construction paper (50 sheets) plastic wrap (1 roll) insulating materials transparent tape (6 rolls) 2-L plastic bottles (12)		scissors (6) alcohol-based thermometers (6) safety goggles (30)
26.2	small plastic balls (30) heavy-duty sewing needles (30)	white unlined paper (30 sheets) transparent tape (1 roll) large, flat cardboard pieces (5) marking pens (30) heavy thread (2 spools)		scissors (30) calculators (30)
27.1	shallow pans (10)	paper towels (1 roll) tap water toothpicks (1 box) feathers (60) string (1 spool) cotton balls (90) cardboard, small pieces (10) sponges (10)	olive oil (2 bottles) liquid detergent (1 bottle) gravel (1 bag)	droppers (10) aprons (30) safety goggles (30) gloves (30 pairs)
27.2	1-L glass jars with lids (60)	distilled water (30 L) pond water (15 L) marking pens (15)	liquid fertilizer (150 mL)	100-mL graduated cylinders (15) microscopes (3) microscope slides (60) coverslips (60) droppers (15) aprons (30) splash-resistant safety goggles (30) gloves (30 pairs)
28.1	bathroom scale			calculators (30)
28.2	15-cm glass tubes, fire pol- ished and taped (10) plastic-foam balls (10) metal washers (400)	duct tape (3 rolls) fishing line paper clips (1 package) marking pens (10)		scissors (10) metric rulers (10) stopwatches (10) calculators (10)

Materials List per Lab, *continued*

Lab	Non-consumables	Consumables	Chemicals	Standard Equipment
29.1	lenses with long focal lengths, sets of 3 (10 sets) lenses with short focal lengths, sets of 3 (10 sets) lenses with identical focal lengths and different diameters, sets of 3 (10 sets) screens (10) screen holders (10) foam lens holders (20)	nested cardboard tubes (20)		ring stands (10) burette clamps (10) metersticks (10) lens holders (20) safety goggles (30)
29.2	plumb lines with weights, 2 m or 3 m (2) stepladders (2) simple ladder rope map compass with crosshairs			stopwatch calculators (30) safety goggles (30)
30.1	straight pins (10) single-edge razor blades (10) clipboards (10) small telescopes (10) small telescope stands (10)	index cards (20) transparent tape (10 rolls) aluminum foil (1 roll) white unlined paper (10 sheets)		metersticks (10) scissors (10) safety goggles (30)
30.2	stiff, thin wire (1 m) small weights (10) binoculars (10)	tracing paper (10 sheets)		protractors, each with a hole at the origin (10) safety goggles (30)
31.1	teaspoons (15) buckets (15)	tap water (3 L) powdered nondairy creamer (1 container)	cooking oil (1 bottle) rock samples, assorted small (15)	250-mL beakers (15) aprons (30) safety goggles (30)
31.2	heavy needles (10)	cardboard pieces (30 cm × 20 cm) (10) fishing line or thread (40 m)	modeling clay (10 containers)	metric rulers (10) scissors (10)

Suppliers

Equipment Suppliers

American Science & Surplus
3605 Howard St.
Skokie, IL 60076
(847) 982-0874

Bio-Rad Laboratories
2000 Alfred Nobel Dr.
Life Science Group
Hercules, CA 94547
(800) 876-3425
ron_mardigian@bio-rad.com

Carolina Biological Supply Co.
2700 York Road
Burlington, NC 27215
(800) 334-5551
www.carolina.com

Edmund Scientific Company
60 Pierce Avenue
Tonawanda, NY 14150
(800) 728-6999
scientifics@edsci.com

Fisher Science Education
Educational Materials Division
485 S. Frontage Rd.
Burr Ridge, IL 60521
(800) 955-1177
www.fisheredu.com

Nasco Science
901 Janesville Avenue
P.O. Box 901
Fort Atkinson, WI 53538-0901
(800) 558-9595
www.enasco.com

Nebraska Scientific
3823 Leavenworth St.
Omaha, NE 68105-1180
(800) 228-7117
nescientif@aol.com

PASCO Scientific
10101 Foothills Blvd.
P.O. Box 619011
Roseville, CA 95747
(800) 772-8700
sales@pasco.com

Sargent-Welch/VWR Scientific
Products
P.O. Box 5229
Buffalo Grove, IL 60089-5229
(800) SAR-GENT
www.SargentWelch.com

Ward's Natural Science Est.
5100 W. Henrietta Road,
P.O. Box 92912
Rochester, NY 14692-9012
(800) 962-2660
www.wardsci.com

Audiovisual Distributors

Bullfrog Films
P.O. Box 149
Oley, PA 19547
(800) 543-FROG
www.bullfrogfilms.com

Coronet/MTI Film & Video
2349 Chaffee Dr.
St Louis, MO 63146
(800) 221-1274
bfaeduc@worldnet.att.net

Discovery Channel Education/TLC
7700 Wisconsin Avenue
Bethesda, MD 20814
(301) 986-0444
www.school.discovery.com

Films for the Humanities and
Sciences
P.O. Box 2053
Princeton, NJ 08543
(800) 257-5126

Flinn Scientific
P.O. Box 219
770 N. Raddant Rd.
Batavia, IL 60510
(800) 452-1261
www.flinnsci.com

Frey Scientific, Div. of
Beckley Cardy
100 Paragon Parkway
Mansfield, OH 44901
(800) 235-3739

Media Design Associates
1093 Albion Rd.
P.O. Box 3189
Boulder, CO 80307-3189
(800) 228-8854
www.indra.com/mediades

National Geographic Society
Educational Services
1145 17th Street, N.W.
Washington, DC 20036
(800) 368-2728

Optical Data School Media
512 Means St., N.W.
Atlanta, GA 30318
(800) 524-2481
www.opticaldata.com

Scholastic, Inc.
555 Broadway
New York, NY 10012-3999
(800) 325-6149
www.scholastic.com

Time Life
P.O. Box 85026
Richmond, VA 23285-5026
(800) 474-4928
www.timelife.com

Suppliers, *continued*

Videodiscovery
1700 Westlake Ave., N.
Suite 600
Seattle, WA 98109-3012
(800) 548-3472
www.videodiscovery.com

Software Distributors

Boreal Laboratories, Ltd.
399 Vansickle Rd.
St. Catharines, Ontario, L2S 3T4
Canada
(800) 387-9393
boreal@niagara.com

Cross Educational Software
508 E. Kentucky Ave.
Ruston, LA 71270
(800) 768-1969
MarkHongCross@yahoo.com

Educational Activities, Inc.
1937 Grand Ave.
Baldwin, NY 11510
(800) 645-3739
www.edact.com

IBM Global Education
4111 Northside Parkway
Atlanta, GA 30301-2150
(800) 426-4968
www.solutions.ibm.com/k12

ABC Clio
130 Cremora Drive
P.O. Box 1911
Santa Barbara, CA 93116-1911
(800) 346-8355

J. Weston Walch, Publisher
321 Valley St.
P.O. Box 658
Portland, ME 04104-0658
(800) 341-6094
www.walch.com

Scholastic, Inc.
555 Broadway
New York, NY 10012-3999
(800) 325-6149
www.scholastic.com

Science Kit and Boreal
    Laboratories
777 East Park Dr.
Tonawanda, NY 14150
(800) 828-7777
www.sciencekit.com

Sunburst Communications
101 Castleton St.
Pleasantville, NY 10570
(800) 321-7511
www.SUNBURST.com

GLENCOE

EARTH SCIENCE
Geology, the Environment, and the Universe

Laboratory Manual

Student Edition

New York, New York   Columbus, Ohio   Woodland Hills, California   Peoria, Illinois

A Glencoe Program

Earth Science: Geology, the Environment, and the Universe

Laboratory Manual, SE and TE

GeoLab and MiniLab Worksheets

Exploring Environmental Problems, SE and TE

Study Guide for Content Mastery, SE and TE

Chapter Assessment

Performance Assessment in Earth Science

ExamView™ Pro CD-ROM Windows/Macintosh

Cooperative Learning in the Science Classroom

Performance Assessment in the Science Classroom

Alternate Assessment in the Science Classroom

Lesson Plans

Block Scheduling Lesson Plans

Section Focus Transparencies and Masters

Teaching Transparencies and Masters

MindJogger Videoquizzes, VHS/DVD

Puzzlemaker Software, Windows/Macintosh

Guided Reading Audio Program

Interactive Teacher Edition CD-ROM

Interactive Lesson Planner CD-ROM

Using the Internet in the Science Classroom

Glencoe Science Web Site: science.glencoe.com

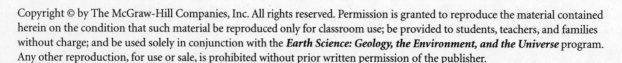

Glencoe/McGraw-Hill
A Division of The **McGraw·Hill** Companies

Send all inquiries to:
Glencoe/McGraw-Hill
8787 Orion Place
Columbus, OH 43240

ISBN 0-07-824567-2
Printed in the United States of America.
1 2 3 4 5 6 7 8 9 10   045   08 07 06 05 04 03 02 01

Contents

Contents, *continued*

Contents, *continued*

Contents, *continued*

How to Use This Laboratory Manual

Working in the laboratory throughout the course of the year can be an enjoyable part of your Earth science experience. **Earth Science: Geology, the Environment, and the Universe,** *Laboratory Manual* is a tool for making your laboratory work both worthwhile and fun. The laboratory activities are designed to fulfill the following purposes:

- to stimulate your interest in science in general and especially in Earth science
- to reinforce important concepts studied in your textbook
- to allow you to verify some of the scientific information learned during your Earth science course
- to allow you to discover for yourself Earth science concepts and ideas not necessarily covered in class or in the textbook readings
- to acquaint you with a variety of modern tools and techniques used by today's Earth scientists

Most importantly, the laboratory activities will give you firsthand experience in how a scientist works.

The activities in this manual are of three types: Investigation, Mapping, or Design Your Own. In an Investigation activity, you will be presented with a problem. Then, through use of scientific methods, you will seek answers. Your conclusions will be based on your observations alone or on those made by the entire class, recorded experimental data, and your interpretation of what the data and observations mean. In a Mapping activity, you will use existing maps or create your own to help you solve or understand various problems in Earth science. Some of the labs are called Design Your Own, which are similar to the Design Your Own labs in your textbook. In Design Your Own labs, you will design your own experiments to find answers to problems.

In addition to the activities, this laboratory manual has several other features— a description of how to write a lab report, diagrams of laboratory equipment, and information on safety that includes first aid and a safety contract. Read the section on safety now. Safety in the laboratory is your responsibility. Working in the laboratory can be a safe and fun learning experience. By using **Earth Science: Geology, the Environment, and the Universe,** *Laboratory Manual*, you will find Earth science both understandable and exciting. Have a good year!

Writing a Laboratory Report

When scientists perform experiments, they make observations, collect and analyze data, and formulate generalizations about the data. When you work in the laboratory, you should record all your data in a laboratory report. An analysis of data is easier if all data are recorded in an organized, logical manner. Tables and graphs are often used for this purpose.

A written laboratory report should include all of the following elements.

TITLE: The title should clearly describe the topic of the report.

HYPOTHESIS: Write a statement to express your expectations of the results and as an answer to the problem statement.

MATERIALS: List all laboratory equipment and other materials needed to perform the experiment.

PROCEDURE: Describe each step of the procedure so that someone else could perform the experiment following your directions.

RESULTS: Include in your report all data, tables, graphs, and sketches used to arrive at your conclusions.

CONCLUSIONS: Record your conclusions in a paragraph at the end of your report. Your conclusions should be an analysis of your collected data.

Read the following description of an experiment. Then answer the questions.

Mass movements of Earth materials can cause damage to property and lives. The movements are influenced by several factors, such as gravity, a material's resistance to flow, and water. A geologist experimented with different Earth materials to determine how water impacted their soil, and placed the materials separately on three boards. The boards were tilted at an angle of 15°. Beginning with the clay, the geologist carefully poured one liter of water down the board and measured the rate of movement of the clay. Using the same amount of water and the same rate of water flow, she repeated the experiment on the gravel and grass-covered soil. She conducted three trials on each material, recording her data in a table. Lastly, she plotted rates of movement on a graph.

1. What was the purpose of this experiment?

_____

2. What materials were needed for this experiment?

_____

3. Write a step-by-step procedure for this experiment.

_____

_____

_____

_____

_____

_____

Writing a Laboratory Report, *continued*

4. Table 1 shows the data collected in this experiment. Based on these data, state a conclusion for this experiment.

_____

_____

_____

_____

Table 1

Material on Board	Rate of Movement of Material
Clay-covered board	
Gravel-covered board	
Soil-covered board	

5. Plot the data in Table 1 on a bar graph. Show rate of movement on the vertical axis. Use a different colored pencil for each material plotted.

Laboratory Equipment

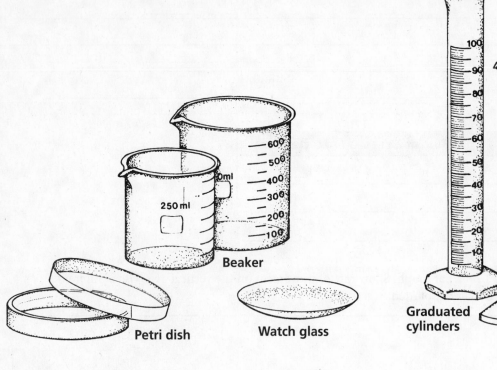

Beaker

Petri dish

Watch glass

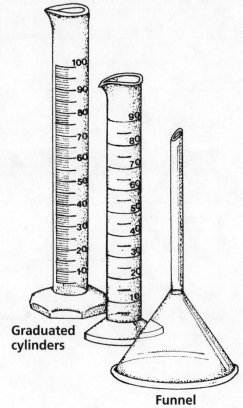

Graduated cylinders

Funnel

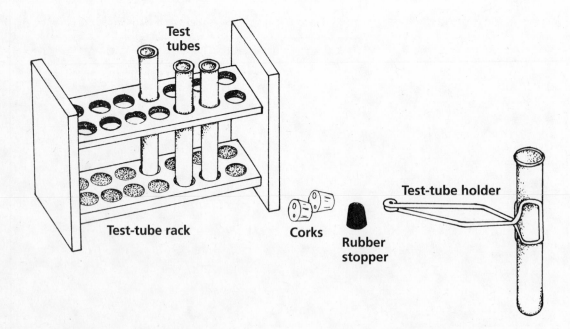

Test tubes

Test-tube rack

Corks

Rubber stopper

Test-tube holder

Laboratory Equipment, *continued*

Stirring rod

Spatula

Thermometer

Dropper

Metal ring

Hot plate

Bunsen burner

Ring stand

Laboratory Equipment, *continued*

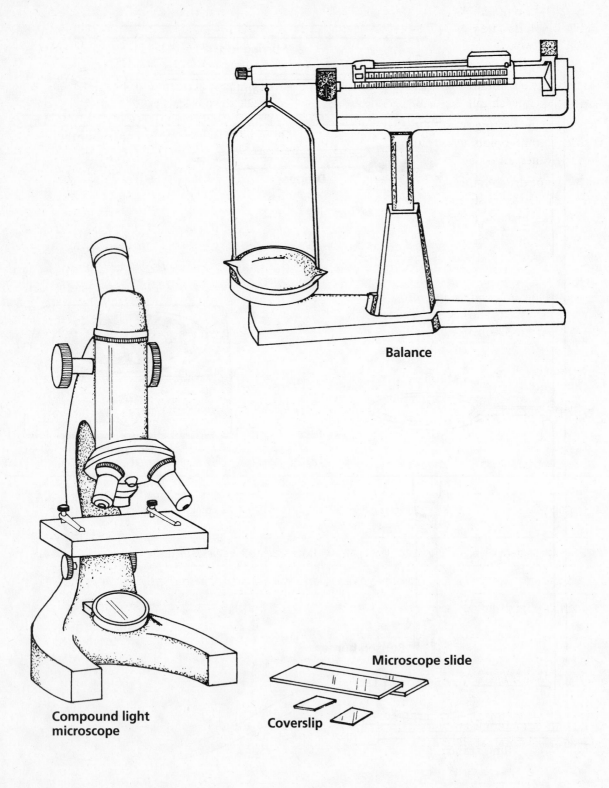

Balance

Microscope slide

Compound light microscope

Coverslip

Safety in the Laboratory

1. Always obtain your teacher's permission to begin a lab.

2. Study the procedure. If you have questions, ask your teacher. Be sure you understand all safety symbols shown.

3. Use the safety equipment provided for you. Goggles and a laboratory apron should be worn when any lab calls for using chemicals.

4. When you are heating a test tube, always slant it so the mouth points away from you and others.

5. Never eat or drink in the lab. Never inhale chemicals. Do not taste any substance or draw any material into your mouth.

6. If you spill any chemical, immediately wash it off with water. Report the spill immediately to your teacher.

7. Know the location and proper use of the fire extinguisher, safety shower, fire blanket, first aid kit, and fire alarm.

8. Keep all materials away from open flames. Tie back long hair and loose clothing.

9. If a fire should break out in the lab, or if your clothing should catch fire, smother it with the fire blanket or a coat, or get under a safety shower. **NEVER RUN.**

10. Report any accident or injury, no matter how small, to your teacher.

Follow these procedures as you clean up your work area.

1. Turn off the water and gas. Disconnect electrical devices.

2. Return materials to their places.

3. Dispose of chemicals and other materials as directed by your teacher. Place broken glass and solid substances in the proper containers. Never discard materials in the sink.

4. Clean your work area.

5. Wash your hands thoroughly after working in the laboratory.

First Aid in the Laboratory

Injury	Safe response
Burns	Apply cold water. Call your teacher immediately.
Cuts and bruises	Stop any bleeding by applying direct pressure. Cover cuts with a clean dressing. Apply cold compresses to bruises. Call your teacher immediately.
Fainting	Leave the person lying down. Loosen any tight clothing and keep crowds away. Call your teacher immediately.
Foreign matter in eye	Flush with plenty of water. Use an eyewash bottle or fountain.
Poisoning	Note the suspected poisoning agent and call your teacher immediately.
Any spills on skin	Flush with large amounts of water or use safety shower. Call your teacher immediately.

Safety Contract

I, _____ , have read and understand the safety rules and first aid information listed above. I recognize my responsibility and pledge to observe all safety rules in the science classroom at all times.

_____   _____

signature   date

The *Earth Science: Geology, the Environment, and the Universe* program uses safety symbols to alert you and your students to possible laboratory dangers. These symbols are provided in the student text in Appendix B and are explained below. Be sure your students understand each symbol before they begin an activity that displays a symbol.

SAFETY SYMBOLS	HAZARD	EXAMPLES	PRECAUTION	REMEDY
DISPOSAL	Special disposal procedures need to be followed.	certain chemicals, living organisms	Do not dispose of these materials in the sink or trash can.	Dispose of wastes as directed by your teacher.
BIOLOGICAL	Organisms or other biological materials that might be harmful to humans	bacteria, fungi, blood, unpreserved tissues, plant materials	Avoid skin contact with these materials. Wear mask or gloves.	Notify your teacher if you suspect contact with material. Wash hands thoroughly.
EXTREME TEMPERATURE	Objects that can burn skin by being too cold or too hot	boiling liquids, hot plates, dry ice, liquid nitrogen	Use proper protection when handling.	Go to your teacher for first aid.
SHARP OBJECT	Use of tools or glassware that can easily puncture or slice skin	razor blades, pins, scalpels, pointed tools, dissecting probes, broken glass	Practice common-sense behavior and follow guidelines for use of the tool.	Go to your teacher for first aid.
FUME	Possible danger to respiratory tract from fumes	ammonia, acetone, nail polish remover, heated sulfur, moth balls	Make sure there is good ventilation. Never smell fumes directly. Wear a mask.	Leave foul area and notify your teacher immediately.
ELECTRICAL	Possible danger from electrical shock or burn	improper grounding, liquid spills, short circuits, exposed wires	Double-check setup with teacher. Check condition of wires and apparatus.	Do not attempt to fix electrical problems. Notify your teacher immediately.
IRRITANT	Substances that can irritate the skin or mucus membranes of the respiratory tract	pollen, moth balls, steel wool, fiber glass, potassium permanganate	Wear dust mask and gloves. Practice extra care when handling these materials.	Go to your teacher for first aid.
CHEMICAL	Chemicals that can react with and destroy tissue and other materials	bleaches such as hydrogen peroxide; acids such as sulfuric acid, hydrochloric acid; bases such as ammonia, sodium hydroxide	Wear goggles, gloves, and an apron.	Immediately flush the affected area with water and notify your teacher.
TOXIC	Substance may be poisonous if touched, inhaled, or swallowed	mercury, many metal compounds, iodine, poinsettia plant parts	Follow your teacher's instructions.	Always wash hands thoroughly after use. Go to your teacher for first aid.
OPEN FLAME	Open flame may ignite flammable chemicals, loose clothing, or hair	alcohol, kerosene, potassium permanganate, hair, clothing	Tie back hair. Avoid wearing loose clothing. Avoid open flames when using flammable chemicals. Be aware of locations of fire safety equipment.	Notify your teacher immediately. Use fire safety equipment if applicable.

Eye Safety
Proper eye protection should be worn at all times by anyone performing or observing science activities.

Clothing Protection
This symbol appears when substances could stain or burn clothing.

Animal Safety
This symbol appears when safety of animals and students must be ensured.

Radioactivity
This symbol appears when radioactive materials are used.

LAB **1.1** **INVESTIGATION**

Observing and Analyzing Stream Flow

*O*ne way that scientists learn about the world is by modeling natural phenomena and observing and describing what happens. For example, Earth scientists can model how flowing water moves soil by using a stream table, which is a large, shallow pan that is propped at an angle and partly filled with sand or other material (Figure 1). Water is allowed to flow from the higher end of the stream table down through the sand to the lower end of the table. By observing the water's path and its effects on the sand and by altering the rate of water flow, scientists can learn a great deal about stream development.

PREPARATION

PROBLEM
What conclusions can you draw about some of the processes represented in a stream table?

OBJECTIVES
- **Observe** a model of natural phenomena.
- **Communicate** observations clearly and accurately.
- **Choose** criteria to classify observed phenomena.

MATERIALS
pen or pencil
Figures 2–7 in lab manual

PROCEDURE

1. Examine Figures 2–7. They are diagrams of stream development as modeled on a stream table. The table shown is about 4 meters long and 1 meter wide. Before the modeling began, a mass of sand sloped gently and smoothly from the back of the table to about the halfway point on the table. The figures show the water's path and the transport and deposition of sand that occurred as water trickled from a spigot for 2 days.

2. Write a detailed description in the Analyze section on page 3 of what you observe in the figures.

Figure 1

DATA AND OBSERVATIONS

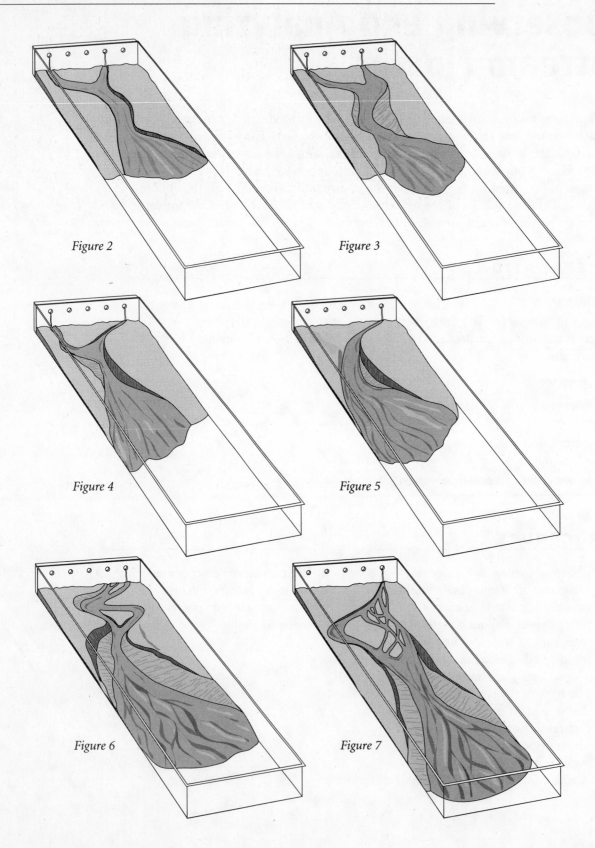

Figure 2

Figure 3

Figure 4

Figure 5

Figure 6

Figure 7

LAB ◆ **1.1**   **INVESTIGATION**

ANALYZE

Figure 2

_____

_____

_____

_____

Figure 3

_____

_____

_____

_____

Figure 4

_____

_____

_____

_____

Figure 5

_____

_____

_____

_____

Figure 6

_____

_____

_____

_____

Figure 7

_____

_____

_____

_____

1. Based on your descriptions, make up a classification scheme for the figures. You may decide to classify them all in the same way. Or you may group individual figures into two or more classifications. Describe your classification system.

_____

_____

_____

_____

_____

LAB **1.1**   **INVESTIGATION**

CONCLUDE AND APPLY

1. Describe the process of stream development based on your observations of Figures 2–7.

_____

_____

_____

_____

_____

_____

_____

2. What modifications could you make to the stream table to gain further insight into stream development?

_____

_____

_____

_____

LAB **1.2**   **DESIGN YOUR OWN**

Formulating a Hypothesis

A scientific method is a planned, organized approach to solving a problem. While the steps taken to solve the problem can vary, the first step involved in scientific problem solving is usually determining what it is you want to know. Often scientific problem solving involves researching the problem. Once the problem is defined and research is complete, a hypothesis, or suggested explanation for an observation, is made. Often the hypothesis is stated in the form of a question that can be answered by the results of a test or an experiment.

PREPARATION

PROBLEM

How can you create a phenomenon on which a hypothesis can be based and formulate a hypothesis to explain a phenomenon created by others?

OBJECTIVES

- **Design** a hidden phenomenon in a box.
- **Use** various observational methods to **examine** the unknown phenomenon.
- **Write** a hypothesis to **explain** or **describe** the phenomenon.

POSSIBLE MATERIALS

box
small objects
modeling clay
string
bubble wrap
newspaper
tape
magnet
balance or scale
measuring tape
scissors

SAFETY PRECAUTIONS

Be careful when using scissors or handling other sharp objects. Any objects with sharp points or edges could puncture your skin.

LAB ◁ 1.2   DESIGN YOUR OWN

PLAN THE EXPERIMENT

With your group, discuss how you can use the materials to create a hidden phenomenon. How might the phenomenon be observed by another person? Visually? By touch? By weighing or measuring the box? By smelling it? By shaking or otherwise moving the box? Choose items accordingly, and construct a hidden phenomenon in a box. Describe the contents and arrangement of the box your group designs.

What kinds of observations might you make about an unknown phenomenon to form a hypothesis about what it is? Use Table 1 to organize your ideas. Write a procedure for investigating an unknown phenomenon. After you design the phenomenon in a box, exchange with another group and investigate its box, following your plan.

DATA AND OBSERVATIONS

Test or Observation	Result or Description	Possible Conclusion

LAB **1.2** DESIGN YOUR OWN

ANALYZE

1. What was the most significant observation you made about the box containing the unknown contents examined by your group?

_____

_____

_____

_____

_____

2. How did you combine observations to draw conclusions about the contents of the box?

_____

_____

_____

_____

_____

_____

LAB **1.2**   **DESIGN YOUR OWN**

CONCLUDE AND APPLY

1. Based on your observations of the unknown phenomenon and your analysis of these observations, state your hypothesis about the contents and structure of the box.

_____

_____

_____

2. While formulating a hypothesis about the unknown contents of the box you examined, did you apply anything you learned while creating your group's box ? If so, what?

_____

_____

_____

3. How well did your hypothesis match the actual contents of the box examined by your group? What could you have done to get more information?

_____

_____

_____

_____

_____

4. How is this activity similar to actual methods that scientists use to explain unknown phenomena?

_____

_____

_____

_____

_____

_____

LAB 2.1   **MAPPING**

Modeling Topographic Maps

Maps are important tools in studies of the physical characteristics of Earth. Spatial relationships and changes in the shapes and sizes of landforms throughout geologic time can be illustrated using a variety of mapping techniques. Topographic maps show changes in elevation on Earth's surface through the use of contour lines, which connect points of equal elevation above sea level. These contour lines provide useful information about the gradient, shape, and height of Earth's landforms.

PREPARATION

PROBLEM

How can you develop a model of a topographic map and use a topographic map to interpret the shape of a landform?

OBJECTIVES

- **Construct** a model of a mountain with a minimum of two different elevations.
- **Use** contour lines on the model to represent changes in elevation.
- **Model** a topographic map by transferring the contour lines to a flat surface.
- **Interpret** a map constructed by another student to **identify** the appropriate model mountain.

MATERIALS

5-gallon aquarium tank
modeling clay
waterproof black marker
metric ruler or meterstick
masking tape
grease pencil
turkey baster
transparency paper
black yarn
water

SAFETY PRECAUTIONS

- Wear an apron when working with clay to help prevent stains on clothing.
- Wear safety goggles during the lab procedure.
- Wipe up any spills immediately.

LAB ◇ **2.1**   **MAPPING**

PROCEDURE

1. Use the grease pencil to draw a 5-cm line on each of the four sides of the tank at 2-cm intervals, beginning with 2 cm from the bottom of the tank. You will have a series of marks 2 cm apart from the bottom to the top of the tank on each side. These marks are for the purpose of measuring water level.

2. Orient one side of the tank to the north and mark that side "North."

3. Construct a clay model of a mountain. The model should fit into the tank with the mountain peak no higher than the top of the tank. If you wish to make it more interesting, the mountain can have more than one peak. Name your mountain.

4. When the model has been placed in the tank, tie one strand of black yarn around the entire base of a mountain to simulate a contour line.

5. Slowly add water to the tank to the level of the first 2-cm line. At the surface level of the water, tie another strand of black yarn around the model.

6. Continue adding water and tying black yarn around the model at each 2-cm level until the water has reached the top of the mountain.

7. With the turkey baster, carefully remove all of the water from the tank. Place transparency paper over the top of the tank, centering it over the mountain, and tape it to the sides of the tank.

8. Place the tank on a low table. Look down at the top of the tank and trace the contour lines from the mountain onto the transparency paper. Label the appropriate end of the map "North." Identify your map as instructed by your teacher and place it on a flat surface to dry. IMPORTANT: At this point, do not put the name of your mountain on the map.

DATA AND OBSERVATIONS

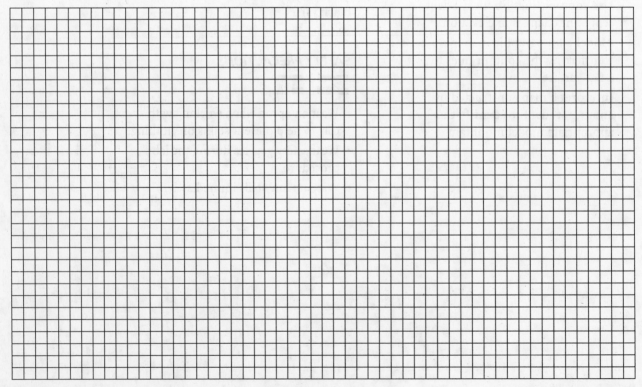

LAB ◁ **2.1** ▷ **MAPPING**

ANALYZE

1. What is the height of your mountain?

_____

2. What is the contour interval of your mountain?

_____

3. Compare the parts of your map that represent the steep gradients with those parts that represent gentler slopes or flat areas. How are the configurations alike or different?

_____

_____

_____

CONCLUDE AND APPLY

1. Exchange maps with another group. You will use this map to identify the group's mountain among the collection of models in your classroom. Observe the map carefully and analyze the shapes and placement of the contour lines. Infer what the mountain might look like. Sketch the mountain in the space below.

LAB 2.1   **MAPPING**

CONCLUDE AND APPLY, *continued*

2. Orient the map and your sketch to the north. Examine the models of mountains on display in your classroom. Identify the model that is represented by the map.

_____

3. Did you select the correct model?

_____

If not, make a new sketch of the mapped mountain, using the method illustrated in the figure below. On the graph paper in the Data and Observations section, use the transect line method to convert the contour map into a profile. Draw a straight line horizontally across the middle of the contour map. At the points where the contour lines intersect the straight horizontal line (the transect), draw perpendicular lines downward to create the profile. See the figure below. Use this profile to identify the model of the mountain. HINTS: What are the main features indicated by the map? Where are the lines closest together and farthest apart? What do these lines tell you about the shape of the landform?

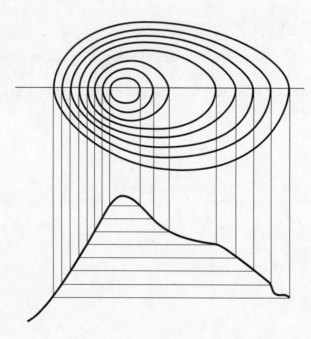

LAB ◆ **2.2**   **INVESTIGATION**

Interpreting Political and Landform Maps

Among the many uses of maps are those of scientific study and the recording of political, geographic, and geological data for commercial, travel, and recreational purposes. A map is appropriate for a particular purpose only if it contains information in a form consistent with the use to which it will be put. For example, a relief map without political boundaries would be of little use to the tax collector for a specific township, while a road map would not give a hiker or petroleum geologist the full range of information necessary for their pursuits. Although some maps contain more than one type of information, too many different types of data on the same map can be difficult to read. In this investigation, you will be working with political, topographic, and physical maps and analyzing the types of information that each provide.

PREPARATION

PROBLEM
How can different types of maps be prepared and interpreted for various uses?

OBJECTIVES
- **Draw** a political map and a landform map of a single location in or near your school or home.

- **Describe** the strengths and limitations of each map.
- **Compare** the information provided by political, topographic, and physical maps.

MATERIALS
calculator
pencil

PROCEDURE

1. Select an area in or around your school (classroom and hallways area, gym, football field, school neighborhood) or your neighborhood to map.

2. Obtain measurements for drawing the map to scale by pacing the perimeter of the area. A pace is a large step forward. Count the number of paces it takes to travel each side of the area.

3. Decide upon the scale that you will use for your map. Example: Suppose a map is 20 cm on each side. If you measured 43 paces for one side, each centimeter would

represent 2.15 paces (43 divided by 20), and your scale would be 2.15 paces = 1 cm. All of your measurements for the map will then be done in paces and converted to centimeters for the map drawing.

4. Draw the map in the blank space provided. Include a pointer to north, the locations and names of features such as entrances, rooms, corridors, gates, streets, highways, railroads, bodies of water, and town/city boundaries. Label this map "Political."

LAB 2.2 INVESTIGATION

PROCEDURE, *continued*

5. Draw a second map of the same area in the blank space provided, using the same perimeter outline from your first map. On this map, draw the physical form of any objects and buildings that exist within the area of the map. Pace off the length and width measurements of these features. From math class, you may know how to determine indirectly the height of buildings, trees, and other tall objects. If not, estimate the heights. Label this map "Physical."

DATA AND OBSERVATIONS

Map 1

Map 2

LAB ◆ **2.2** ▸ INVESTIGATION 🔍

ANALYZE

1. Compare and contrast the two maps. What similarities and differences do you observe?

_____

_____

_____

_____

_____

2. Which map provides you with the information that you need to travel by car or bicycle? Explain your answer.

_____

_____

_____

_____

_____

3. If you wanted to hike across the area covered by the map in the fastest way possible, which map would be most helpful? Explain your answer.

_____

_____

_____

_____

_____

_____

_____

LAB **2.2** INVESTIGATION

CONCLUDE AND APPLY

1. Suppose that some landowners allowed hikers to cross their properties but others had high fences and locked gates. What could be added to a map of the properties to make them more useful to hikers?

_____

2. Which of the maps shown below is like your physical map? Which is like your political map? What type of map is Map C?

_____

_____

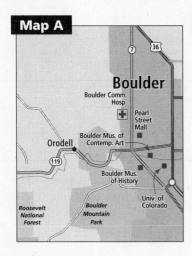

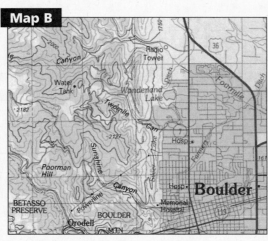

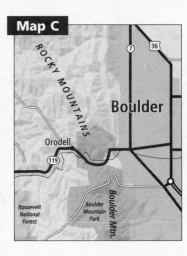

3. If you were in Colorado for the first time and were planning a bicycle trip from Boulder to Orodell, what route would you use if you had only Map A to consult?

_____

_____

_____

4. Would your bicycle route differ if you had Map B or C to consult instead of Map A? Why or why not?

_____

_____

_____

LAB **3.1**   **DESIGN YOUR OWN**

Changes in State

Elements cycle through the lithosphere, hydrosphere, and atmosphere of Earth as different forms of matter change in state. On Earth, most substances are found in three states: solid, liquid, and gaseous. These states reflect the relative amount of thermal energy in a substance. Changes in thermal energy change the speed of molecular motion. For example, when a solid absorbs enough thermal energy from the environment, it melts into a liquid. When a liquid loses enough thermal energy to the environment, it condenses to a solid. Changes in states of matter are important processes on Earth.

PREPARATION

PROBLEM

How can the melting and boiling points of water (a liquid at room temperature) be demonstrated and compared with those of carnauba wax (a solid at room temperature)? Which states of matter will be observed in this demonstration?

_____

_____

_____

_____

OBJECTIVES

- **Describe** methods of measuring the boiling and freezing points of liquids.
- **Plan** and **carry out** a demonstration of changes in state of liquids and solids.
- **Generalize** your results to the scale of the hydrologic, lithospheric, and atmospheric systems of Earth.
- **Predict** the variables involved in further investigation of changes in state.

HYPOTHESIS

Think about how to demonstrate the boiling and freezing points of matter. Determine what method and materials you will use. Make a hypothesis about the nature of the variables involved and what scale of measure will be appropriate for your demonstration. What is the best way to communicate your findings? How can you graph your results?

_____

_____

_____

POSSIBLE MATERIALS

hot plate
ring stand
test-tube clamp
beaker
flask
clear plastic tubing or distillation apparatus
test-tube corks or stoppers
water
test tubes
carnauba wax
alcohol-based thermometer
graph paper

SAFETY PRECAUTIONS

- Do not touch the hot plate while it is on.
- Use caution when handling hot glassware. Wear thermal mitts if needed.
- Melted wax and boiling water can cause burns. Handle carefully.
- Avoid using mercury-based thermometers. Mercury is toxic.
- Wear safety goggles and an apron during the lab procedure.

LAB ◆ **3.1** DESIGN YOUR OWN

PLAN THE EXPERIMENT

Brainstorm the steps of the demonstration and any necessary safety precautions. List the materials you will use. Prepare charts for recording your data. Select an appropriate style of graph (line, bar, or circle) for communicating your results. Which variables will your graph show? What scale of measurement will you use? What will the labels for the axes be?

_____

_____

_____

_____

_____

_____

DATA AND OBSERVATIONS

DATA CHART

LAB ⬦ **3.1**   **DESIGN YOUR OWN**

ANALYZE

1. How might you improve the method and/or materials?

_____

_____

2. At what time intervals did you record the temperatures?

_____

_____

How did this help you to display your data?

_____

_____

3. What did the graphs show about the behavior of water and wax as they absorb and release thermal energy?

_____

_____

_____

CHECK YOUR HYPOTHESIS

Was your **hypothesis** supported by your data? Why or why not?

_____

_____

LAB ◆ **3.1** DESIGN YOUR OWN

CONCLUDE AND APPLY

1. What conclusion have you reached about changes in state of water and wax?

_____

_____

_____

2. On the graphs of the melting and freezing points of wax, draw a red line around the section of the graph that illustrates the absorption of thermal energy by the wax. Draw a blue line around the section of the graph that illustrates the release of thermal energy. At what point do the two graphs cross? What can you conclude from this data?

_____

_____

_____

_____

_____

3. The following table lists changes in state of matter caused by changes in the amount of thermal energy contained in each substance. Fill in the blank sections to describe the dynamics of these changes.

Form of Matter	State of Matter #1	Change in Thermal Energy (absorbed or released)	State of Matter #2
Ice	Solid	Absorbed	Water
Water	Liquid		Steam
Water	Liquid		Ice
Glue stick			Liquid glue
Liquid glue	Liquid		Bonded glue
Gasoline	Liquid		Gaseous gasoline
Stick of butter		Absorbed at room temperature	Soft butter
Stick of butter	Solid	Absorbed when heated	
Melted chocolate	Liquid		Solid chocolate
Kerosene			Gaseous kerosene
Magma			Solid rock

Laboratory Manual

Rates of Chemical Reactions

*T*he change of one or more substances into other substances is called a chemical reaction. Chemical reactions require different lengths of time for completion, depending on the substances and the conditions for the reaction. While many reactions can be over in a fraction of a second, others, such as those associated with changes in Earth systems, can take much longer. Chemists use collision theory to explain the effects of surface area, concentration, and temperature on reactions.

Below is the equation for the chemical reaction you will observe in this lab.

$$Zn \text{ (solid)} + 2 HCl \text{ (aqueous)} \Rightarrow ZnCl_2 \text{ (aqueous)} + H_2 \text{ (gas)}$$

PREPARATION

PROBLEM
Investigate the effects of surface area, concentration, and temperature on the reaction between zinc and hydrochloric acid.

OBJECTIVES
- **Observe** and **record** the results of chemical reactions.
- **Use** collision theory to **interpret** reaction data.
- **Illustrate** the dynamics of chemical reactions in the context of collision theory.
- **Describe** the relationship between the rate of chemical reactions and surface area, concentration, and temperature.

MATERIALS
forceps
6 test tubes
test-tube rack
glass marker
5 large pieces of granulated zinc
several small pieces of granulated zinc
HCl solution A (2 *M*)
HCl solution B (1 *M*)
alcohol-based thermometer
beaker
water
hot plate

SAFETY PRECAUTIONS

- Use forceps to handle the zinc.
- Point the open end of the test tube away from you while heating it.
- If the HCl splatters, wash the area immediately with cold water.
- Use caution when handling hot glassware. Wear thermal mitts if needed.
- Avoid using mercury-based thermometers. Mercury is toxic.
- Wear safety goggles and an apron during the lab procedure.

LAB ⟨ **3.2** ⟩   **INVESTIGATION**

PROCEDURE

1. Put on the safety goggles, gloves, and a lab apron.

2. Put two clean test tubes in the test-tube rack. Label one tube "A" and the other "B." Drop one of the larger pieces of zinc into each tube.

3. Add HCl solution A to one-quarter of the height of tube A and HCl solution B to the same height in tube B. After a minute or two, observe carefully to see how fast the gas in each tube is bubbling. Record the results in the table below.

4. Put two clean test tubes in the test-tube rack. Label the test tubes "L" and "S." Drop one of the larger pieces of zinc in tube L and several small pieces in tube S.

5. Add HCl solution A to one-quarter of the height of each tube. Observe the rate of bubbling in each tube and record the results.

6. Label two clean test tubes "R" and "H." Drop a large piece of zinc in each test tube. Put test tube R in the rack at room temperature, and place test tube H in a beaker half full of water on a hot plate. Add HCl solution A to one-quarter of the height of each tube.

7. Put a thermometer in test tube H and note the temperature. Heat the tube to raise the temperature by 10°C. Observe the rate of bubbling in each tube and record the results in the table. Turn off the hot plate and put test tube H in the rack.

8. Review the results that you have recorded in your table and, for each set of two test tubes, determine which effect caused the faster reaction rate: surface area, concentration, or temperature. Enter the cause in the last column of the table.

DATA AND OBSERVATIONS

Reactants	Bubbles Faster	Bubbles Slower	Cause of Faster Reaction
Tube A: large zinc + dilute HCl			
Tube B: large zinc + 1/2 dilute HCl			
Tube L: large zinc + dilute HCl			
Tube S: small zinc + dilute HCl			
Tube R: zinc + HCl at room temperature			
Tube H: Zinc + heated HCl			

LAB 3.2 INVESTIGATION

ANALYZE

1. The diagrams below show how collision theory explains the effect of concentration on reaction rate. Draw additional diagrams illustrating the effect on reaction rate of temperature and surface area.

Low concentration of acid

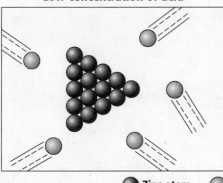

Concentration higher— more chance of particles colliding

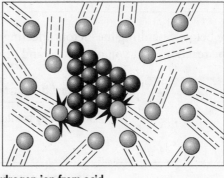

● Zinc atom ○ Hydrogen ion from acid

Low Temperature   **High Temperature**

Small Surface Area   **Large Surface Area**

LAB **3.2** INVESTIGATION

CONCLUDE AND APPLY

`1. What chemical reaction results in the formation of rust?

_____

2. When metal is painted to prevent the formation of rust, which factor
(concentration, surface area, or temperature) is being reduced?

_____

3. Complete the table below describing the factors affecting reaction rate. In the last
three rows, describe reactions that you observe in and on Earth.

Reaction	Rate Reduced or Increased	Factor Involved
Metal rusting	Reduced by painting	
Acid burning skin	Reduced by rinsing	
Food spoiling		
Apple slices turning brown		
Coffee brewing		
Limestone formations dissolving, producing caves (Hint: Where are limestone caves found?)		

 **LAB** **4.1**  **INVESTIGATION**

Growing Crystals

Weak solutions of mineral salts can result when rainwater percolates through rock. When the solution reaches a hole in the rock, such as a fracture, the solution may evaporate and become more concentrated. When the solution becomes saturated, further evaporation deposits some of the salt as crystals. This evaporation is responsible for many common forms of crystal deposition. We can simulate this process by using small amounts of supersaturated solutions.

PREPARATION

PROBLEM
How do crystals form from solutions?

OBJECTIVES
- **Form** crystals by evaporating solutions.
- **Identify** several of the major crystal systems.

MATERIALS
solutions A–D
solutes A–D
4 test tubes
test-tube rack
glass marker
4 small petri dishes
metal spatula
Bunsen burner
lighter
test-tube tongs
pipette
4 microscope slides
table lamp
compound microscope

SAFETY PRECAUTIONS

- Wear safety goggles, gloves, and an apron during the lab procedure. Tie back long hair and do not wear loose clothing.
- Circuits must be protected by a GFI (ground fault interrupter) when electricity is used near a water source.
- Some of the solutions are toxic and may irritate skin; wash your hands at the end of lab. Rinse spills with water.
- Do not inhale any powder or fumes; chemicals can be toxic if inhaled.
- Wear thermal mitts when handling hot objects.
- Follow your teacher's instructions to dispose of used slides and hazardous chemicals.

PROCEDURE

1. Label four test tubes A–D. Half fill each one with the corresponding solution provided by your teacher.

2. Label four small petri dishes A–D. Place a few heaped spatulas of each solute into its corresponding dish.

3. Use tongs to heat test tube A with a Bunsen burner to a temperature that is about midway between room temperature and the boiling point of water (approximately 66°C).

LAB ◁ **4.1** ▷   **INVESTIGATION**

PROCEDURE, *continued*

4. Add a spatula of each solute to its corresponding solution. Stir with a clean spatula to dissolve the solute. Repeat this step until nearly all of the solute dissolves.

5. Label four microscope slides A–D. Use a pipette to place a drop of warm supersaturated solution A on slide A. Rinse and dry the pipette. Repeat this step for each solution. Record the time in Table 2.

6. Collect the slides in one place. Bring the bulb of a table lamp within about 15 cm of the collected slides to keep them warm.

7. Observe each slide under the microscope about every 2 minutes as crystals form. Record your observations, including the time at which crystals first appear and how they look. Note how the crystal structure develops.

8. After 15–20 minutes, draw the crystals in the space on the next page.

DATA AND OBSERVATIONS

Table 1

Solution	Chemical	Formula
A	Alum	$AlK(SO_4)_2 \cdot 12H_2O$
B	Rochelle salt	$KNaC_4H_4O_6 \cdot 4H_2O$
C	Copper acetate monohydrate	$Cu(CH_3COO)_2 \cdot H_2O$
D	Calcium copper acetate hexahydrate	$CaCu(CH_3COO)_4 \cdot 6H_2O$

Table 2

Solution	Start Time	Observations
A. Alum		
B. Rochelle salt		
C. Copper acetate monohydrate		
D. Calcium copper acetate hexahydrate		

LAB ◆ **4.1**   **INVESTIGATION**

DATA AND OBSERVATIONS, *continued*

DRAWING OF CRYSTALS

ANALYZE

1. Consider the four examples of crystallization that you observed. Describe the process of evaporative crystallization. Identify trends that apply to all the samples, and summarize those trends.

_____

_____

_____

_____

_____

_____

_____

_____

_____

_____

_____

_____

LAB 4.1   **INVESTIGATION**

CONCLUDE AND APPLY

1. Summarize in Table 3 the major crystal system and color that results from the evaporation of each solution. Refer to Table 4-1 on page 78 in your textbook.

Table 3

Solution	Crystal System	Color
A. Alum		
B. Rochelle salt		
C. Copper acetate monohydrate		
D. Calcium copper acetate hexahydrate		

2. Compare your model to natural formations of crystals.

_____

_____

_____

_____

_____

_____

Rockhounding

*R*ocks can tell you a lot about your area's geologic history. Every area has places *that are good for rockhounding, or seeking and collecting rocks. For example, there may be quartz mines where, for a small fee, those searching for rocks can gently hammer away at special seams to obtain delicate crystals. You may be able to find interesting outcrops of rock with minerals embedded in them along timber roads and in gravel bars and creek drainages.*

PREPARATION

PROBLEM

What rocks and minerals are found in your area?

OBJECTIVES

- **Identify** a local spot of geologic interest.
- **Plan** a field trip to collect samples of rocks and minerals.
- **Collect** samples of different rocks and minerals.
- **Identify** rocks and minerals.

HYPOTHESIS

What kinds of rocks and minerals do you expect to find in your area? Write your hypothesis below.

_____

_____

_____

_____

POSSIBLE MATERIALS

resources on local geology
small backpack
chisel-edged hammer
short pry bar
cloth or leather gloves

newspaper
bag for samples
notebook
masking tape
markers
hand lens
field guide to rocks and minerals
food
water
sunscreen
porcelain tile
hardness testing kit
dilute hydrochloric acid
long-sleeved shirt or jacket

SAFETY PRECAUTIONS

- Avoid treacherous terrain.
- Wear safety goggles to protect your eyes from flying chips of rock.
- Use caution when hammering.
- Carefully examine your surroundings. Avoid contact with poisonous plants and animals. Watch out for ticks.
- Wear your cloth or leather gloves during the entire lab procedure.
- Hydrochloric acid is corrosive. Keep it away from your skin and eyes.

LAB ◁ **4.2** ▷   **DESIGN YOUR OWN** 📐

PLAN THE EXPERIMENT

As a group, research the geology of your area on the Internet, in pamphlets about the local geology, and with geologic maps. Write about two or three locations that are accessible and geologically interesting. As a class, consider all proposals and choose a site to visit, bearing in mind geologic merit and practical considerations, such as time and transport. Once the class has decided where to go, compile a table of a dozen or so rocks and minerals that you might expect to find there. Note a few characteristics of each that will help you with field identifications.

Look at the possible materials. A notebook is essential for writing directions to the site, sketching outcrops, and describing the rocks you collect. Other essentials are water and safety equipment. Plan to collect 10–12 samples. Write a checklist of what you will need to pack at home and what you will need from school.

DATA AND OBSERVATIONS

FIELD IDENTIFICATION TABLE

LAB ◁ **4.2** ▷   **DESIGN YOUR OWN**

ANALYZE

1. After the field trip, confirm your field identifications by checking hardness, specific gravity, color, streak, cleavage, luster, and crystal form. Compile a table with an identification number for each sample, your tentative identification, tests performed, and a confirmed identification.

2. As a class, compile a table of everyone's sample information.

3. Exhibit your specimens with informative labels. View your classmates' samples. Take notes on the minerals and rocks that you did not collect yourself.

DATA TABLES

LAB ⟨ **4.2** ⟩   **DESIGN YOUR OWN**

CHECK YOUR HYPOTHESIS

Was your **hypothesis** supported by your data? Why or why not?

_____

_____

CONCLUDE AND APPLY

1. What is your most remarkable specimen? What is the most remarkable specimen in the class?
Explain your answer.

_____

_____

_____

2. What were the most common types of rocks and minerals at the collection site?
Were these the most frequently collected samples?

_____

_____

_____

3. Were the samples what you expected to find? If they were different, explain why.

_____

_____

_____

LAB **5.1**   **INVESTIGATION**

Comparing Lunar Rocks to Earth Rocks

Igneous rocks form when molten rock called magma cools. Igneous rocks are classified by mineral composition and texture. Their mineral composition indicates the nature of the magma. Texture indicates how the magma cooled. Rocks collected from the Moon have characteristics like those of igneous rocks on Earth. These characteristics provide insight about the composition of the Moon and how it was formed.

PREPARATION

PROBLEM

How do lunar rocks compare with Earth rocks?

OBJECTIVES

- **Estimate** mineral percentages in igneous rock samples.
- **Identify** types of igneous rocks.
- **Compare** lunar rocks to Earth rocks.

MATERIALS

4 igneous rocks from Earth
igneous-rock key
pictures of lunar rocks

SAFETY PRECAUTIONS

Use caution when handling rocks; edges can be sharp. Do not wear sandals during the lab procedure.

IGNEOUS-ROCK KEY

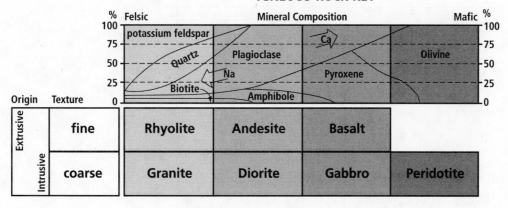

LAB 5.1   **INVESTIGATION**

PROCEDURE

1. Observe a rock sample provided by your teacher and determine whether the texture is fine-grained or coarse-grained. Record this data in the table.

2. Estimate and record the percentage of dark minerals. This percentage will allow you to classify the rock as felsic (few dark minerals, light-colored or gray), intermediate (about 50 percent dark minerals, dark gray), or mafic (more than 70 percent dark minerals, very dark or black).

3. Estimate and record the percentage of feldspar. Classify the feldspar as potassium (pink, white, or gray) or plagioclase (white or gray with striations).

4. Estimate and record the percentage of quartz. If the sample has no quartz, it belongs in the gabbro-basalt group. If it has less than 10 percent quartz, it belongs in the diorite-andesite group. If it has 10–40 percent quartz, it belongs in the granite-rhyolite group.

5. Using the igneous-rock key on page 33, identify the unknown igneous-rock sample. Write the correct name of the sample in the table.

6. Repeat steps 1–5 for the other rock samples.

7. Look at pictures of lunar rocks, and use your observations to answer the questions in Analyze and Conclude and Apply.

DATA AND OBSERVATIONS

TABLE

Rock Sample	Texture	Estimated % of Dark Minerals	Felsic, Mafic, or Intermediate	Name of Rock
1				
2				
3				
4				

LAB **5.1**   **INVESTIGATION**

ANALYZE

1. What elements appear to be prevalent in the lunar rocks?

_____

_____

_____

_____

2. Which igneous rocks from Earth are most like the lunar rocks? Explain your answer.

_____

_____

_____

_____

3. What similarities and differences did you notice between lunar rocks and Earth rocks?

_____

_____

_____

_____

LAB ◆ **5.1** ▶   **INVESTIGATION** 🔍

CONCLUDE AND APPLY

1. Scientists theorize that numerous lavaflows have erupted on the surface of the Moon millions of years ago. What evidence proves this?

_____

_____

_____

_____

2. Darkened spots on the Moon's surface are visible from Earth. These dark spots are created by huge fields of mafic rock located deep in the valleys of craters. How do you think these mafic rocks got there? Why are these areas darker than the surface of the Moon?

_____

_____

_____

_____

_____

3. The grain size of lunar rocks is relatively small. What does a fine grain size suggest about how the magma cooled on the surface of the Moon?

_____

_____

_____

_____

LAB 5.2 **MAPPING**

Locating Igneous Rocks on Earth

Intrusive igneous rocks form beneath Earth's crust when magma cools slowly. Extrusive igneous rocks form on the surface when lava cools very rapidly. Differences in cooling rate determine the texture of igneous rocks. When magma cools slowly, it forms large crystals and coarse-grained rocks. When magma cools quickly, it forms small crystals and fine-grained rocks. When magma cools even more rapidly, such as in water, it forms extremely small crystals and glassy rocks. At times, two stages of cooling occur, forming rocks that are porphyritic. These rocks have large crystals surrounded by small crystals.

The color of igneous rocks indicates their mineral composition. Dark rocks usually contain large amounts of iron and magnesium and are called mafic. Light rocks contain large amounts of feldspar and silicon and are called felsic. Intermediate rocks are a mixture of light and dark colors.

PREPARATION

PROBLEM

How can you identify where rocks originate?

OBJECTIVES

- **Classify** igneous rocks based on texture and color.
- **Recognize** that the characteristics of rocks are linked to their formation conditions and origins.
- **Plot** the location of igneous rocks on a map.

MATERIALS

9 igneous rocks

SAFETY PRECAUTIONS

Use caution when handling rocks; edges can be sharp. Do not wear sandals during the lab procedure.

PROCEDURE

1. Observe nine igneous rock samples. Using Table 1 and Figure 1 as guides, record your observations of color, texture, and type for each sample in Table 3.

2. Using the coordinates in Table 2, match each letter with the appropriate point on the map in Figure 2. Each labeled point is the origin of a rock sample that you have observed.

3. Using your data in Table 3, match each rock (1–9) with its proper point on the map. Write the rock number next to the labeled point (A–I). It may be possible that a rock originated in several places. List each potential point of origin in Table 3.

LAB ◆ **5.2** ◆ ──────────────────────────── **MAPPING** 🌐

DATA AND OBSERVATIONS

Table 1

Igneous Rock Type	Common Colors	Minerals
Felsic	white, tan, gray, pink, red	silica, quartz, orthoclase and plagioclase feldspar, some mica and hornblende
Intermediate	gray, green	plagioclase feldspar, hornblende, augite, biotite, amphibole, and pyroxene
Mafic	dark green, dark gray, black	iron, magnesium, plagioclase feldspar, augite, biotite, amphibole, pyroxene, and olivine

Table 2

Location	Latitude (N)	Longitude (W)	Depth (m)
A	21°	102°	−2.5
B	40°	120°	−195
C	27°	73°	−80 below water
D	52°	47°	−120 below water
E	17°	136°	−105 below water
F	38°	79°	−0.5
G	62°	112°	−93
H	28°	142°	−1.5
I	61°	162°	−772

Figure 1

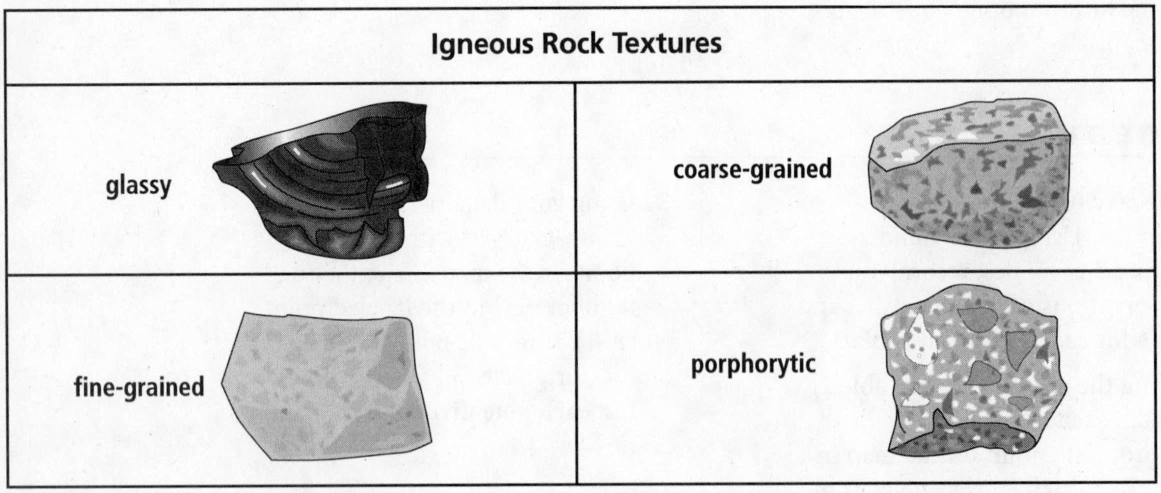

Igneous Rock Textures

glassy

coarse-grained

fine-grained

porphorytic

LAB ◆ **5.2** ═══════════════════════════════ **MAPPING** 🌐

Table 3

Rock	Color(s)	Felsic, Mafic, or Intermediate	Texture (glassy, fine-grained, coarse-grained, or porphyritic)	Intrusive or Extrusive
1				
2				
3				
4				
5				
6				
7				
8				
9				

Figure 2

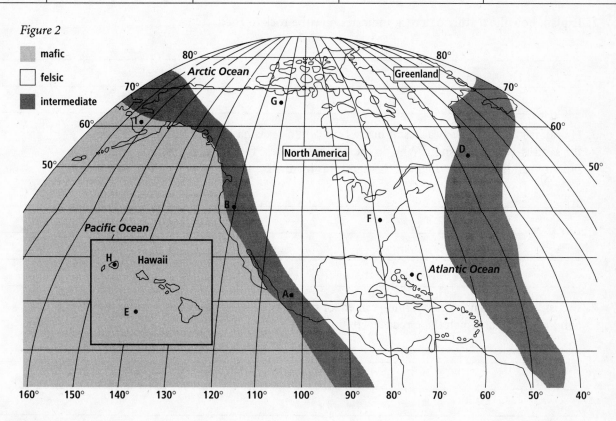

■ mafic
□ felsic
■ intermediate

ANALYZE

1. Where on the map is felsic rock found?

_____

LAB **5.2** **MAPPING**

ANALYZE, *continued*

2. Where on the map is mafic rock found?

_____

3. Where on the map is intermediate rock found?

_____

CONCLUDE AND APPLY

1. How did you determine whether the rocks were felsic, mafic, or intermediate?

_____

_____

_____

_____

2. Explain how the texture of a rock indicates how the rock formed.

_____

_____

_____

3. Hawaii is known for its beaches of black sand, while Texas has miles of beaches where the sand is as white as snow. Why do the beaches in these two states have such different types of sand? How do you think this sand was formed?

_____

_____

_____

_____

4. Extrusive rocks may be glassy, fine-grained, or porphyritic. Compare and contrast the conditions under which these rocks form.

_____

_____

_____

_____

_____

_____

LAB ◆ **6.1**   **INVESTIGATION**

Comparing Chemical Sedimentary Rocks and Modeling Their Formation

There are three main types of sedimentary rock: clastic, organic, and chemical. Clastic sedimentary rocks form when sediments such as sand or clay are cemented together. Organic sedimentary rocks form from the remains of once-living organisms that have been buried and lithified. Chemical sedimentary rocks may form when minerals precipitate out of a solution as a result of evaporation of water. They may also form from chemical reactions of ions in a solution. Common chemical sedimentary rocks include chert, rock salt, rock gypsum, and travertine.

PREPARATION

PROBLEM

How can you distinguish among different types of chemical sedimentary rocks? How do chemical sedimentary rocks form?

OBJECTIVES

- **Differentiate** among several types of chemical sedimentary rocks.
- **Simulate** the formation of chemical sedimentary rocks.

MATERIALS

4 chemical sedimentary rocks
sodium chloride solution
silver nitrate solution
water   500-mL beaker
2 test tubes   hot plate
test-tube rack   dropper
test-tube holder

SAFETY PRECAUTIONS

- Be careful when using the hot plate and handling hot glassware. Wear thermal mitts if needed.
- Silver nitrate stains clothing and skin. Stains on skin cannot be removed. Stains on clothing can be removed with a stain remover. Silver nitrate is highly toxic.
- Wear safety goggles, gloves, and an apron during the lab procedure.

PROCEDURE

1. Fill a beaker three-quarters full of water. Place the beaker on a hot plate and heat it to boiling.

2. Label two test tubes 1 and 2. Use a graduated cylinder to fill each one half full of sodium chloride solution and set the test tubes in a test-tube rack.

Copyright © Glencoe/McGraw-Hill, a division of the McGraw-Hill Companies, Inc.

LAB **6.1** **INVESTIGATION**

PROCEDURE, *continued*

3. Using the test-tube holder, place test tube 1 upright in the boiling water, and hold it in the water without letting it rest on the bottom of the beaker. Heat the test tube until much of the water in the test tube has boiled away and white crystals become visible (about 10 minutes). Record your observations in Table 1.

4. Use a dropper to add two drops of silver nitrate to test tube 2. Watch what happens and record your observations.

5. Now examine the chemical sedimentary rocks provided by your teacher.

DATA AND OBSERVATIONS

Table 1

Test Tube	Observations
1	
2	

Table 2

Rock	Color	Characteristics
Travertine	White or cream	Has dense, closely compacted layers; generally occurs in banded layers
Rock salt	Colorless to white	Has cubic crystals; generally occurs as a mass of intergrown crystals
Rock gypsum	White, gray, brown, red, or green	Is very soft, may have thin layers, generally appears massive, may be crumbly

ANALYZE

1. Use the information in Table 2 to help identify the chemical sedimentary rock samples provided by your teacher. Record your identifications in Table 3 below.

Table 3

Sample	Rock Name
1	
2	
3	

2. How did the crystals in test tube 1 form?

_____

_____

_____

_____

_____

3. How did you know that a chemical reaction was taking place in test tube 2?

_____

_____

_____

_____

_____

LAB **6.1** **INVESTIGATION**

CONCLUDE AND APPLY

1. In this lab, you observed the formation of precipitates from a salt solution. The same chemical elements make up common table salt and the mineral halite, or rock salt. What are these elements?

_____

_____

_____

_____

_____

2. What are some of the characteristic features of sedimentary rock?

_____

_____

_____

_____

_____

3. Where do you think you are most likely to find chemical sedimentary rock? Why?

_____

_____

_____

_____

_____

LAB ◆ **6.2** **MAPPING**

Grand Canyon Formations

The Grand Canyon is not only a famous recreational site, but it is the subject of intense scientific research. The Grand Canyon is composed of many layers of rock, most of which are sedimentary. These rocks often contain fossils that help scientists determine how and when the rock formed. If you were to hike through the Grand Canyon today, you would be exposed to numerous rock layers that represent more than 2 billion years of geologic history.

PREPARATION

PROBLEM

How can you use a geologic map of the Grand Canyon to interpret the geologic history of the area?

OBJECTIVES

- **Interpret** information about rock layers in the Grand Canyon.
- **Create** a geologic cross section.
- **Hypothesize** about how rock layers formed.

MATERIALS

colored pencils

PROCEDURE

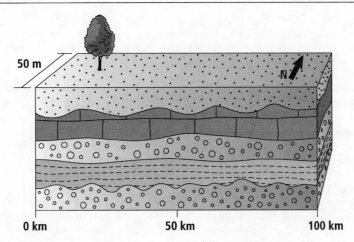

1. Examine the geologic cross section in the figure above.

2. Using the figure above as a guide, construct a cross section of the Grand Canyon rock layers listed in

Table 1. Draw the cross section on the grid in Data and Observations.

3. Once you have drawn in the rocks, color each layer to match the colors in Table 1.

LAB 6.2   **MAPPING**

PROCEDURE, *continued*

Table 1

Rock Layer	Composition	Color	Age (millions of years)	Thickness (feet) East to West
Kaibab Limestone	Sandy limestone	Grayish white	250	300–500
Toroweap Formation	Sandy limestone	Grayish yellow	255	250–450
Coconino Sandstone	Quartz sand	Cream	260	350–50
Hermit Shale	Shale	Rusty red	265	250–1000
Supai Formation	Shale	Red	285	950–1350
Redwall Limestone	Marine limestone	Red	335	450–700
Temple Butte Limestone	Freshwater limestone	Cream	350	0–450
Muav Limestone	Limestone	Gray	515	400–1000
Bright Angel Shale	Mudstone shale	Greenish brown	530	300–450
Tapeats Sandstone	Sandstone	Dark brown	545	250–150
Great Unconformity	Rock layers eroded or never deposited			
Chuar Group	Sandstone Shale Limestone	Tan Black Green	825–1000	6900
Nankoweap Formation	Sandstone	Gray	1050	6900
Cardenas Basalt	Basalt	Dark brown	1100	980
Dox Sandstone	Sandstone	Orange red	1190	3000
Shinumo Quartzite	Sandstone	Purplish brown	1200	1070–1560
Hakatai Shale	Shale	Orange red	1225	430–830
Bass Formation	Limestone	Grayish	1250	120–340
Early Unconformity	Rock layers eroded or never deposited			
Zoroaster Granite	Granite	Dark gray	1700–1900	?
Vishnu Schist	Mica schist	Black	2000	?

LAB ⟨ **6.2** ⟩   **MAPPING**

DATA AND OBSERVATIONS

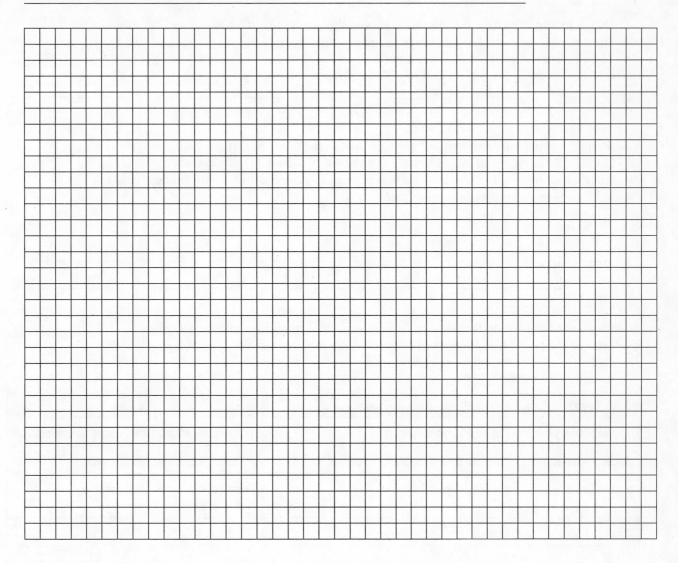

ANALYZE

1. What problems did you have with the vertical scale of the cross section? Will the cross section be the same in a different area? How will it change?

_____

_____

_____

2. Which layers in the Grand Canyon are metamorphic rocks? What factors contributed to their formation?

_____

_____

LAB ◇ **6.2**   **MAPPING**

CONCLUDE AND APPLY

1. Over 2 billion years ago, the area that is now to the north of the Grand Canyon in Colorado and Utah was once a mountain range taller and wider than the Rocky Mountains. What happened to those mountains over time?

_____

_____

2. Scientists have found two spans of geologic time in the Grand Canyon for which no rock layers exist. These are called the Great Unconformity (~550–820 million years ago) and the Early Unconformity (~1255–1695 million years ago). How are the unconformities related to changes in depositional environment?

_____

_____

_____

Scientists have been able to hypothesize the environmental conditions that existed when the layers of the Grand Canyon formed by examining the characteristics of each layer. Use Table 2 to answer the following questions.

Table 2

Rock Layer	Composition	Fossils
Redwall Limestone	Marine limestone	Brachiopods, clams, snails, corals, fish, trilobites
Coconino Sandstone	Pure quartz sand, basically a petrified sand dune	No bone fossils; invertebrate tracks and burrows
Hermit Shale	Soft, easily eroded shale	Ferns, conifers, other plants; reptile and amphibian tracks; no bones
Zoroaster Granite	Granite	None

3. Hypothesize about the environment that existed when the Coconino Sandstone formed. Give reasons for your hypothesis.

_____

_____

4. What does the information given about the Hermit Shale suggest about the environment that existed when it formed?

_____

_____

5. Why do you suppose that no fossils are present in Zoroaster Granite?

_____

_____

LAB ◆ **7.1**   **INVESTIGATION**

Chemical Weathering and Temperature

Chemical weathering takes place when rocks and minerals undergo changes in their composition as a result of a chemical reaction. Significant agents of chemical weathering include water, oxygen, carbon dioxide, and acids. Acids contribute to the chemical weathering of limestone, which produces carbon dioxide gas as the calcium carbonate dissolves. This gas production may be too slow to observe, but the loss of mass can be measured with a balance.

PREPARATION

PROBLEM
What effect does temperature have on the chemical weathering of limestone?

OBJECTIVES
- **Determine** the effect of an acid on limestone.
- **Model** the effect of temperature on the chemical weathering of limestone.
- **Calculate** the relationship between temperature increase and chemical breakdown.

MATERIALS
100 g pea-sized limestone chips
balance
paper towels
glass marker
200-mL beakers (2)
500-mL beakers (2)
400 mL vinegar
100-mL graduated cylinder
ice
aluminum foil
alcohol-based thermometer
hot water
plastic spoons

SAFETY PRECAUTIONS

- Vinegar is a weak acid and can burn sensitive skin. Wear your goggles at all times.
- Avoid using mercury-based thermometers. Mercury is toxic.
- Wash your hands after handling the limestone chips and vinegar.
- Label all solutions.
- Wear an apron during the lab procedure.
- Follow your teacher's suggestions for disposing of lab materials.

PROCEDURE

1. Get about 100 g of limestone chips. Make two piles of chips, on two paper towels, and blot them as dry as possible.

2. Label two 200-mL beakers "C" and "W." Weigh one of the two piles of

chips to the nearest 0.1 g, and put them in beaker C. Record the mass in the table provided. Weigh the other pile of chips and put them in beaker W. Record the mass.

LAB ◆ **7.1** **INVESTIGATION**

PROCEDURE, continued

3. Add about 100 mL of cold vinegar to beaker C and 100 mL of warm vinegar to beaker W. Put about 400 mL of an ice-water mixture in one 500-mL beaker, and about 400 mL of hot water in the other beaker. **CAUTION:** *Direct contact with hot water can burn skin.* Place beaker C in the ice-water mixture, and beaker W in the hot water. Measure and record the temperature in beakers W and C.

4. Look for evidence of a chemical reaction in the two beakers. Record what you observe in the table.

5. Cover both beakers with aluminum foil. After 20–30 minutes, use a plastic spoon to fish out the limestone pieces from each beaker. Place them on separate labeled paper towels and blot them dry.

6. Measure and record the mass of the chips from both beakers.

7. Put the chips back into their respective beakers. Add 100 mL of cold vinegar to the chips in beaker C and 100 mL of warm vinegar to the chips in beaker W. Cover both beakers with aluminum foil.

8. Refrigerate beaker C. Put beaker W in the lab where it can sit overnight.

9. The next day, record the temperature of the vinegar in the two beakers. Pour out the vinegar and rinse away small black pieces and residue. Place the chips on separate labeled paper towels and blot them dry.

10. Measure and record the mass of each pile of chips.

11. Calculate and record the percentage change in mass.

12. Use the figure following the table to create a bar graph of your results.

DATA AND OBSERVATIONS

TABLE

		Beaker C	Beaker W
	Mass before weathering		
	Mass after weathering		
Day 1	Temperature of vinegar		
	Change in mass		
	Percentage change in mass		
	Mass before weathering		
	Mass after weathering		
Day 2	Temperature of vinegar		
	Change in mass		
	Percentage change in mass		

LAB **7.1**   **INVESTIGATION**

DATA AND OBSERVATIONS, *continued*

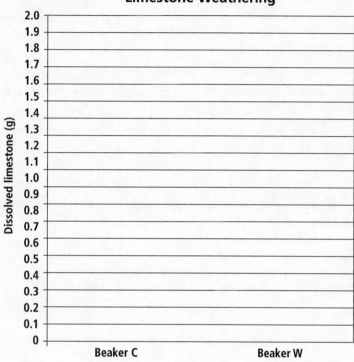

Limestone Weathering

ANALYZE

1. What evidence of a chemical reaction did you see when you added vinegar to the limestone chips?

_____

2. What evidence of chemical weathering appeared on the second day?

_____

_____

_____

3. What effect did temperature have on the weathering of the limestone chips?

_____

4. What are some ways to express the amount of change to the limestone due to weathering?

_____

_____

LAB 7.1   **INVESTIGATION**

CONCLUDE AND APPLY

1. Do the data suggest how climate could affect the rate of chemical weathering? Explain your answer.

_____

_____

_____

2. What changes could you make in the investigation to increase chemical weathering of the limestone?

_____

_____

_____

3. Where do you think chemical weathering of limestone would be faster—in a hot desert or in a rainy northern valley? Explain your answer.

_____

_____

_____

Laboratory Manual

LAB ◆ **7.2**   **MAPPING**

Global Soils and Climate

Soil is one of our most important natural resources. Humans and other animals depend on plants, which usually grow in soil, for their food and shelter. Except for some mountainous terrain and extremely cold areas on Earth, soil is found everywhere. Soil formation depends on the weathering of bedrock. The type and amount of weathering is closely related to the local climate. Because soils form from different parent bedrock and undergo different climatic conditions, soils vary greatly from one place to another.

PREPARATION

PROBLEM

Are soil types influenced by precipitation and temperature?

MATERIALS

ruler

OBJECTIVES

- **Use** maps to **compare** climate and soils in different regions.
- **Relate** regional soil types to temperature and rainfall.

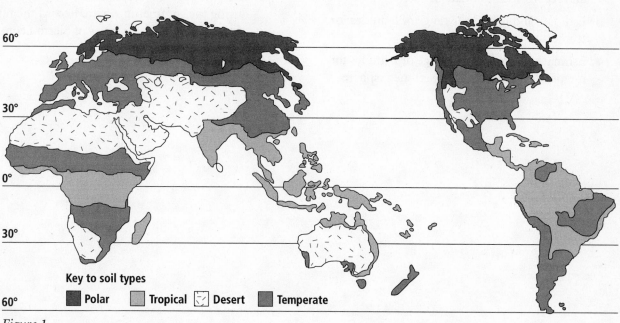

Figure 1

LAB 7.2 **MAPPING**

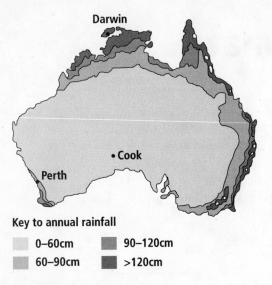

Figure 2

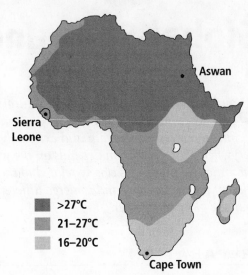

Figure 3

PROCEDURE

1. Examine Figure 1. The map covers roughly 70°N to 60°S latitude. Notice the key to the four soil types.

2. Estimate the range of latitudes for polar soils, and record your estimate in Table 1.

3. Estimate and record the range of latitudes for tropical soils.

4. Estimate and record the range of latitudes for temperate soils in the northern hemisphere.

5. Examine Figure 2, an annual rainfall map of Australia. In Table 2, record the range of rainfall for the cities of Perth, Cook, and Darwin.

6. Examine Figure 3, a typical temperature day during the summer in Africa. Record the range of temperatures in the cities of Sierra Leone, Aswan, and Cape Town.

LAB **7.2**   **MAPPING**

DATA AND OBSERVATIONS

Table 1

Soil Type	Range of Latitudes
Polar	
Tropical	
Northern temperate	

Table 2

City	Range of Rainfall
Perth	
Cook	
Darwin	
	Range of Temperature
Sierra Leone	
Aswan	
Cape Town	

ANALYZE

1. At what latitudes in the northern and southern hemispheres are desert soils found?

_____

_____

2. What might be the reason for polar soils reaching down to about 40°N in the United States, while in the rest of the world they stay up around 50°N?

_____

_____

3. Compare the rainfall pattern in Australia to the soil types found there.

_____

_____

_____

_____

LAB **7.2**

ANALYZE, *continued*

4. Compare the temperature map of Africa with the soil types found in that country.

_____

_____

_____

_____

_____

CONCLUDE AND APPLY

1. Are the soil types found in different areas of Earth related to the climate of that area? Explain your answer.

_____

_____

_____

_____

_____

2. Are the soil types more closely related to temperature or to rainfall?

_____

_____

_____

3. If you had to predict the type of soil found in an area on Earth, what information would you seek?

_____

_____

_____

LAB 8.1   **INVESTIGATION**

How Does Wind Erosion Take Place?

Winds transport materials by causing sediment particles to move in different ways. One method of transport is called suspension, in which strong winds cause particles to stay airborne for long distances. Another method of wind transport, called saltation, causes a jumping motion of particles. You will investigate saltation, the most common method of sand transport, when you move sand in a box with the use of a hair dryer.

PREPARATION

PROBLEM

How does wind-blown sand behave around small rocks and other obstructions?

OBJECTIVES

- **Observe** and **compare** the effects of moving air on different particle sizes.
- **Observe** some features of wind deposits.

MATERIALS

hair dryer with cool heat setting
box, cardboard (approximately
  30 cm wide, 60 cm long, 10 cm high)
samples of sand and gravel
400-mL beaker
twigs with a number of branches
  (or steel wool and pencils)
candle
matches
rocks or rubber stoppers of
  various sizes
protractor
cardboard strip (15 cm × 5 cm)
20-cm thin string
paper clip
tape

SAFETY PRECAUTIONS

- If possible, plug the hair dryer into a ground fault interruptor (GFI) outlet.
- Do not get the hair dryer wet or use it with wet hands.
- Blown sand, clay, or silt can cause injury to the eyes or irritate skin. Do not use the high speed.
- Wear safety goggles and apron during the lab procedure.
- Make sure the heat setting on the hair dryer is set to off if possible.
- Do not stick metal objects into the hair dryer; electrocution can result.
- Wear thermal mitts if the hair dryer becomes hot to the touch.
- Follow your teacher's suggestions for disposing of lab materials.

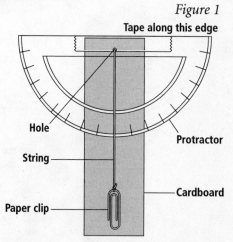

Figure 1

Tape along this edge

Hole

String

Paper clip

Protractor

Cardboard

LAB 8.1   **INVESTIGATION**

PROCEDURE

1. First, you will make a type of inclinometer to measure the slope of your sand dunes. With tape, attach the straight side of the protractor to the top of the cardboard strip, as show in Figure 1. Use a straightened paper clip to punch a hole in the cardboard through the hole in the protractor. Thread one end of the string through the hole and tie it. Attach a paper clip to the other end of the string. The paper clip must hang between the bottom of the cardboard and the bottom of the protractor. Set the inclinometer aside.

2. Use the beaker to obtain a sample of sand. Pour enough sand over the bottom of the box to form a layer about 1 cm thick. Distribute the sand evenly over the bottom.

3. Make sure your hands are dry while handling the hair dryer. Plug in and turn on the hair dryer, using the lowest setting. Move the hair dryer so the air is blowing horizontally over the sand. Adjust the speed and/or distance so that sand is moving toward the back of the box. Observe how the sand is moving. Turn off the dryer and record your observations in the table on the next page.

4. Redistribute the sand evenly over the bottom of the box. Place two or three rocks (or rubber stoppers) in the sand. Repeat this step until a sand dune forms. Turn off the dryer and carefully remove the rocks or stoppers from the box.

5. Using the inclinometer constructed in step 1, carefully measure the angle of the sand on the windward and lee-ward sides of the dune (Figure 2). Subtract the reading on the protractor indicated by the hanging string from 90 degrees. Record these values in the table.

Figure 2

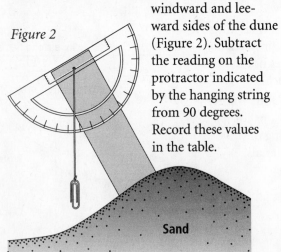

Sand

6. Smooth out the sand in the box. Place a twig in the sand. If you're using steel wool, then pull it apart slightly, so that there is more open space. Anchor the steel wool with a pencil or a small rock. Repeat step 4. Record your observations in the table. Remove the twig and smooth the sand.

7. Invert the beaker and press it into the sand. Place the candle in the sand directly behind the beaker and light it. **CAUTION:** *Make sure the candle is anchored securely in the sand. Do not burn candles near any combustibles.* Hold the dryer at a distance of about 30 cm in front of the beaker. Direct the dryer at the beaker and observe the results. While keeping the dryer at a fixed distance in front of the beaker, back the candle up about 3 cm at a time and observe the results. Turn off the dryer. Record your observations in the table.

8. Remove the beaker and candle and smooth the sand. Invert the beaker and press it into the sand again. Direct the dryer at the beaker. Observe how the sand moves around the beaker. Turn off the dryer. Record your observations in the table.

9. Extinguish the candle and remove it and the beaker from the box. While continuing to operate the dryer, have a partner add more sand very slowly to the box by pouring it from a height of 30 cm. Be sure this is done near the end of the box closest to the hair dryer to avoid blowing the sand out of the box. Record your observations in the table.

10. Remove all but 100 mL of the sand from the box and return it to its container. Put a handful of gravel in the box. Spread the gravel out slightly. Put the sand on top of the gravel, covering it completely. Use more sand if necessary. Direct the hair dryer at the sand. Adjust the speed/distance until the sand is moving slowly. Turn off the dryer and record your observations in the table.

11. Remove the gravel from the box and return it to its container. Put the sand in the beaker and dampen the sand slightly so that it barely sticks together. Pour the wet sand into the center of the box. Direct the dryer at the pile of damp sand and observe what happens. Turn off the dryer and record your observations in the table.

LAB **8.1**   **INVESTIGATION**

DATA AND OBSERVATIONS

	Observations
Procedure 4	
Procedure 6	Windward side = Leeward side =
Procedure 7	
Procedure 8	
Procedure 9	
Procedure 10	
Procedure 11	
Procedure 12	

ANALYZE

1. Where did the sand dune form relative to any obstacle you placed in the sand?

_____

_____

2. Which side of the dune was steeper? On which side was erosion dominant? On which side was deposition dominant?

_____

_____

_____

3. The twigs and steel wool simulated plants on the surface of the sand. How did they affect the movement of the sand?

_____

_____

_____

4. Describe the burning of the candle as you backed it slowly away from the beaker.

_____

_____

_____

LAB **8.1** INVESTIGATION

CONCLUDE AND APPLY

1. How would you characterize the force of wind behind an obstruction, and how does this relate to the deposition of sand behind such an obstruction?

_____

_____

_____

_____

_____

2. What could be used to slow the movement of wind-blown sand across a highway?

_____

_____

_____

3. Did the sand movement take place by saltation or suspension? Give evidence for your answer.

_____

_____

_____

LAB **8.2**   **DESIGN YOUR OWN**

Analysis of Glacial Till

Glaciers deposit two kinds of materials-till and outwash. Till consists of material that was carried by the glacier and deposited as the ice melted. A till deposit contains particles of all sizes in an unlayered mass. Outwash is material deposited by streams flowing from the ice. The moving water sorts the materials so that in an outwash sample, one particle size is more common than other sizes. Outwash deposits usually occur in distinct layers.

PREPARATION

PROBLEM

We want to determine the various particle sizes and what percentage each particle size is of the whole sample. In order to do this, we have to come up with a method of sorting the glacial till and outwash into different particle sizes. We then will measure the relative amount of each particle size in the sample.

OBJECTIVES

• **Determine** the particle sizes in samples of glacial till and outwash.

• **Measure** the relative amounts of each particle size.

• **Compare** the particle sizes and relative amounts of each size in glacial till and outwash.

HYPOTHESIS

Think about the material that might be left behind by a glacier. Would you expect to see more of one particle size than other particle sizes? What would be largest and smallest particle size you might find?

Make a hypothesis about the sizes of particles that will be found in the glacial till and outwash, as well as the percentage of each particle size that will be found in the sample. Write your hypothesis below.

_____

_____

_____

POSSIBLE MATERIALS

unknown glacial till and/or outwash
pan set
balance
beakers
screening sieves
filter paper

SAFETY PRECAUTIONS

• Wear safety goggles and apron during the lab procedure.

• Plan to dispose of wastes as directed by your teacher.

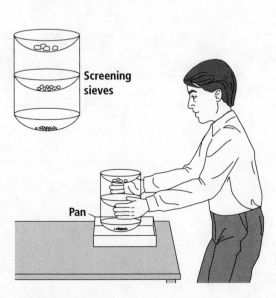

Screening sieves

Pan

LAB 8.2 **DESIGN YOUR OWN**

PLAN THE EXPERIMENT

- Think about ways in which you can separate the till and outwash. As you look at this till, what differences do you see between the various particles in the till? Can you use these differences to separate the particles? What could you use that would allow the smallest particles to pass through, but keep the larger pebbles behind? What separating tools will you need to separate the various sizes of particles? You will not be able to separate the till or outwash into just one size. Instead, you will have a range of sizes in each group.

- Once you separate the particles into various groups, how will you measure the amount of material in each group? What measuring tools will you need?

- What data will you need to record? Look at the objectives to get a hint. What kind of data table will you construct to make your measurements meaningful? Use or modify the chart below to record your data. Use the bar graph as a model for your data presentation. Use other graphs, as you feel necessary, to make the data more meaningful.

- Use the mesh-size table below as a guide to presenting some of your data.

  Talk with the members of your group until your ideas are well thought out, and then write below the procedures that your team will follow.

DATA AND OBSERVATIONS

Object	Mass of Empty Container (g)	Mass of Container plus Sediment (g)	Mass of Sediment (g)	Percent of Total Mass of Sediment

LAB **8.2** **DESIGN YOUR OWN**

DATA AND OBSERVATIONS, *continued*

MESH SIZES

Top, or largest, screen   =   _____ mm

Second screen from top   =   _____ mm

Third screen from top   =   _____ mm

Bottom, or smallest screen   =   _____ mm

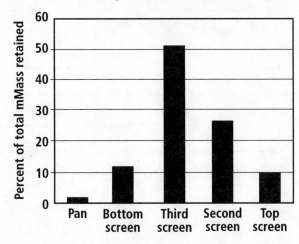

Percentage of Various Sizes in Sample

ANALYZE

1. What method did you use to separate the till and outwash?

_____

_____

_____

2. After separating the till, how many groups did you have?

_____

_____

3. What were the sizes of the particles in each group?

_____

_____

_____

LAB ◆ **8.2** DESIGN YOUR OWN

ANALYZE, *continued*

4. What size particles formed the largest group?

_____

_____

CHECK YOUR HYPOTHESIS

Was your **hypothesis** supported by your data? Why or why not?

_____

_____

CONCLUDE AND APPLY

1. Do you think that the glacial sediment you analyzed came from outwash or till? Explain your answer.

_____

_____

_____

2. Use a chart similar to the one below to categorize your groups' particle sizes as they relate to standardized particle sizes.

0.01 (size in mm)   0.0625   0.125   0.25   0.5   1.0   2.0   4.0   8.0

Fine Silt	Medium Silt	Coarse Silt	Very Fine Sand	Fine Sand	Medium Sand	Coarse Sand	Very Coarse Sand	Granules	Small Pebbles

3. How would you change the investigation if you wanted to measure the outwash in a glacial region of Wisconsin and were going to publish your findings?

_____

_____

_____

_____

LAB 9.1 **INVESTIGATION**

Analyzing Watersheds

A watershed is the land area whose water drains into a particular stream system. Any pollutants from the surface or in the groundwater will find their way into wells, surface streams, and lakes in a watershed. A watershed is also affected by any construction that disrupts its drainage pattern. You can gauge the health of a watershed by looking at condition indicators and vulnerability indicators. A condition indicator represents present conditions, such as contaminated sediments and groundwater that contains chemicals. Vulnerability indicators represent conditions that may adversely affect the watershed in the future, such as large human populations and the potential for agricultural runoff.

PREPARATION

PROBLEM
Determine the health of a watershed by analyzing indicators and establish goals to improve the health of the watershed.

OBJECTIVES
- **Examine** maps showing condition and vulnerability indicators.
- **Analyze** maps and **establish** a watershed health report.

- **Develop** a list of goals aimed at reversing damage and improving the health of the watershed.

MATERIALS
ruler
colored markers

PROCEDURE

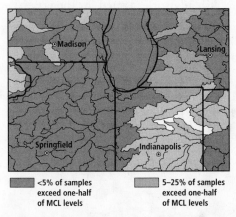

Figure 1. Chemicals from many different sources in the groundwater. Before the water is used, many of these chemicals will be filtered out or neutralized. (1997)

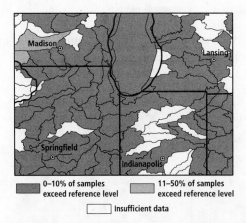

Figure 2. Copper, chromium, nickel, and zinc in the groundwater. Consumption of high concentrations of these chemicals causes illness or death. (1997)

PROCEDURE, *continued*

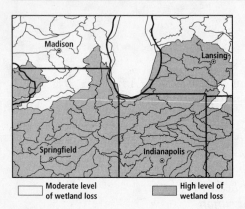

Moderate level of wetland loss   High level of wetland loss

Figure 3. Wetlands lost because of human use. Wetlands make important contributions to the health of a watershed by purifying water, filtering runoff, abating floods, and decreasing erosion. (1997)

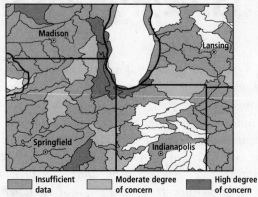

Insufficient data   Moderate degree of concern   High degree of concern

Figure 4. Chemicals found in bottom sediments. These chemicals can harm or kill bottom-dwelling organisms. They can also accumulate in organisms and move up the food chain to fish, shellfish, and humans. (1997)

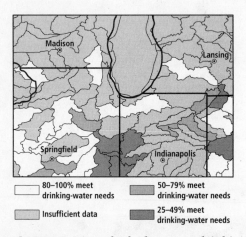

80–100% meet drinking-water needs   50–79% meet drinking-water needs

Insufficient data   25–49% meet drinking-water needs

Figure 5. Watersheds that meet drinking-water needs of a human population. (1997)

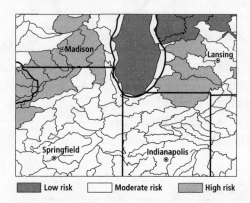

Low risk   Moderate risk   High risk

Figure 6. Fish advisories issued for the watershed. Advisories indicate the accumulation of toxic substances in fish and shellfish, making them unsafe for human consumption. (1997)

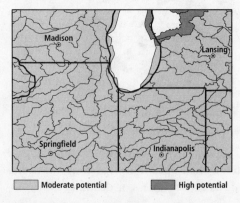

Moderate potential   High potential

Figure 7. Pesticide runoff from farms. Watersheds with high scores are at greater risk of contamination of surface water by pesticides. (1997)

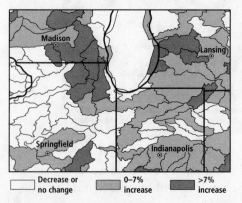

Decrease or no change   0–7% increase   >7% increase

Figure 8. Growth of human population. Population increases can result in increased pollution of the water. (1997)

LAB **9.1** **INVESTIGATION**

PROCEDURE, *continued*

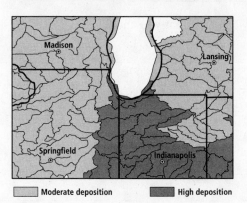

Moderate deposition   High deposition

Figure 9. Atmospheric deposition of nitrogen. Nitrogen and phosphorus are nutrients that can cause algal and cyanobacterial blooms and other problems in surface water and groundwater. (1997)

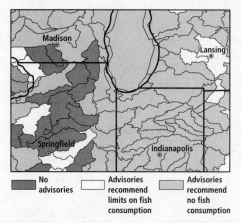

No advisories | Advisories recommend limits on fish consumption | Advisories recommend no fish consumption

Figure 10. Nitrate risk from various sources, such as fertilizers, atmospheric deposition, and karst aquifers. (1997)

1. Examine the six condition indicators (Figures 1–6) and four vulnerability indicators (Figures 7–10). Each irregular area on the map represents a watershed.

2. Pick one watershed and draw around its perimeter on each map. This will be the watershed that you examine for each indicator.

3. Analyze each condition indicator. In Figure 11, draw a bar for each condition indicator to represent your interpretation of the map.

4. Analyze each vulnerability indicator. Draw a bar for each vulnerability indicator in Figure 12.

DATA AND OBSERVATIONS

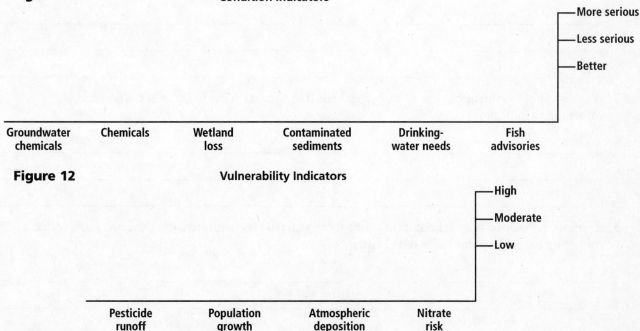

Figure 11   **Condition Indicators**

— More serious

— Less serious

— Better

Groundwater chemicals | Chemicals | Wetland loss | Contaminated sediments | Drinking-water needs | Fish advisories

Figure 12   **Vulnerability Indicators**

— High

— Moderate

— Low

Pesticide runoff | Population growth | Atmospheric deposition | Nitrate risk

LAB ◇ **9.1** INVESTIGATION

ANALYZE

1. Write a short narrative describing the present condition of the watershed that you chose.

_____

_____

_____

2. Describe the vulnerability of the watershed.

_____

_____

_____

3. Are the watershed conditions similar to those of surrounding watersheds? Why do you suppose they are or are not?

_____

_____

_____

_____

CONCLUDE AND APPLY

1. Taking into consideration the many pressures on the watershed you chose, predict what will happen if conditions remain the same for the next 50 years.

_____

_____

2. What is your assessment of most of the watersheds that appear on the maps of condition and vulnerability indicators?

_____

_____

_____

3. If you were the governor of the state in which these watersheds are located, what specific goals would you set up to improve the health of the citizens?

_____

_____

LAB 9.2 **MAPPING**

Interpreting a River's Habits

All stream systems generally start from rain running off the land. A stream develops further, depending on the amount of available water, the slope of the land, and the underlying type of bedrock. Fast-moving streams follow a straighter path than do slow-moving streams, which tend to form meanders. Oxbow lakes often form from meandering streams and rivers. Below is a topographic map of the Souris River valley in north-central North Dakota. This area was under a continental glacier during the ice ages. The surface is largely covered with moraine deposits.

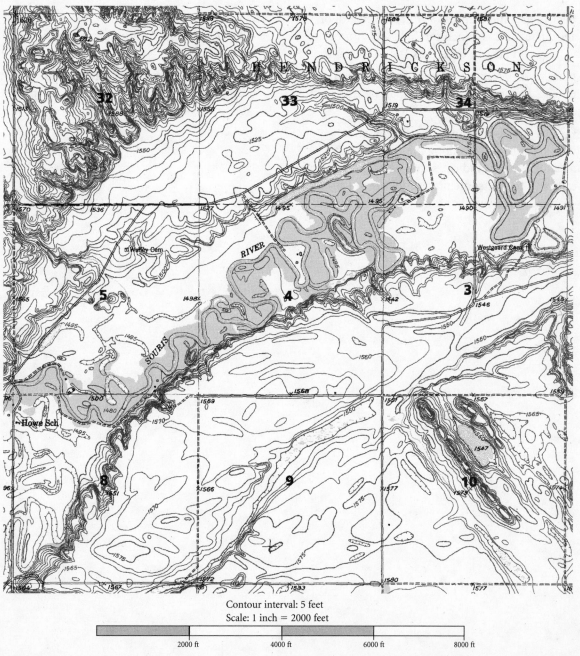

Contour interval: 5 feet
Scale: 1 inch = 2000 feet

2000 ft   4000 ft   6000 ft   8000 ft

LAB ◆ **9.2**   **MAPPING** 🌐

PREPARATION

PROBLEM
What can a topographic map tell about a river and its surroundings?

MATERIALS
ruler

OBJECTIVES
Use a topographic map to **answer** questions about a river and its valley.

PROCEDURE

1. The topographic map has a contour interval of 5 feet. The scale is 1 inch for 2000 feet. Study the map and answer questions 1–4 in the table.

2. The river drops about 2 feet in elevation across the map. Determine the gradient and answer questions 5–7.

3. Examine the floodplain of the river. Notice that the contour lines along the river run into one another. This indicates that natural levees occur and that at some places they are at least 5 feet high. Answer questions 8–10.

4. Notice that there are numerous elongated depressions in the floodplain. Answer question 11.

5. Examine the structures across the top of the map in sections 32, 33, and 34. Answer questions 12 and 13.

LAB 9.2   **MAPPING**

DATA AND OBSERVATIONS

Table

Question	Answer
1. What is the approximate difference between the lowest point and the highest elevation?	
2. What is the straight-line distance from where the river enters the map to where it leaves the map?	
3. What is the approximate length of the river's course that you can see on the map?	
4. What does the difference between the two distances in questions 2 and 3 tell you about the river's gradient?	
5. What is the river's gradient per 100 feet?	
6. What is the river's gradient per mile?	
7. Estimate the rate at which the river flows: very slowly, slowly, or rapidly.	
8. Approximately how wide is the floodplain of the river?	
9. What happened just east of Westgaard Cemetery in section 3?	
10. Has what you described in question 9 occurred anywhere else on the map? If so, where?	
11. What are the depressions in the floodplain called?	
12. Is there any evidence of erosion in sections 32, 33, and 34?	
13. Is there any evidence of other stream valleys?	

LAB 9.2

ANALYZE

1. How is a structure like the one identified in question 9 formed?

_____

_____

_____

2. What do you suspect is the origin of the generally flat land between the present floodplain bluff and the steep bank in the northern third of section 33 and most of section 32?

_____

_____

_____

CONCLUDE AND APPLY

1. From your interpretation of the topographic map, describe the Souris River's shape, flow rate, and amount of downcutting into the bedrock.

_____

_____

_____

_____

_____

2. Describe the geography around the Souris River.

_____

_____

_____

_____

3. What do you think the overall rain pattern in this area might be: little rain, moderate, or heavy? Support your answer with an explanation.

_____

_____

_____

_____

LAB ◆ **10.1** **INVESTIGATION**

Measuring Permeability Rate

*A*fter a rain, you may have noticed that puddles are left on the sidewalks, but not on the grass next to them. If the same amount of rain falls on both surfaces, why does more water remain on one surface? A lawn is usually much more permeable than a cement or asphalt sidewalk. Permeability is the ability of a material to let water pass through it.

PREPARATION

PROBLEM
How does the water permeability of different soil components vary?

OBJECTIVES
• **Measure** the water permeability of various types of soil.

• **Compare** and **contrast** the permeability of pure and mixed materials.

MATERIALS
hand lens
100 mL sand
100 mL pebbles
100 mL potter's clay
100 mL unsorted soil
100-mL graduated cylinder

water
stopwatch
4 rubber bands
4 cheesecloth squares
4 large funnels
500–1000-mL beakers (4)

SAFETY PRECAUTIONS

• Potter's clay that is airborne can irritate eyes and nose; wear goggles while handling dry clay.

• Wipe up any spills immediately.

• Wear an apron during the lab procedure to avoid staining your clothing.

LAB   **10.1**   **INVESTIGATION**

PROCEDURE

1. Examine the sand, pebbles, clay, and unsorted soil with a hand lens. Look for differences in the particle size as well as other observable characteristics. Record this information under Observations.

2. Line four funnels with squares of cheesecloth. Secure the cheesecloth with a rubber band. Set each funnel on top of a beaker.

3. Put 100 mL of sand in one funnel, 100 mL of pebbles in a second, 100 mL of clay in a third, and 100 mL of unsorted soil in a fourth. Leave at least 3–4 cm of space above the material in each funnel.

4. Pour water through the funnel until the water just starts to drip into the beaker. Stop pouring the water and wait until the water stops dripping. Empty the water out of the beaker.

5. Slowly pour 100 mL of water into the funnel containing the sand. Do not let the water overflow the funnel. Start the stopwatch when the water begins to drip out of the funnel.

6. Stop the stopwatch when the water stops dripping out of the funnel or after 5 minutes. Record the time to the nearest second in the table below.

7. Measure the water that drained into the beaker and record the amount.

8. Repeat steps 4–7 for the pebbles and clay.

9. Calculate the permeability of the three materials by dividing the amount of water that drained from each funnel by the drainage time in seconds. Express the value as milliliters per second.

10. Based on the permeability of the first three materials, estimate and record the permeability of the unsorted material.

11. Repeat steps 4–7 for the unsorted material. Calculate the permeability.

12. Do not put the wet materials in the sink or trash. Store them where your teacher directs you.

DATA AND OBSERVATIONS

OBSERVATIONS

_____

_____

_____

_____

_____

_____

_____

	Sand	Pebbles	Clay	Unsorted
Time for draining (s)				
Drained water (mL)				
Estimated permeability rate (mL/s)				
Calculated permeability rate (mL/s)				

Copyright © Glencoe/McGraw-Hill, a division of the McGraw-Hill Companies, Inc.

ANALYZE

1. Create a bar graph for your data, using the empty graph below.

Permeability Rate

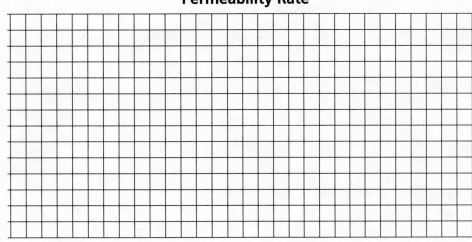

Permeability (mL/sec)

Material

2. Compare the permeability rate of the four materials.

_____

_____

_____

3. Did you accurately predict the permeability rate through the unsorted soil? If not, why not?

_____

_____

LAB ◁ **10.1** ▷   **INVESTIGATION**

CONCLUDE AND APPLY

1. Based on your observation of each sample, suggest an explanation for the differences in their permeability.

_____

_____

_____

_____

_____

_____

_____

2. How does sorting of material affect permeability?

_____

_____

3. Based on the results of this investigation, would you expect to get more water from a well dug in sand, pebbles, clay, or unsorted material? Give reasons for your answer.

_____

_____

_____

_____

DESIGN YOUR OWN

Analysis of Drinking Water

In many areas of the United States, groundwater is the only economical source of household water. If groundwater becomes contaminated, it can be cleaned up only with difficulty and at great expense. The contaminants originate above ground and often result from human activities. Wells bring groundwater up and are a source of drinking water and a direct pathway from the land surface into the water supply. Well water should be tested at least once a year. If the well is in an area of potential pollution sources such as farms, landfills, and toxic disposal sites, it should be tested periodically.

PREPARATION

PROBLEM
How can you tell if drinking water from a well is safe?

OBJECTIVES
- **Examine** test results for well water.
- **Interpret** the test results and **assess** health risks.
- **Write** a report describing test results, listing health risks, and making recommendations.

HYPOTHESIS
As a group, write a hypothesis about the safety of the well water.

_____

_____

_____

POSSIBLE MATERIALS
paper
computer

PLAN THE EXPERIMENT

Study Table 1, listing contaminants, their maximum contaminant level (MCL), health risks to humans, possible sources of the pollutants, and possible treatments to clean the water. The MCL is the maximum contamination allowed by the Environmental Protection Agency (EPA). The suggested water treatments would be fairly cheap to do

on site and do not affect the water in the well or in the ground. Examine the well test results (Table 2), and determine any risk to humans. Design and write a report of your discoveries. Include health risks and other information and suggestions that you think are necessary. Keep your report about a page long.

LAB 10.2   **DESIGN YOUR OWN**

DATA AND OBSERVATIONS

Table 1

Contaminant	MCL (mg/L)	Risks to Humans	Contaminant Sources	On-Site Treatment
Arsenic	0.05	Weight loss, depression, cancer	Pesticides, improper waste disposal, mining	Reverse osmosis, filtration, distillation
Barium	2	Toxic to heart, blood vessels, and nerves	Paints, diesel-fuel combustion, mining	Reverse osmosis, filtration, distillation
Benzopyrene	0.0002	Cancer	Coal-tar coating, fossil fuels	Activated carbon
Cadmium	0.005	Kidney damage, mutations	Fertilizers, sewage, discarded batteries	Reverse osmosis, filtration, distillation
Chromium	0.1	Lung tumors, nervous-system damage, accumulation in organs	Septic systems, industrial discharge, mining sites	Reverse osmosis, filtration, distillation
2-4 D	0.07	Cancer, liver and kidney damage	Herbicides, aquatic-weed control	Activated carbon
Dioxin	0.00000003	Cancer, mutations	Impurity in herbicides, chemical by-products	Activated carbon
Cyanide	0.2	Thyroid and nervous-system damage	Fertilizer; mining; electronics, steel, and plastic manufacturing	Ion exchange, reverse osmosis, chlorination
Lead	0.015	Reduced mental capacity, neurological problems	Paint, diesel-fuel combustion, discarded batteries, old paints and solder	Activated carbon, ion exchange, reverse osmosis
Methoxychlor	0.04	Reduced growth; impact on liver, kidneys, and nerves	Insecticide for fruits, vegetables, alfalfa, livestock, pets	Activated carbon
Nitrate	10	Blue-baby disease	Livestock facilities, septic systems, fertilizers	Ion exchange, distillation, reverse osmosis
Picloram	0.5	Kidney and liver damage	Herbicide on broadleaf plants	Activated carbon
Thallium	0.002	Skin irritation	Electronics, glass, and pharmaceuticals manufacturing	Ion exchange, distillation

LAB 10.2   DESIGN YOUR OWN

DATA AND OBSERVATIONS, *continued*

Table 2

Results for Well 1		Results for Well 2	
Contaminant	**Amount (mg/L)**	**Contaminant**	**Amount (mg/L)**
Arsenic	0.045	Arsenic	0.06
Cadmium	0.007	Barium	3.0
2-4 D	0.01	Benzopyrene	0.0000
Lead	0.017	Cadmium	0.001
Methoxychlor	0.04	2-4 D	0.00
Nitrate	0.01	Dioxin	0.00000000
Picloram	0.000	Lead	0.000
Thallium	0.000	Nitrate	0.00

ANALYZE

1. What information did you provide to the well owner and why?

_____

_____

_____

2. What criterion did you use to determine if a health warning was necessary?

_____

_____

_____

_____

3. Did you suggest additional water tests? Why or why not?

_____

_____

_____

_____

ANALYZE, *continued*

4. Which water treatments did you suggest, and why?

_____

_____

_____

_____

_____

_____

CHECK YOUR HYPOTHESIS

Was your **hypothesis** supported by your data? Why or why not?

_____

_____

CONCLUDE AND APPLY

1. What did you conclude about the water from wells 1 and 2?

_____

_____

_____

_____

2. If you had more room on the report, what additional information would you provide?

_____

_____

_____

_____

3. If you were the EPA director, what directives would you make to warn people of possible health risks from their well water?

_____

_____

_____

LAB ◆ 11.1 ◆ INVESTIGATION

Temperature Inversion

In some cities, the weather report often warns of high air-pollution levels. People are asked not to drive unless it is absolutely necessary, and open fires and barbecues are forbidden. A frequent reason for high levels of air pollution near the ground is a temperature inversion in the atmosphere. Although temperature and pressure in the overall troposphere decrease with height, the temperature inversion is an exception to this rule.

PREPARATION

PROBLEM

How can you detect a temperature inversion, and how does it trap pollution?

OBJECTIVES

- **Graph** temperature data for the atmosphere.
- **Describe** how a temperature inversion affects ground-level pollution.

MATERIALS

ruler
calculator

PROCEDURE

1. Use Box 1 to graph data sets A and B. The horizontal axis will be height and the vertical axis will be temperature. Label these axes.

2. Look at the data sets and choose suitable ranges and intervals for the axes. Mark the axes accordingly.

3. Plot data set A on your graph. Connect the points with a solid line. Plot data set B on the same graph but connect the points with a dashed line.

4. Indicate on your graph which line represents which data set. Give the graph a title.

5. When air is heated, it expands. As air expands, the number of molecules in a particular volume,

for example, 1 m³, decreases. So the mass of air molecules per cubic meter—or its density—decreases. Because of this relationship, if the pressure of the air remains unchanged, then its density is inversely proportional to its temperature, provided the temperature is expressed in kelvins (K). The Kelvin scale starts at absolute zero, which corresponds to −273.15°C. To convert a temperature in degrees Celsius to kelvins, you simply add 273.15. Convert the temperatures in the table into kelvins.

6. You can work out the density of air at a particular height from the temperature data if you know the density of air at ground level.

Chapter 11 *Earth Science: Geology, the Environment, and the Universe* **81**

LAB ◆ 11.1   INVESTIGATION

PROCEDURE, *continued*

Density is inversely proportional to absolute temperature; therefore, the density at height x is equal to the density at ground level times the absolute temperature (kelvins) at ground level divided by the absolute temperature at height x. Use this information to calculate the density at each height for both data sets. Assume that the air density at ground level in both data sets is 1 kg/m^3.

7. Use Box 2 to make a graph of density versus height similar to the first graph you made.

DATA AND OBSERVATIONS

Table

Height (m)	Data Set A			Data Set B		
	Temperature (°C)	Absolute Temperature (K)	Density (kg/m³)	Temperature (°C)	Absolute Temperature (K)	Density (kg/m³)
0	20.0			20.0		
100	19.5			19.3		
200	18.7			18.8		
300	18.0			18.0		
400	17.5			19.0		
500	16.9			19.5		
600	16.0			19.4		
700	15.5			18.8		

Box 1

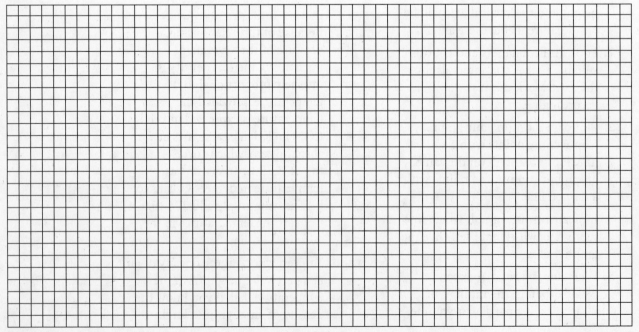

LAB **11.1**   **INVESTIGATION**

Box 2

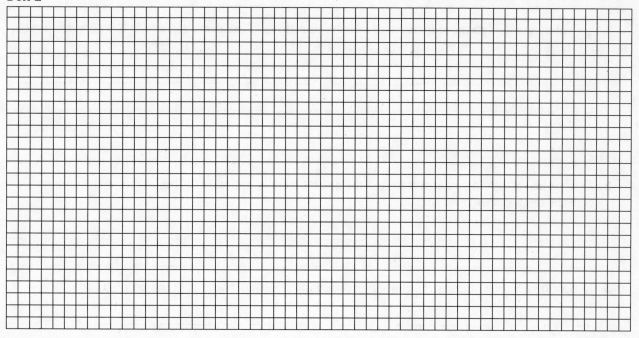

ANALYZE

1. For data set A, does the temperature increase or decrease as height increases? At what altitude does the temperature first change by 1°C?

_____

2. At what point do the two plotted lines from data sets A and B intersect?

_____

_____

3. Describe the plotted data of set B above 300 m.

_____

_____

4. Which data set shows normal conditions and which shows a temperature inversion?

_____

5. In the data set with the temperature inversion, use your graph in Box 2 to compare the density in two regions: 300–500 m and 500–700 m.

_____

_____

_____

LAB **11.1**   **INVESTIGATION**

CONCLUDE AND APPLY

1. Air pollutants tend to move from more dense regions toward less dense regions. What does this imply for the movement of air pollutants in the data set with the temperature inversion?

_____

_____

_____

_____

2. At what height would you expect to find the greatest concentration of air pollutants in the data set with the temperature inversion?

_____

_____

3. In your own words, summarize how temperature inversions increase air pollution at ground level.

_____

_____

_____

_____

_____

LAB **11.2**   **DESIGN YOUR OWN**

What is in the air?

Air is mostly composed of nitrogen and oxygen, with varying amounts of water vapor. However, air also contains particulates like dust, smoke, and pollen. It can be very useful to know just what particulates are in the air, especially for health reasons. One source of data is the daily pollen count; pollen affects hay fever and asthma sufferers. The concentration of particulates varies with time and weather. Health and safety authorities also monitor particulates in workplaces and schools.

PREPARATION

PROBLEM

What is the particulate content of the air? How does it change from day to day?

OBJECTIVES

- **Observe** how the daily weather affects the number and type of particulates in the air.
- **Research** the number and type of particulates in the air around your school.

HYPOTHESIS

As a group, discuss the atmospheric changes caused by different weather patterns. Write a hypothesis about how the weather affects the concentration of particulates outside and inside your school.

_____

_____

_____

_____

POSSIBLE MATERIALS

coffee filters
rubber band
thermometer
microscope
vacuum cleaner with intake hose
outdoor extension cord
masking tape
5 microscope slides
petroleum jelly
5 petri dishes with lids

SAFETY PRECAUTIONS

- Wear safety goggles and an apron during the lab procedure.
- Do not use the vacuum cleaner outside in inclement weather. Keep the cord away from water.

LAB ⟨ **11.2** ⟩   **DESIGN YOUR OWN**

PLAN THE EXPERIMENT

Review the list of possible materials. Plan how to monitor the daily variation of the atmosphere's particulate content both outside and inside the school during a particular period of time. Choose the sites you will monitor. How will you determine the concentration of particulates in the air each day at each location? What daily location measurements will you make? Plan to collect a week's worth of data. Design a table to record your data. Outline your plan and have your teacher approve it before you begin the experiment.

_____

_____

_____

_____

_____

_____

_____

_____

_____

_____

_____

_____

_____

_____

_____

LAB **11.2** DESIGN YOUR OWN

DATA AND OBSERVATIONS

DATA TABLE

LAB 11.2   DESIGN YOUR OWN

ANALYZE

1. Which locations had the highest particle count? Which had the lowest?

_____

_____

2. What types of particles did you collect outdoors?

_____

3. Which elements of the weather most clearly affected the number of particles collected outdoors?

_____

4. Did any of your indoor locations show the same trend of variation as the outdoor locations?
If so, which ones?

_____

_____

5. Did any of your indoor measurements vary with the weather in a significantly different way
from the outdoor counts? Explain your answer.

_____

_____

_____

CHECK YOUR HYPOTHESIS

Was your **hypothesis** supported by your data? Why or why not?

_____

_____

CONCLUDE AND APPLY

1. Based on your research, is a person with allergies more likely to have trouble indoors or outdoors
at your school? Explain your answer.

_____

_____

2. Under what circumstances would you expect a pollen warning to be issued?

_____

_____

_____

LAB ◆ 12.1   INVESTIGATION

Modeling the Coriolis Effect

The rotation of Earth in an easterly direction causes the Coriolis effect. The Coriolis effect, in turn, influences the direction of all free-moving objects, such as air and water. For example, in the northern hemisphere, air moving from the north pole toward the equator is deflected to the right. In the southern hemisphere, air moving from the south pole toward the equator is deflected to the left. The Coriolis effect greatly influences the movement of global wind patterns and ocean currents.

PREPARATION

PROBLEM
How does the Coriolis effect deflect the movement of air and water in each hemisphere?

OBJECTIVES
- **Model** the Coriolis effect in the northern and southern hemispheres.
- **Sketch** various movements caused by the Coriolis effect.

- **Infer** how the Coriolis effect influences global wind patterns and ocean currents.

MATERIALS
globe
red, blue, yellow, and green chalk

PROCEDURE

1. Working with a partner, place a globe on a steady, flat surface. Locate the equator, the north pole, and the south pole on the globe.

2. Have your partner rotate the globe in a counterclockwise direction at a slow, steady speed. As the globe rotates, use blue chalk to draw a line from the north pole to the equator. Sketch the line in circle A on the next page. Mark the four compass directions and the equator.

3. Use red chalk to draw a line from the equator to the north pole while your partner continues to rotate the globe. Sketch this line in circle B. Then add compass directions and the equator.

4. As your partner rotates the globe in a counterclockwise direction, use green chalk to draw a line from the south pole to the equator. Sketch the line in circle C. Then add compass directions and the equator.

5. As your partner rotates the globe in a counterclockwise direction, use yellow chalk to draw a line from the equator to the south pole. Sketch the line in circle D. Then add compass directions and the equator.

LAB 12.1 INVESTIGATION

DATA AND OBSERVATIONS

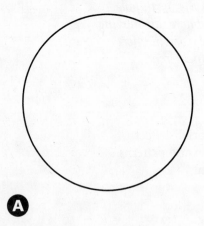

A

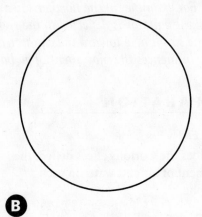

B

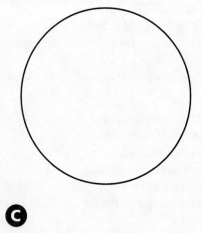

C

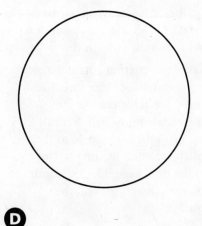

D

LAB ◆ **12.1**   **INVESTIGATION**

ANALYZE

1. Compare your four sketches. Describe any patterns that you observe.

_____

_____

_____

2. Why was it necessary to rotate the globe in a counterclockwise direction?

_____

_____

3. Suppose that each line represents a wind system. Describe where each originates and in which direction it moves.

_____

_____

_____

_____

_____

_____

4. Ocean surface currents, which affect weather and climate, move in circular patterns. Use sketches A and C to infer the direction in which these currents move in the northern and southern hemispheres.

_____

_____

_____

_____

LAB **12.1** **INVESTIGATION**

CONCLUDE AND APPLY

1. Summarize how freestanding objects are deflected by the Coriolis effect in the northern and southern hemispheres.

_____

_____

_____

_____

2. How would these objects move if the Coriolis effect did not exist? Explain your answer.

_____

_____

_____

_____

 **LAB 12.2** DESIGN YOUR OWN

Predicting the Weather

A ccurate weather forecasts depend on a variety of factors that can change by the minute, such as temperature, wind speed and direction, relative humidity, and air pressure. In addition, meteorologists must incorporate data from the lower atmosphere and the upper atmosphere when they make forecasts. Because so many factors affect weather—and because these factors constantly change—predicting the weather is a complex task.

PREPARATION

PROBLEM

How can you make an accurate weather forecast?

OBJECTIVES

- **Analyze** and **interpret** weather data from a variety of sources.
- **Measure** and **record** weather conditions.
- **Predict** the weather.
- **Determine** the accuracy of weather forecasts.

HYPOTHESIS

As a group, discuss what sources you will use to predict the weather. You may want to use the Glencoe Science Web Site, newspapers, television, radio, or your own weather observations. Write a general prediction of the weather for the next 5 days.

_____

_____

_____

_____

POSSIBLE MATERIALS

weather maps
alcohol-based thermometer
barometer
anemometer
wind vane
rain gauge

SAFETY PRECAUTIONS

- Be careful when handling weather instruments. If a thermometer or other glass instrument should break, do not attempt to clean it up. Notify your teacher immediately.
- Avoid using mercury-based thermometers. Mercury is toxic.
- Wear safety goggles during the lab procedure.

PLAN THE EXPERIMENT

As a group, decide how you will make your weather forecast. Will you use television, Internet, radio, or newspaper weather reports? Will you gather your own weather data? Or will you use a combination of sources? Assign tasks to each member of your group. For example, who will be responsible for measuring or obtaining data about each of the weather conditions in Tables 1 and 2? Who will summarize your data and judge the accuracy of the predictions? Have your teacher approve your plan before you begin.

Use Table 1 to record your weather predictions for the next 5 days. Make a prediction for each of the weather elements listed in the table. Then use Table 2 to record actual weather conditions for each day.

DATA AND OBSERVATIONS

Table 1

Predicted Weather					
	Day 1	**Day 2**	**Day 3**	**Day 4**	**Day 5**
Temperature					
Wind speed					
Wind direction					
Cloud cover					
Precipitation					
Presence of high or low pressure					

LAB 12.2 **DESIGN YOUR OWN**

DATA AND OBSERVATIONS, *continued*

Table 2

	Actual Weather				
	Day 1	Day 2	Day 3	Day 4	Day 5
Temperature					
Wind speed					
Wind direction					
Cloud cover					
Precipitation					
Presence of high or low pressure					

ANALYZE

1. What sources did you use to make your weather predictions? Be specific.

_____

_____

_____

2. Which weather conditions were most helpful in terms of making a forecast? Which weather conditions were least helpful?

_____

_____

_____

LAB ◀ **12.2** ▶   **DESIGN YOUR OWN**

ANALYZE, *continued*

3. Were your predictions for some weather conditions more accurate than others?
Explain your answer.

_____

_____

_____

4. Compare your predictions to those of other groups. Was one source consistently more
accurate than others? If so, why was it?

_____

_____

_____

CHECK YOUR HYPOTHESIS

Was your **hypothesis** supported by your data? Why or why not?

_____

_____

CONCLUDE AND APPLY

1. Summarize your data. Describe how the accuracy of your forecast changed over time.

_____

_____

2. As a group, brainstorm ways to improve the accuracy of your forecast. Record your ideas.

_____

_____

_____

3. Based on your results, infer why long-term weather forecasts are less reliable than
short-term weather forecasts.

_____

_____

LAB ◆ **13.1**   **INVESTIGATION**

Observing Flood Damage

Floods are the main cause of thunderstorm-related deaths in the United States each year. Floods can happen in a number of ways. Sometimes rain falls over a large area and drains into a river faster than the water can move downstream. The river overflows its banks and floods low-lying areas surrounding it. Floods can also occur when large amounts of rain fall on asphalt, concrete, or other surfaces that cannot easily absorb water. Yet another type of flooding, a flash flood, occurs when torrential rains cause a sudden overflow of a river or other water-drainage feature.

PREPARATION

PROBLEM
How do floods affect rates of erosion and human-built structures?

OBJECTIVES
- **Model** different types of floods.
- **Observe** and **record** rates of erosion.
- **Determine** how floods affect local communities.
- **Discuss** ways to reduce flood damage.

MATERIALS
stream table
sand
water source
hose
metric ruler
wooden sticks
large sheet of plastic

SAFETY PRECAUTIONS

- Wear safety goggles and an apron during the lab procedure.
- Be careful when using the hose. To avoid getting shocked, do not use the hose near an electrical receptacle.
- If spills occur, wipe them up immediately to prevent accidents.

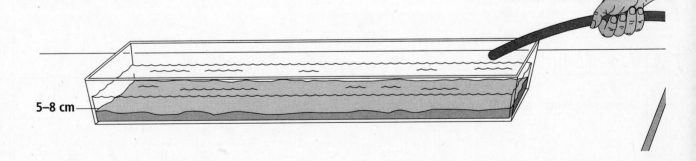

5–8 cm

Copyright © Glencoe/McGraw-Hill, a division of the McGraw-Hill Companies, Inc.

LAB **13.1** **INVESTIGATION**

PROCEDURE

1. As a group, set up the stream table on a long, low table. Carefully pour sand into the stream table. The sand should cover the bottom to a depth of 5 to 8 cm.

2. Attach the hose to the water source. Start the water flowing slowly and observe any erosion that occurs. Stop the water and record your observations in the table.

3. Smooth out the sand so that it once again covers the bottom of the stream table to a depth

of at least 5 cm. Insert a wooden stick, which represents a bridge support, in the middle of the stream table. Repeat step 2.

4. Remove the wooden stick and smooth out the sand. Repeat steps 2 and 3 with the water flowing rapidly.

5. Remove the wooden stick and smooth out the sand. Cover the sand with the sheet of plastic and repeat step 2.

DATA AND OBSERVATIONS

Conditions	Observations
Slow-moving water	
Slow-moving water with stick	
Fast-moving water	
Fast-moving water with stick	
Slow-moving water with plastic	

ANALYZE

1. Compare and contrast the flow of the water in steps 2 through 5.

_____
_____
_____
_____

2. When the wooden stick was in the sand, in what parts of the stream did the water flow fastest and slowest?

_____
_____
_____

3. During which step did most erosion occur? How could you tell?

_____
_____
_____
_____

4. How could you revise this lab to increase the duration of the model flood?

_____
_____
_____

5. Which step in the procedure modeled a flash flood? Which step modeled a flood in an urban area? Explain your answers.

_____
_____
_____
_____
_____

LAB **13.1**   **INVESTIGATION**

CONCLUDE AND APPLY

1. Based on your observations, why do bridges become unsafe during floods?

_____

_____

_____

_____

_____

2. What kind of damage might a flash flood cause to houses along a riverbank?

_____

_____

_____

_____

_____

3. As a group, brainstorm ways of reducing flood damage to homes and other human-built structures. Record your ideas here.

_____

_____

_____

_____

_____

LAB  **13.2**   **DESIGN YOUR OWN**

Building Hurricane-Proof Homes

Hurricanes are the most powerful of all storms, so they can cause tremendous damage to property and lives. Much of this damage is a result of violent winds that can exceed 250 km/h. Winds of more than 60 km/h can affect areas as far as 400 km from the center of the storm. In the United States, the National Weather Service issues hurricane warnings that help reduce loss of lives. Before a hurricane strikes a particular area, people temporarily move out of the path of the storm. Buildings, however, cannot be moved. Many are damaged or destroyed by high winds. Scientists and engineers are continually working to design stronger buildings that can withstand hurricane-strength winds.

PREPARATION

PROBLEM
What sort of structure can best withstand hurricane-strength winds?

OBJECTIVES
- **Design** and **construct** a model home using an assortment of building materials.
- **Test** the strength of the structure in a model hurricane.
- **Analyze** different structural designs and **infer** which would best withstand severe storm conditions.

HYPOTHESIS
As a group, discuss how you could use the materials provided by your teacher to design and build a model home. Form a hypothesis about the factors that might affect the ability of your structure to withstand a model hurricane. Write your hypothesis below.

_____

_____

_____

_____

POSSIBLE MATERIALS
wooden sticks
toothpicks
cardboard squares of various sizes
modeling clay
marshmallows
scissors
tape
glue
fan with variable speeds

SAFETY PRECAUTIONS

- Be careful when using the scissors and the electric fan.
- Follow your teacher's suggestions for disposing of lab materials.
- Wear safety goggles and an apron during the lab procedure.

LAB 13.2   **DESIGN YOUR OWN**

PLAN THE EXPERIMENT

Review the list of possible materials. Working in pairs, design a building that could withstand hurricane-strength winds. Sketch and label the design in the blank space provided below. Share your design with your group and decide on the best design. You might incorporate elements from several designs. Then, sketch and label the revised plan. Discuss how you will test your design. What will your control be? How will you model the hurricane? How will you vary hurricane conditions? How many times should you repeat the test? Construct your model. When your model is complete, test its strength. Draw a data table to record your observations. Have your teacher approve your plan before you begin.

_____

_____

_____

_____

_____

_____

_____

_____

_____

DATA AND OBSERVATIONS

DESIGNS AND DATA TABLE

LAB **13.2** **DESIGN YOUR OWN**

ANALYZE

1. Describe your model. Explain the function of each part.

_____

_____

_____

_____

2. Explain how you modeled hurricane-strength winds. How did you determine the strength of your model building?

_____

_____

_____

3. Did your building withstand the storm as planned? Why or why not?

_____

_____

_____

_____

4. Compare your design to those of other groups. Suggest improvements to your design. What could you change to increase its strength?

_____

_____

_____

_____

CHECK YOUR HYPOTHESIS

Was your **hypothesis** supported by your data? Why or why not?

_____

_____

LAB ◆ **13.2** 　　　　　　　　　　　　　　　　　**DESIGN YOUR OWN**

CONCLUDE AND APPLY

1. Add your suggested improvements to the sketch of your design. Describe each of its functional parts. Explain how the improvements will increase the strength of the design.

_____

_____

_____

_____

_____

2. Review your results and those of other groups. Which factors appear to affect the strength of the model homes?

_____

_____

_____

_____

3. In the tests, which held up best, solid or open walls? Why?

_____

_____

_____

4. Infer why skyscrapers are designed to bend in the wind.

_____

_____

_____

LAB ◆ 14.2 **MAPPING**

Classifying Climates

A variety of factors influence the climate of an area, including latitude, topography, closeness to a lake or an ocean, availability of moisture, global wind patterns, and air masses. These various factors cause Earth's climates to range from scorching deserts to tropical rain forests to ice-covered polar regions. In general, climates are classified by natural vegetation and average monthly values for temperature and precipitation.

PREPARATION

PROBLEM

How do climates differ from one another?

OBJECTIVES

• **Interpret** climatic data on a world map.

• **Compare** and **contrast** different climates.

• **Analyze** the factors that make climates different.

MATERIALS

world map or globe

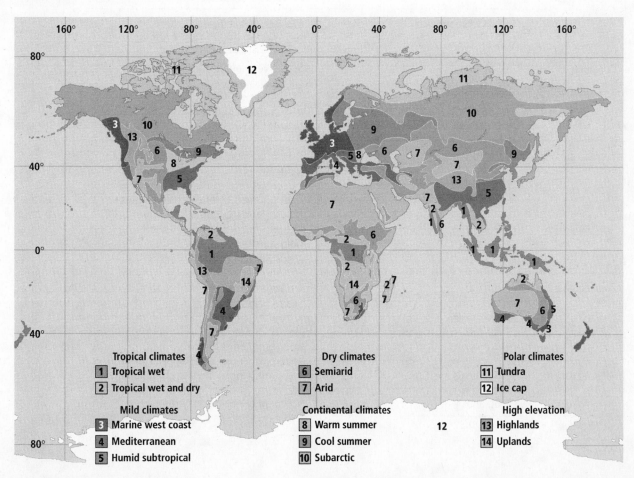

Tropical climates	**Dry climates**		**Polar climates**
1 Tropical wet	6 Semiarid		11 Tundra
2 Tropical wet and dry	7 Arid		12 Ice cap
Mild climates	**Continental climates**		**High elevation**
3 Marine west coast	8 Warm summer	12	13 Highlands
4 Mediterranean	9 Cool summer		14 Uplands
5 Humid subtropical	10 Subarctic		

LAB 14.2   **MAPPING**

PROCEDURE

1. Carefully study the figure on the previous page. Note the latitudes and longitudes. Locate your area on the map to orient yourself. Compare the figure to a world map or globe that includes the names of countries.

You will need both maps to answer the questions on the next page.

2. Study the table below, which briefly describes the various types of climates included in the figure.

DATA AND OBSERVATIONS

Type of Climate	Description	Defining Characteristics
Tropical climates	Tropical wet	High temperatures year-round High rates of precipitation
	Tropical wet and dry	High temperatures year-round Wet summers, dry winters
Mild climates	Marine west coast	Cool summers, mild winters Abundant precipitation
	Mediterranean	Warm summers, mild winters Moderate precipitation
	Humid subtropical	Wet, warm summers Dry, cool winters
Dry climates	Semiarid	Scarce vegetation Little precipitation
	Arid	Very scarce vegetation Very little precipitation
Continental climates	Warm summer	Warm summers, relatively cold winters Moderate precipitation
	Cool summer	Cool summers, relatively cold winters Moderate precipitation
	Subarctic	Cold summers, cold winters Moderate precipitation
Polar climates	Tundra	Cold year-round Scarce vegetation
	Ice cap	Very cold year-round No vegetation
High elevation	Highlands	Variation of polar climate on mountains
	Uplands	Variation of polar climate on high plateaus

LAB **14.2** MAPPING

ANALYZE

1. What is the climate of your area? Use the table to describe your climate.

_____

_____

2. What country is located at 25°N, 20°E? Describe the climate of this country.

_____

_____

3. In terms of latitude, where are most tropical wet climates located?

_____

_____

4. Study the locations of marine west coast and mediterranean climates. What factor appears to have the most influence on these climates?

_____

_____

5. Compare and contrast the climates of the west and east coasts of Nicaragua.

_____

_____

_____

_____

_____

6. Clashes between air masses can cause extreme variations in temperature. In the United States, which climate types appear to be most affected by air masses? Explain your answer.

_____

_____

_____

_____

LAB **14.2** **MAPPING**

CONCLUDE AND APPLY

1. How do climates differ on either side of the Rocky Mountains in the northwest United States? What can you infer about the influence of the mountains on climate?

_____

_____

_____

_____

_____

_____

2. Which part of Australia would be best suited for growing crops that need plenty of moisture and mild temperatures year-round? Why?

_____

_____

_____

3. South America and Africa do not extend to the poles, yet parts of these continents experience polarlike climates. Why?

_____

_____

_____

LAB 15.1

MAPPING

Ocean Surface Temperatures

Ocean water has distinct chemical and physical properties, such as level of salinity, temperature, and the ability to absorb light. Because the oceans constantly intermix, these properties can vary from day to day and from place to place. Scientists use satellite data to track changes in some of these properties. Ocean surface temperatures, for example, can be determined by using satellite imagery that detects differences in thermal energy. These data are then compiled into maps.

PREPARATION

PROBLEM

How do ocean surface temperatures vary from place to place?

MATERIALS

globe

OBJECTIVES

- **Interpret** a world map of ocean surface temperatures.
- **Compare** the surface temperatures of different oceans.
- **Analyze** why ocean surface temperatures vary.

PROCEDURE

1. Study the map, which shows ocean surface temperatures in October 2000. Compare it to a globe.

2. Use the globe to label the oceans and the continents on the map. Add latitude and longitude coordinates to the map. Also label north, south, east, and west on the map.

LAB 15.1   MAPPING

DATA AND OBSERVATIONS

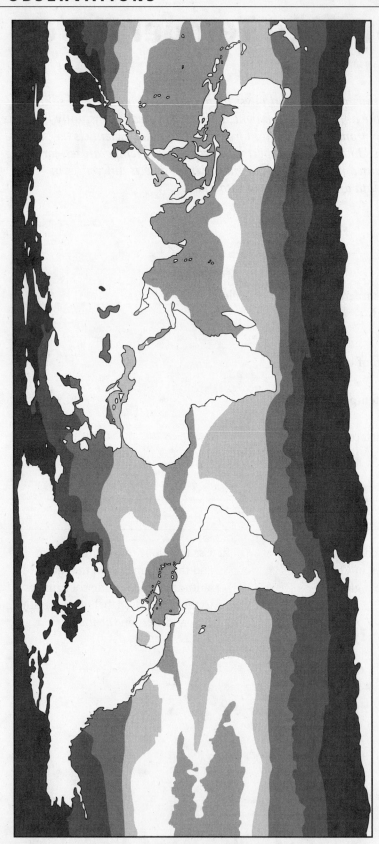

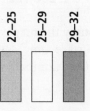

22–25

25–29

29–32

0–8

8–16

16–22

LAB 15.1 MAPPING

ANALYZE

1. What is the range of ocean surface temperatures shown in the scale on the map?

_____

_____

2. Look for and describe patterns on the map. For example, which surface temperature or range of temperatures appears to be most common?

_____

_____

_____

_____

_____

_____

3. What is the surface temperature of the ocean nearest to the place you live? Convert this temperature to the Fahrenheit scale.

_____

_____

4. Describe how ocean surface temperatures change from the northern Pacific Ocean southward to Antarctica.

_____

_____

_____

_____

_____

_____

_____

LAB 15.1   **MAPPING**

CONCLUDE AND APPLY

1. Where are the coldest surface temperatures found? Where are the warmest found? What accounts for these differences in temperature?

_____

_____

_____

_____

_____

_____

2. Global warming is an increase in global temperatures caused by increases in certain atmospheric gases. How might scientists use maps such as the one in this lab to analyze global warming? What might be some other uses of this map?

_____

_____

_____

_____

_____

3. How might this map change if the satellite data were gathered in February? In July?

_____

_____

_____

_____

LAB ◁ **15.2** ▷   **INVESTIGATION**

Making Waves

As wind blows across the surface of the ocean, friction causes the water to move with the wind. If conditions are right, water begins to pile up and forms a wave. Ocean waves vary greatly in height. Those that reach shallow water and break on shore may be less than 1 m high. In the open ocean, waves can reach towering heights of 30 m. A monster wave is usually caused by a powerful storm.

PREPARATION

PROBLEM
What factors affect the heights of waves?

OBJECTIVES
- **Model** the movement of waves.
- **Measure** and **record** differences in wave heights.
- **Infer** what factors affect the heights of waves.

MATERIALS
electric fan with variable speed and a grounded/polarized plug
overhead light with reflector
ring stand
white paper
timer
clear, shallow, rectangular container
water
metric ruler

SAFETY PRECAUTIONS

- If you are using any electrical outlets near water, be sure there is GFI (ground fault interruptor) protection.
- Wear safety goggles during the lab procedure.
- Be careful when handling the overhead light and the fan. The light could get very hot. Do not let the light, the fan, or their cords touch the water.
- Do not stick your fingers or other objects in the fan blades.
- Wipe up spills immediately to help prevent slipping or falling.

PROCEDURE

1. Lay a large sheet of white paper on a flat surface, then place the container on the paper. Position a ring stand to the side of the container. Clamp a light on the ring stand so that the light shines directly into the container.

2. Fill the container nearly to the top with water. Place a fan at one end of the container. Turn it on low.

3. After 3 minutes, measure the heights of the waves created by the fan. Record your measurements in the table provided.

LAB **15.2** **INVESTIGATION**

PROCEDURE, *continued*

4. Keep the fan on low and carefully observe the shadows of the waves on the white paper. Record your observations.

5. After 5 minutes, measure and record the heights of the waves again.

6. Repeat steps 3–5 with the fan on medium speed and on high speed.

7. Turn off the fan. Observe and record what happens to the water.

DATA AND OBSERVATIONS

Fan Speed	Wavelength	Observations
Low, 3 minutes		
Low, 5 minutes		
Medium, 3 minutes		
Medium, 5 minutes		
High, 3 minutes		
High, 5 minutes		

LAB ◄**15.2**►   **INVESTIGATION**

ANALYZE

1. Compare the heights of the waves when the fan was on low, medium, and high speeds.

_____

_____

_____

_____

2. Did the heights of the waves change with time? Explain your answer.

_____

_____

_____

_____

_____

3. Describe how the shadows of the waves changed when the speed of the fan changed.

_____

_____

_____

_____

4. Describe the movement of the water when the fan was turned off.

_____

_____

_____

_____

LAB ◆ **15.2** INVESTIGATION

CONCLUDE AND APPLY

1. Based on your results, what factors influence wave height?

_____

_____

_____

2. What might happen to wave height if you repeated the experiment using a much longer container? What might happen if the container was deeper?

_____

_____

_____

_____

_____

_____

3. The heights of ocean waves vary greatly. Describe some conditions that might generate both high and low ocean waves.

_____

_____

_____

_____

_____

LAB ◆ **16.1**   **MAPPING**

Changes in Sea Level

$\mathbf{S}$ea level continually changes in response to numerous factors, including glacial melting, tectonic forces, and climatic changes. Currently, sea level is rising at a rate of 1.5 to 3.9 mm/year. Studies by the U.S. Environmental Protection Agency and other organizations indicate that global warming may be linked to increases in sea level. Global warming is a worldwide rise in surface temperatures. Scientists hypothesize that global warming is caused by human activities, such as the burning of fossil fuels. Even a small rise in global temperatures can melt glaciers and make seawater expand, both of which increase the volume of water in the oceans.

PREPARATION

PROBLEM
How have coastlines and sea level changed during geologic time?

OBJECTIVES
- **Observe** and **measure** changes in coastlines.
- **Describe** changes in sea level over geologic time.
- **Predict** the impact of rising sea level on coastal regions.

MATERIALS
ruler
string

PROCEDURE

1. Take a few minutes to study the sea-level map on the next page. Note the map scale. You will use the map and the map scale to answer the questions in this lab.

2. Use the string to measure distances along the coast or between two points that are not in a straight line. For example, you can lay the string along the coast so that it follows the outline of the coast, then measure the distance by laying the string along a ruler.

LAB 16.1   MAPPING

DATA AND OBSERVATIONS

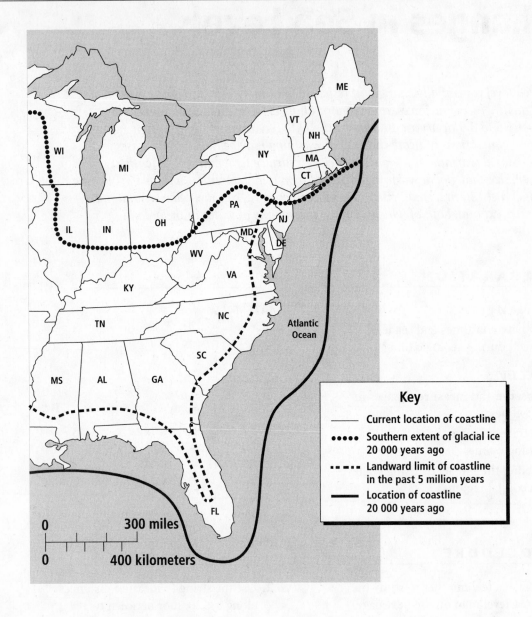

Key
— Current location of coastline
●●●● Southern extent of glacial ice
20 000 years ago
– – – Landward limit of coastline
in the past 5 million years
—— Location of coastline
20 000 years ago

0 ———— 300 miles

0 ———— 400 kilometers

LAB ◁ **16.1** ▷   **MAPPING**

A N A L Y Z E

1. How does the landward limit of the coastline 5 million years ago compare to its current location? How does it compare to the location of the coastline 20 000 years ago?

_____

_____

_____

_____

2. Locate South Carolina on the map. How far did its coastline extend into the Atlantic Ocean 20 000 years ago? How far inland was its coastline 5 million years ago?

_____

_____

_____

_____

3. Measure and record the entire length of the current coastline and its length 20 000 years ago. Describe how it has changed. What caused these changes?

_____

_____

_____

_____

_____

_____

4. Use the map to describe how sea level has changed in the last 20 000 years. Why do you think these changes occurred?

_____

_____

_____

_____

LAB ◁ **16.1** ▷   **MAPPING**

CONCLUDE AND APPLY

1. The last ice age peaked roughly 10 000 years ago. Since then, sea level has risen approximately 130 m. Describe the effect of small rises in sea level on coastal areas.

_____

_____

_____

2. The mass of huge glaciers exerts pressure on underlying land and causes it to sink. When these glaciers retreat, the land that they covered often rises, or rebounds. Where on the map would you expect glacial rebound to be occurring? How might this rebound affect the levels of seas and other large bodies of water?

_____

_____

_____

3. Global sea level could rise by 30 cm within the next 70 years. Predict which areas on the map would be affected most. Explain your answer.

_____

_____

_____

4. Discuss the potential impacts of rising sea level on low-lying coastal areas.

_____

_____

_____

_____

_____

LAB **16.2**   INVESTIGATION

Observing Brine Shrimp

Oceans cover 70 percent of Earth, and these vast waters support an amazing array of marine life. Marine organisms range from massive whales to microscopic plankton, but all marine organisms must be able to survive in seawater. In this lab, you will examine how salinity affects aquatic organisms called brine shrimp. Brine shrimp are tiny crustaceans that have hard exoskeletons, jointed legs, and antennae. They live in salty lakes and ponds.

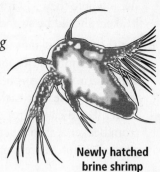

Newly hatched brine shrimp

PREPARATION

PROBLEM
Under what conditions do brine shrimp hatch and thrive?

OBJECTIVES
- **Culture** brine shrimp.
- **Observe** and **record** data about the structure and behavior of a crustacean.
- **Analyze** the effects of different salt concentrations on an aquatic organism.

MATERIALS
500-mL beakers (4)
glass marker
100-mL graduated cylinder
room-temperature water
alcohol-based thermometer
75 g noniodized salt
balance
4 stirring rods

wooden stick
brine-shrimp eggs
plastic wrap
4 droppers
4 petri dishes
microscope

SAFETY PRECAUTIONS

- If you break a thermometer or beaker, notify your teacher right away. Do not attempt to clean up broken glass.
- Avoid using mercury-based thermometers. Mercury is toxic.
- Wipe up any spills immediately.
- Wear safety goggles during the lab procedure. Salt water can irritate your eyes.

PROCEDURE

1. Use a glass marker to label four beakers A, B, C, and D. Measure 500 mL of room-temperature water into each beaker. Use a marker to label the petri dishes similarly.

2. Add 5 g of noniodized salt to beaker B. Add 20 g of salt to beaker C. Add 50 g of salt to beaker D. Do not add salt to beaker A.

3. Use the rounded end of a wooden stick to transfer some brine-shrimp eggs to beaker A. Mix the solution with a stirrer. The eggs are tiny and difficult to count, but try to transfer roughly the same number of eggs into beakers B and C. Use a clean, dry stirrer each time.

4. Record the temperature of the water in each beaker in a data table.

LAB **16.2** **INVESTIGATION**

PROCEDURE, *continued*

5. Cover the beakers with plastic wrap and store them where they will not be disturbed. All beakers should be stored at around 21°C.

6. On the following day, uncover the beakers and use a thermometer to measure water temperatures. Record these temperatures in your data table. Stir each beaker with a clean stirrer. Use a clean dropper to place a few drops from beaker A into a petri dish. Repeat this procedure for the remaining solutions.

7. Observe the petri dishes under a microscope. Count the number of hatched brine shrimp in each dish. Record your observations in Table 1.

8. Repeat steps 5 through 7 for 3 more days.

DATA AND OBSERVATIONS

Table

Beaker	Number of Hatched Brine Shrimp							
	Day 1	Temperature	Day 2	Temperature	Day 3	Temperature	Day 4	Temperature
A								
B								
C								
D								

LAB **16.2**   **INVESTIGATION**

ANALYZE

1. How long did it take the brine shrimp to hatch? Did they hatch in all the beakers?

_____

_____

_____

2. Which beaker had the most hatched brine shrimp? Which beaker had the least?

_____

_____

_____

3. Calculate the percentage of salt in each solution, using grams per milliliter.

_____

_____

_____

4. Describe the structure and color of the hatched brine shrimp. Be specific. Draw one brine shrimp below Table 1.

_____

_____

_____

_____

5. Describe the behavior of the brine shrimp. For example, how do they move about in the water?

_____

_____

_____

_____

_____

_____

LAB ◁ **16.2** ▷ **INVESTIGATION**

CONCLUDE AND APPLY

1. Under which conditions did brine shrimp thrive best?

_____

_____

2. How might changes in salinity affect the brine shrimp?

_____

_____

_____

_____

_____

3. Like many marine organisms, brine shrimp respond to light. Based on this information, what can you conclude about their natural habitat?

_____

_____

_____

_____

_____

LAB 17.1 DESIGN YOUR OWN

Magnetism and Ocean Ridges

Evidence of seafloor spreading includes magnetic measurements of the basaltic rocks at the bottom of the ocean. Earth's magnetic field at different places along the seafloor is stronger than Earth's current field, and some places have a weaker than normal field. These variations indicate that Earth's magnetic field reverses periodically over geologic time.

The plausibility of this interpretation can be demonstrated with a model. You can put iron filings in a test tube, set a magnet near the end of the table, and tap it. The individual filings become magnetized and line up, effectively becoming a collection of small bar magnets that all face in the same direction. The magnetized iron filings model iron-bearing minerals in molten material that wells up along a divergent plate boundary. As the molten material cools, it preserves the magnetic orientation at the time of crystallization. Magnetic fluctuations on the seafloor form symmetrical patterns in relation to an ocean ridge (Figure 1).

PREPARATION

PROBLEM
How are patterns of magnetic-field strength in seafloor rocks related to changes in the polarity of Earth's magnetic field?

OBJECTIVES
- **Investigate** the mechanism of magnetization.
- **Model** how magnetic patterns preserved in seafloor rocks arise.

HYPOTHESIS
With your group, write a description of how patterns of magnetic fluctuations arise on the seafloor.

_____

_____

_____

POSSIBLE MATERIALS
test tube
test-tube stopper
iron filings
bar magnet
small plotting compass
meterstick

SAFETY PRECAUTIONS

Use caution when handling iron filings. Wear safety goggles to help keep filings away from your eyes.

Figure 1

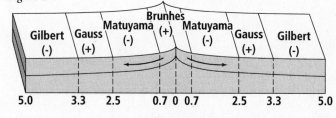

Age (millions of years)

LAB 17.1   **DESIGN YOUR OWN**

PLAN THE EXPERIMENT

Consider the possible materials and design an experiment that supports the theory that patterns observed in seafloor rocks indicate reversals in Earth's magnetic field. Seafloor measurements do not indicate that the field is currently reversed; rather, they show that the field is weaker or stronger than the average. So, you need to confirm that a weak magnetic field (like that of iron-bearing minerals in rocks as represented by the iron filings), in the presence of a strong magnetic field (like that of Earth as represented by the bar magnet), can produce a combined field that is stronger or weaker than the average magnetic field is alone. What can you use to discover the turning point, where the field's effect changes? List the materials you will need and outline your experiment in Data and Observations. You may also choose to draw a diagram as part of your outline. Have your teacher approve your plan before you start.

DATA AND OBSERVATIONS

OUTLINE OR DIAGRAM

_____

_____

_____

_____

_____

_____

_____

_____

_____

_____

LAB 17.1   **DESIGN YOUR OWN**

ANALYZE

1. Consider the magnetic field strength at the following four locations: the surface of Earth, the surface of a bar magnet, the surface of a test tube containing magnetized iron filings, and the seafloor. List these four surfaces from strongest to weakest.

_____

_____

_____

2. How far from the bar magnet does its field equal Earth's magnetic field? How could you tell?

_____

_____

_____

3. If you were to move the compass a few extra centimeters away from the magnet, do you think the strength of the combined magnetic field at that point would be greater than, less than, or equal to the strength of Earth's magnetic field? Why?

_____

_____

_____

4. Do the magnetized iron filings have a stronger or weaker magnetic field than the bar magnet?

_____

_____

CHECK YOUR HYPOTHESIS

Was your **hypothesis** supported by your data? Why or why not?

_____

_____

_____

LAB ⟨ **17.1** ⟩   **DESIGN YOUR OWN**

CONCLUDE AND APPLY

1. Measurements of seafloor magnetic fields show regions of stronger-than-normal and weaker-than-normal fields. The measurements do not actually indicate reversed fields. Explain how the measurements provide evidence that Earth has experienced periods of reversed magnetic polarity.

_____

_____

_____

_____

2. Look at Figure 1. Why is there magnetic symmetry in relation to an ocean ridge?

_____

_____

_____

_____

3. If the ocean ridge ran east-west instead of north-south, would you expect to see patterns of magnetic symmetry in the seafloor rock? Explain your answer.

_____

_____

_____

_____

4. When might the magnetic field of Earth reverse? Explain your answer.

_____

_____

_____

_____

LAB ◆ **17.2** **INVESTIGATION**

Earthquakes and Subduction Zones

Figure 1

T he density of the rock that makes up a subducting
plate is one of the factors that determines how the
plate behaves. The greater the density, the faster the plate
subducts into the mantle and the steeper the angle of
subduction. Older crust is cooler and therefore denser than
younger crust, so it subducts faster and at a steeper angle along a subduction zone.

Most earthquakes occur at tectonic plate boundaries. An earthquake can be classified by the depth
of its focus. Deep-focus earthquakes have foci at more than 300 km, shallow-focus earthquakes have
a focus at less than 70 km, and intermediate-focus earthquakes have foci between 70 km and 300 km.

PREPARATION

OBJECTIVES

- **State** a hypothesis about the relative
  ages of the crust at two convergent
  boundaries.
- **Use** earthquake data to **construct**
  profiles of two convergent boundaries.
- **Compare** the behavior of two subducting plates.

HYPOTHESIS

Consider Figure 1. The East Pacific Rise
is an ocean ridge, running north-south
at about 110°W, where the Pacific Plate
meets the Nazca Plate. Material from
this divergent boundary flows westward
across the Pacific Plate or eastward
across the Nazca Plate. The west-
flowing material runs into the

Australian Plate at the Tonga Trench,
which is north of New Zealand at about
175°W. East-flowing material meets the
South American Plate at the Peru-Chile
Trench, at about 65°W. Assume that the
seafloor spreads at the same rate both
west and east of the East Pacific Rise.
Form a hypothesis about the relative
ages of the East Pacific Rise material at
the two convergent boundaries: the
Tonga Trench and the Peru-Chile Trench.

_____

_____

_____

_____

MATERIALS
calculator

PROCEDURE

1. Table 1 shows earthquake data
   from the region associated with the
   Peru-Chile Trench. Plot these data
   on a graph, using a dot to
   represent each data point.

2. Plot the earthquake data from the
   region associated with the Tonga
   Trench on a second graph.

3. Draw a best-fit line for the Peru-
   Chile Trench data. A best-fit line is
   a smooth line that shows the trend
   of the data; the line does not have
   to pass through the data points.

4. Draw a best-fit line for the Tonga
   Trench data.

LAB 17.2   INVESTIGATION

DATA AND OBSERVATIONS

Peru-Chile Trench		Tonga Trench	
Longitude (°W)	Focus depth (km)	Longitude (°W)	Focus depth (km)
61.7	540	173.8	35
62.3	480	173.8	50
63.8	345	173.8	60
65.2	285	173.9	60
65.5	290	174.1	30
66.2	230	174.6	40
66.3	215	174.7	35
66.4	235	174.8	35
66.5	220	174.9	40
66.7	210	174.9	50
66.7	200	175.1	40
66.9	175	175.4	250
67.1	230	175.7	205
67.3	185	175.7	260
67.5	180	175.8	115
67.5	170	175.9	190
67.7	120	176.0	160
67.9	140	176.0	220
68.1	145	176.2	270
68.1	130	176.8	340
68.2	160	177.0	380
68.3	130	177.0	350
68.3	110	177.4	420
68.4	120	177.7	560
68.5	140	177.7	580
68.6	180	177.7	465
68.6	125	177.8	460
69.1	95	177.9	565
69.2	35	178.0	520
69.3	60	178.1	510
69.5	75	178.2	595
69.7	50	178.2	550
69.8	30	178.3	540
69.8	55	178.5	505
70.8	35	178.6	615
		178.7	600
		178.8	590
		178.8	580
		179.1	675
		179.2	670

LAB **17.2**   **INVESTIGATION**

DATA AND OBSERVATIONS, *continued*

ANALYZE

1. How far is the Tonga Trench from the East Pacific Rise? Note that one degree longitude equals about 100 km. If the seafloor spreads at 3 cm/year, how long would it take material on the plate to travel this distance?

_____

2. What is the depth of the deepest earthquake in the Tonga data set? Estimate the rate of descent of the East Pacific Rise material at the Tonga Trench in centimeters per year.

_____

LAB **17.2** **INVESTIGATION**

ANALYZE, *continued*

3. Estimate the rate of descent of East Pacific Rise material into the Peru-Chile Trench in centimeters per year.

_____

_____

4. The best-fit line on the Peru-Chile graph is an estimate of the location of the boundary between the Nazca Plate and the South American Plate. Indicate on the graph which plate is which. Add an arrow to show the direction of motion of the Nazca Plate.

5. The best-fit line on the Tonga graph is an estimate of the location of the boundary between the Pacific Plate and the Australian Plate. Indicate on the graph which plate is which. Add an arrow to show the direction of motion of the Pacific Plate.

CHECK YOUR HYPOTHESIS

Was your **hypothesis** supported by your data? Why or why not?

_____

_____

CONCLUDE AND APPLY

1. Compare your two graphs. Which has the steeper profile? Which do you think has the denser material? The older material? Explain your answer.

_____

_____

2. Summarize your observations, including a statement about the validity of your hypothesis.

_____

_____

_____

_____

_____

_____

LAB 18.1   **DESIGN YOUR OWN**

Modeling a Lava Flow

Lava flows can form a complicated variety of structures. Levees can form on the outer part of a lava-flow channel, and ridges sometimes develop inside the flow. Shear zones can occur where one part of the flow moves faster than another. Often the easiest way to explore complicated physical systems such as lava flows is to make a model. You can use a model to study how slope and the position in a flow affect the dimensions of the flow.

PREPARATION

PROBLEM

How is a lava flow affected by changes in the conditions that produce it?

OBJECTIVES

- **Model** the geologic processes associated with lava flows.
- **Collect** data on the structure of a model lava flow.

HYPOTHESIS

The slope over which a lava flow travels and lava viscosity are two parameters that determine how a lava flow behaves. What effects do these two parameters have on the width, depth, length, and speed of a flow? How do these two parameters affect structures in a flow? Write a hypothesis about what your experiment might show about flow characteristics.

_____

_____

_____

_____

POSSIBLE MATERIALS

dry cake mix
water
bucket with pouring spout
wire whisk
coffee tin with 2-cm circular
   hole in the bottom
large spatula
wooden board, 1 m × 2 m
paper
plastic wrap
wooden shims and wedges
protractor
plumb line
stopwatch
metric ruler
toothpicks
masking tape

SAFETY PRECAUTIONS

- Wear safety goggles and an apron during the lab procedure.
- Immediately clean up floor spills of cake mix; they can be slippery.
- Handle the coffee tin carefully. The hole in the bottom may have sharp edges that can cut your skin.
- Follow your teacher's instructions to dispose of the cake mix at the end of the lab.

LAB 18.1 DESIGN YOUR OWN

PLAN THE EXPERIMENT

Work with four other students. Review the list
of possible materials. Design an experiment to
simulate the evolution of lava flows on the side
of a volcano. You should consider the slope of
the incline, pouring rate, and viscosity of the
lava. What cases will you consider? How will you
measure the variables? What data will you collect?
Set up a table or tables in which to record the data.
Plan to draw diagrams, including cross sections, of
the flow features. Outline your plan and have your
teacher approve it before you begin the
experiment.

_____

_____

_____

DATA AND OBSERVATIONS

TABLES AND DIAGRAMS

LAB ◆ **18.1**   **DESIGN YOUR OWN**

DATA AND OBSERVATIONS, *continued*

ANALYZE

1. Use your diagrams to describe how the flows evolved.

_____

_____

_____

_____

LAB 18.1 **DESIGN YOUR OWN**

ANALYZE, *continued*

2. Describe the nature and locations of any flow channels, levees, ridges, and shear zones that you observed.

_____

_____

_____

_____

3. Summarize your results with respect to the slope of the incline, viscosity, and pouring rate.

_____

_____

_____

_____

CHECK YOUR HYPOTHESIS

Was your **hypothesis** supported by your data? Why or why not?

_____

_____

CONCLUDE AND APPLY

1. How well did your model represent a real lava flow? Describe the model properties that are identical to those of a lava flow, similar but on a different scale, and not similar at all.

_____

_____

_____

_____

2. Shield volcanoes have gently sloping sides, whereas cinder-cone volcanoes and composite volcanoes usually have steeper sides. Use the results of your experiment to predict how lava flows differ for these types of volcanoes.

_____

_____

_____

LAB **18.2** **INVESTIGATION**

Analyzing Volcanic-Disaster Risk

On May 18, 1980, an earthquake shook Mount St. Helens. A bulge on the side of the mountain and the area surrounding it slid away in a gigantic avalanche, releasing pressure and triggering a major pumice and ash eruption of the volcano. Debris filled 62 km^2 of a valley; a lateral blast damaged 650 km^2 of recreation, timber, and private lands; and volcanic mud flows deposited an estimated 0.15 km^3 of material in the nearby river. Nearly five dozen people died in the eruption. There was over $1 billion in damage.

PREPARATION

PROBLEM

What is the probability that a volcano will erupt in any given year? What does that imply for the cost of insuring people against volcanic disasters?

OBJECTIVES

- **Assess** the probability of a volcanic disaster.
- **Investigate** the feasibility of an insurance policy against volcanic disaster.

MATERIALS

Tables 1 and 2
calculator

PROCEDURE

Mount St. Helens is a volcano in the Cascade Range, which extends from California to British Columbia. Table 2 contains data for the eruption histories of the Cascade Range volcanoes. With these data, you could estimate the annual probability that a particular volcano will erupt.

$$\text{annual probability} = \frac{\text{number of eruptions}}{\text{years}}$$

For example, based on the Holocene data, the probability that Lassen Peak will erupt in any given year is (3 eruptions)/(10 000 years),

or 3/10 000. From Table 1, you can see that this value lies between the annual probabilities that an individual human will die by homicide or die of AIDS.

Only huge eruptions left records before the Holocene. Smaller eruptions in the Pleistocene are poorly documented in the rock record. To calculate eruption probabilities for which there are no Pleistocene data, use the 10 000-year Holocene baseline.

Use the formula above and the data in Table 2 to answer the questions in Analyze.

LAB ◄ **18.2** ▶ **INVESTIGATION**

DATA AND OBSERVATIONS

Table 1

Event	Annual Probability per Person
Experience car theft	1/100
Experience house fire	1/200
Die from heart disease	1/280
Die of cancer	1/500
Die in a car wreck	1/6000
Die by homicide	1/10 000
Die of AIDS	1/11 000
Die of tuberculosis	1/200 000
Win a state lottery	1/1 million
Die from lightning	1/1.4 million
Die from a flood or tornado	1/2 million
Die in a hurricane	1/6 million
Die in a commercial plane crash	1/1 million to 1/10 million

Table 2

Feature	State	Late Pleistocene Huge	Holocene Huge	Large	Medium	Small
Mount Baker	WA				1	3
Glacier Peak	WA			2		7
Mount Rainier	WA	1			1	10
Mount St. Helens	WA				7	
Mount Adams	WA					4
Mount Hood	OR					3
Mount Jefferson	OR	1				
Three Sisters	OR			2		2
Newberry Caldera	OR			1	3	
Crater Lake	OR		1	2		
Medicine Lake	CA				8	8
Mount Shasta	CA	1		2		10
Lassen Peak	CA	4		1		2
Total		**7**	**1**	**10**	**20**	**49**

Note: Huge eruptions = >10 km³ of ejecta; large = 1–10 km³; medium = 0.1–1 km³; small = <0.1 km³.
The periods of the eruptions are late Pleistocene (10 000 years to 100 000 years ago) or Holocene (<10 000 years ago).

LAB 18.2 INVESTIGATION

ANALYZE

1. Based on the Holocene data, what is the probability that Medicine Lake will erupt this year?

_____

2. What is the probability that Medicine Lake will have a medium-size eruption this year?

_____

3. What is the annual probability that Mount Jefferson will erupt?

_____

4. During the last 10 000 years, how many eruptions have occurred in the Cascade Range?

_____

5. What is the annual probability that one of the Cascade Range volcanoes will erupt?

_____

6. What is the annual probability that a small eruption will occur in the Cascade Range? Multiply this by $100 million to obtain the contribution of small eruptions to the annual cost of Cascade volcanic disasters.

_____

7. What is the annual probability that a medium-size eruption will occur in the Cascade Range? Multiply this by $1 billion to obtain the contribution of medium-size eruptions to the annual cost of Cascade volcanic disasters.

_____

8. Calculate the annual probability for large Cascade eruptions. If a large Cascade eruption costs $10 billion, what is the contribution of large eruptions to the annual cost of Cascade volcanic disasters?

_____

9. Using both Pleistocene and Holocene data, what is the annual probability that a huge eruption will occur? Calculate the contribution of huge eruptions to the annual cost of Cascade volcanic disasters if the cost of a huge eruption is $100 billion.

_____

10. What is the total cost per year of Cascade eruptions? If inflation and land development drove the cost per eruption up by a factor of 100, what would the annual cost be?

_____

LAB 18.2   **INVESTIGATION**

CONCLUDE AND APPLY

1. Think of two reasons why your estimates of the probabilities might predict three times fewer volcanic eruptions than the actual number that will occur during the twenty-first century.

_____

_____

_____

_____

_____

2. If there were three times as many volcanoes as predicted, what would the total annual cost be? Use the value that you obtained for question 10. If this cost is distributed evenly among 2 million policyholders, what would the insurance premium be?

_____

_____

_____

3. Suppose that 10 percent of the inhabitants in the Cascade Range owned 90 percent of the property, and that the cost of the insurance premium would prohibit the other 90 percent from becoming policyholders. Divide 90 percent of the cost by 10 percent of 2 million people to find out what the annual insurance premium would be.

_____

_____

4. Explain why insurance companies rarely insure against volcanic-disaster damage, even though volcanic disasters do not occur very often.

_____

_____

_____

_____

_____

LAB ◆ **19.1** **INVESTIGATION**

Predicting Earthquakes

The United States Geological Survey (USGS) compiles and posts on the Internet a list of recent earthquakes. This list is updated every 5 minutes. In a typical month, the list may include 300–400 earthquakes that occurred around the world. The list includes each earthquake's location, magnitude, and depth. These data can be mapped and used to predict where earthquakes will occur next.

PREPARATION

PROBLEM
Where are earthquakes most likely to occur next ?

OBJECTIVES
- **Analyze** the locations, magnitudes, and depths of recent earthquakes.
- **Predict** where earthquakes are most likely to occur in the next few weeks.

MATERIALS
computer with Internet access
fine-point pens, 6 different colors

PROCEDURE

1. Visit sites listed on the Glencoe Science Web Site to retrieve and print out the USGS table of earthquake data.

2. Identify the columns for the time of the earthquake and its latitude, longitude, depth, and magnitude. Use the body-wave magnitude.

3. Decide on a scheme of colors and symbols to map earthquake locations. A symbol's color should indicate the magnitude of the earthquake, and its shape should identify the depth. Define your scheme in the two keys in Figure 1.

4. Identify the data for the most recent earthquake in the USGS table. Use a sharp pencil to plot the position of the earthquake on the world map in Figure 1.

5. Ask your teacher to verify that you have correctly plotted the earthquake's location.

6. Use a fine-point pen and follow your symbol scheme to mark the point.

7. Plot each earthquake on the list or as many as your teacher specifies. This task will go more quickly if one person reads the data aloud while another person plots the point.

8. Locate an area 5° × 5° on the world map where you expect an earthquake to occur in the next few weeks.

9. Use your data to complete columns 1 and 2 of Table 1.

LAB 19.1   **INVESTIGATION**

DATA AND OBSERVATIONS

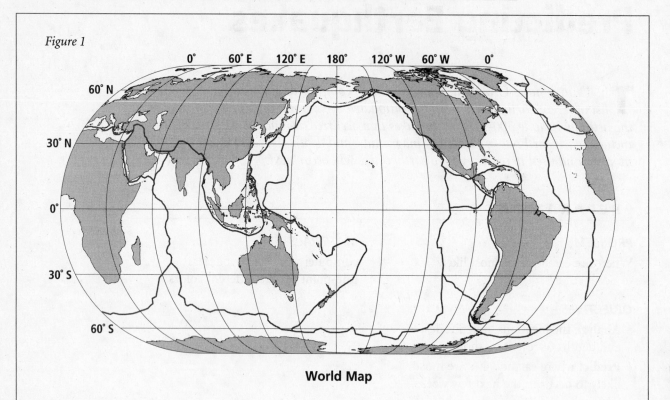

Figure 1

World Map

Magnitude	Color
<4	
4 – 4.9	
5 – 5.9	
6 – 6.9	
7 - 7.9	
>8	
no data	

Depth (km)	Symbol
0 – 50	
51 – 100	
101 – 150	
151 – 200	
201 – 250	
>250	
no data	

LAB **19.1** INVESTIGATION

DATA AND OBSERVATIONS, *continued*

Table 1

	Actual Earthquakes		Predicted Earthquakes in the 5° × 5° Area	
	Number of Earthquakes	**Percentage of Earthquakes**	**Predicted Earthquakes**	**Actual Earthquakes**
Richter Magnitude				
<4				
4–4.9				
5–5.9				
6–6.9				
7–7.9				
>8				
No data				
Depth (km)				
0–50				
51–100				
101–150				
151–200				
>200				
No data				

LAB ◆ **19.1** INVESTIGATION

ANALYZE

1. Find the time interval, to 0. 1 days, between the least recent and most recent earthquakes for the data you plotted. Calculate how many earthquakes occurred per day during this interval. This is the earthquake rate.

_____

2. What is the earthquake rate in your 5° × 5° area on the map?

_____

3. Predict how many earthquakes you expect to occur in your 5° × 5° area during the next week. Give reasons for your prediction.

_____

_____

4. Use the data in Table 1 to help you predict for the next few weeks the number of earthquakes in each magnitude range and each depth range in your 5° × 5° area. Record your predictions in column 3 of Table 1.

CONCLUDE AND APPLY

1. Earth's major tectonic plate boundaries are shown in Figure 1. What can you hypothesize about the distribution of earthquake locations?

_____

_____

2. A week later, get the past week's data from the web site. Use the new data to complete column 4 in Table 1 for your 5° × 5° area . How well do your predictions match the actual events of the past week? Explain your answer.

_____

_____

_____

LAB 19.2

DESIGN YOUR OWN

Earthquake News Report

Many scientific concepts can be described in depth to an audience with no in-depth knowledge of the subject. The key is to consider at the outset the target idea that you want to convey. A scientific idea usually builds off a few other ideas. Once those lower-level ideas are understood, then the target idea is easily accessible. If these lower-level ideas can be presented by analogy to common experience, they are contact points. If a lower-level idea is not a contact point, it can be treated as a target idea that depends on even lower-level ideas, and so on. Most target ideas have a reasonably manageable set of contact points. Conveying the target idea requires establishing contact points with the audience and weaving the points together to construct the target idea.

PREPARATION

PROBLEM

How can you convey technical information to a popular audience?

OBJECTIVES

- **Address** the issues involved in communicating technical ideas to a popular audience.
- **Make** a team presentation about earthquakes.
- **Critique** technical presentations in a constructive way.

HYPOTHESIS

What are the three most important things that a scientist should consider when communicating technical ideas to an audience that may not have a technical background?

_____

_____

_____

POSSIBLE MATERIALS

research resources about earthquakes
overhead projector
poster board
drawing supplies
printer paper

PLAN THE EXPERIMENT

In your group, decide on the kind of presentation your team will make. Do you want it to be a newscast, part of a magazine show, a documentary, or perhaps a studio forum? What's the purpose of the report? Is the main emphasis geologic or historical? Decide what role each team member will play

in the presentation. Table 1 might give you some ideas, but don't limit yourself to the roles there. Each role will require you to research different information. Resources might include the Internet, a library, textbooks, magazine articles, and interviews. How will you decide which of these sources is reliable?

LAB ◆ **19.2** DESIGN YOUR OWN

PLAN THE EXPERIMENT, *continued*

Outline your plans and role assignments. Have your teacher check your plans before you start your research.

Use your research notes to draft your section of a script for the presentation and to prepare any visual aids. As a team, read and discuss one another's work. Compile the final script, get your teacher's approval, and rehearse your presentation.

DATA AND OBSERVATIONS

Table 1

Anchor/host	Coordinates the presentation, including introducing and summarizing, introducing experts, and providing emphasis and continuity.
Geologist	Explains technical definitions, such as *tectonics*, *fault*, and *subduction*. Explains what causes earthquakes.
Seismologist	Describes how earthquakes are measured, including instruments, techniques, and magnitude and intensity scales.
Historian	Knows about major historical earthquakes, the destruction that they caused, and their social consequences. Could provide a history of seismology.
Geographer	Concentrates on the location of earthquakes. Explains which regions of the world are prone to earthquakes and provides details of recent earthquakes associated with tsunami devastation.
Disaster worker	Introduces appropriate government agencies and furnishes viewers with practical information about preparation and recovery.

ANALYZE

Take notes as you watch the other teams' presentations. Focus on the three areas described below.

1. Think about the content of the presentation. How comprehensive is the coverage? Is the introduction effective? Does the summary recap the major points well? Are there any major omissions? How could the presenters have improved their coverage?

2. What techniques did the team use to emphasize points? Were minor points overemphasized, or were major points underemphasized?

3. Was the technical content presented in an easily understandable way? Could some points have used more explanation? Were visual aids used effectively?

ANALYZE, *continued*

NOTES

_____

_____

_____

_____

_____

_____

_____

_____

_____

_____

_____

_____

_____

_____

_____

_____

_____

_____

_____

_____

_____

_____

_____

_____

_____

_____

_____

_____

_____

_____

_____

_____

LAB ◁ **19.2** ▷ **DESIGN YOUR OWN**

CHECK YOUR HYPOTHESIS

Was your **hypothesis** supported by your data? Why or why not?

_____

_____

CONCLUDE AND APPLY

1. Make a transcript, with illustrations, of your team's presentation.

2. On separate sheets of paper, write a one-paragraph review of each of the other teams' presentations.

3. Would your hypothesis be different now than it was before you developed and presented your script? Explain your answer.

_____

_____

_____

_____

LAB ◆ **20.1**   **INVESTIGATION**

Plate Tectonics of North America

Changes in the positions and shapes of Earth's continents and oceans can be explained by the theory of plate tectonics. This theory states that Earth's crust and rigid upper mantle are divided into roughly a dozen slabs, called plates. Tectonic plates move slowly over Earth's surface. Interactions among tectonic plates account for most earthquakes, volcanoes, and mountain ranges.

PREPARATION

PROBLEM
How can the theory of plate tectonics be used to analyze some of the tectonic features of North America?

OBJECTIVES
- **Identify** the major plates associated with North America and their movements.
- **Describe** the locations and orientations of major mountain chains of North America.

- **Explain** how geologic evidence supports the theory of plate tectonics.
- **Predict** how future tectonic processes might affect the North American continent.

MATERIALS
red, blue, and orange markers

PROCEDURE

1. Use a blue marker to draw a line on map B that traces the deep-sea trenches off of the western coasts of the Americas.

2. Using a red marker and map A as a reference, draw lines on map B to mark the edges of the tectonic plates shown. Indicate with arrows their directions of movements.

3. Locate the Mid-Atlantic Ridge on map B and color it orange.

4. Study maps B and C. Answer questions 1–5 in Analyze.

5. An active tectonic plate has a leading edge and a trailing edge. On map B, label the leading and trailing edges of the North American Plate.

6. Look at the map legend for map D. What do the dashed lines in the gulf between the Baja Peninsula and the mainland indicate?

_____

_____

7. Plate boundaries are convergent, divergent, or transform. Identify each boundary that is associated with the North American Plate. Label them on map B. Answer questions 6 and 7 in Analyze.

_____

_____

_____

LAB ◆ 20.1   **INVESTIGATION**

DATA AND OBSERVATIONS

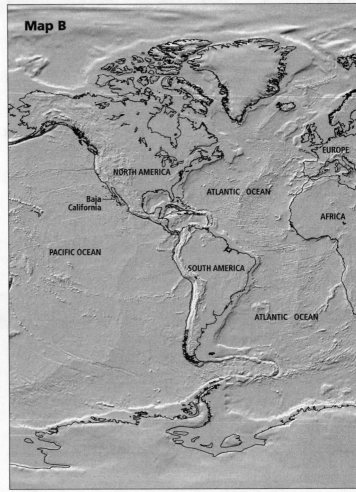

Map B

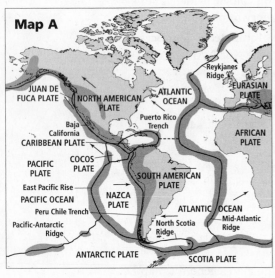

Map A

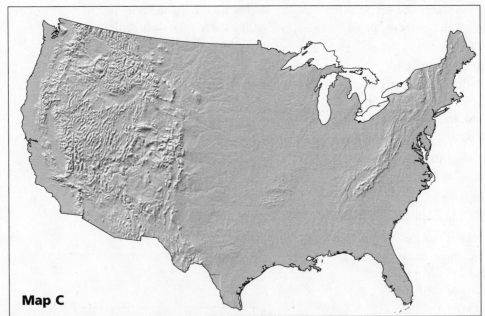

Map C

LAB ⟨20.1⟩ INVESTIGATION

DATA AND OBSERVATIONS, *continued*

Map D

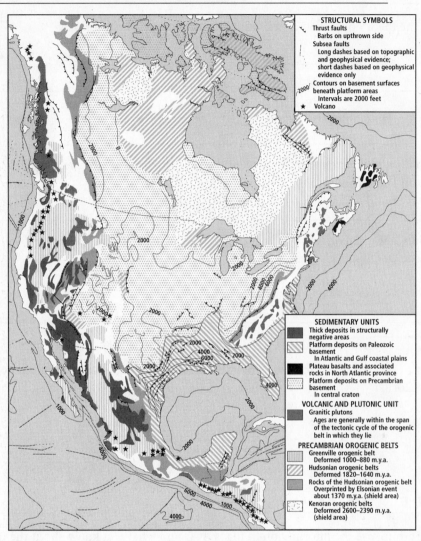

ANALYZE

1. List two features shown on map B that formed or are forming as a result of plate motion.

_____

_____

2. In what direction is the North American Plate moving?

_____

3. Use map C to describe the locations and orientation of the major mountain systems of North America.

_____

_____

_____

LAB **20.1** **INVESTIGATION**

ANALYZE, *continued*

4. How does the theory of plate tectonics explain your answer to question 3?

_____

_____

_____

_____

5. From what direction were the forces that resulted in the formation of the Appalachian Mountains in the eastern United States?

_____

6. Locate Baja, California, on maps A, B, and D. List all of the tectonic features and events that are associated with this area.

_____

_____

_____

7. If the Pacific Plate continues to move along the San Andreas Fault, what might happen to Baja, California?

_____

_____

CONCLUDE AND APPLY

1. With your group, use the information in maps A–D and what you know about the theory of plate tectonics to briefly describe the tectonic processes that have affected North America.

_____

_____

_____

_____

_____

_____

Analysis of Geologic Maps

Throughout Earth's history, continents have undergone many structural changes. Most of these changes are due to tectonism, which includes convergence, divergence, folding, faulting, volcanism, and orogeny. Sedimentation and associated subsidence also played a role in changing Earth's continents. Features present at Earth's surface are evidence of the many processes at work to change our planet.

PREPARATION

PROBLEM

How can geologic maps be used to interpret the processes that have resulted in the major landforms of North America?

OBJECTIVES

• **Identify** structural elements of the North American continent by rock age and type.

• **Describe** the tectonic forces that have shaped the mountain ranges of North America.

• **Describe** some of the geologic characteristics of the Appalachian and Rocky Mountain systems.

• **Compare** the tectonic history of some of the major mountain chains of North America.

MATERIALS

map D from Lab 20.1
markers, 8 different colors

PROCEDURE

1. Map D on page 155 is a tectonic map of North America. Carefully study the map and its legend.

2. Find the thick deposits in structurally negative areas and color them yellow.

3. Platform areas are rocks composed of sedimentary or volcanic deposits intruding or overlying older basement rocks. Color the plateau basalts red, the platform deposits on a Paleozoic basement in the Atlantic and Gulf Coastal Plains gray, and the platform deposits on the Precambrian basement in the central craton orange. The craton is the stable interior of the continent. It is composed of large areas of ancient crystalline rocks.

4. Orogenic belts formed as a result of the compression of Precambrian rocks have been identified by the time at which they were deformed. Color the rocks that formed over 2000 million years before present pink. Color the rocks that formed 1820–1640 million years before present green. Color the rocks that formed 1370 million years before present blue. Color the rocks that formed 1000–880 million years before present brown.

5. Color the granitic plutons purple.

6. Find the Valley and Ridge Province of the Appalachian Mountains on Map E. Map F is a close-up of these rocks. On Map F, color the ridges orange and the valleys green.

Copyright © Glencoe/McGraw-Hill, a division of the McGraw-Hill Companies, Inc.

DATA AND OBSERVATIONS

Map E

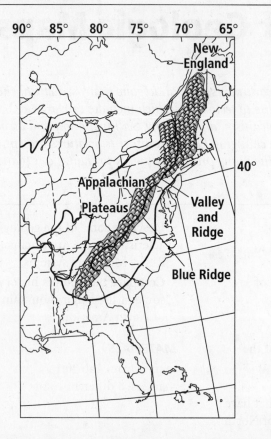

Map F

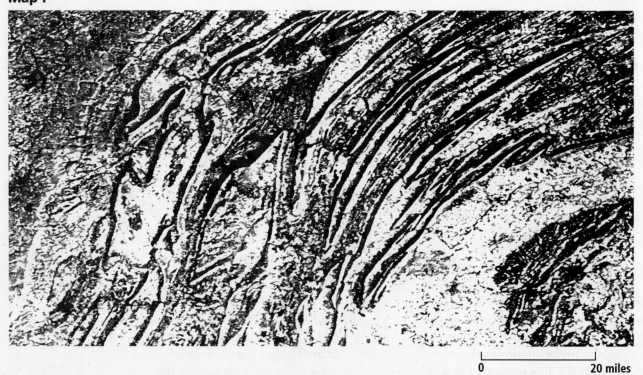

0   20 miles

MAPPING

ANALYZE

1. What are the yellow areas on map D?

_____

_____

_____

2. On map D, locate and label the shield area. The structural patterns of shield rocks show the roots of a series of deformed mountain belts. Use arrows to indicate on map D the direction of the compressive forces that produced the structural trends in each major portion of the shield.

3. On map D, label the Appalachian and the Rocky Mountain ranges. What is the major difference between these two areas and the central craton and Atlantic and Gulf Coastal Plains?

_____

_____

_____

_____

_____

4. Locate the Valley and Ridge Province of the Appalachian Mountains on maps D and E. Map F shows some of the sedimentary rocks that have been deformed into a series of tight folds and then eroded to form the ridges and valleys. Use arrows to indicate the direction of the stresses that produced this deformation.

LAB ◆ **20.2** ◆   **MAPPING**

CONCLUDE AND APPLY

1. Compare the tectonic activity associated with the formation of the Appalachian Mountains with that of the Rocky Mountains.

_____

_____

_____

_____

_____

_____

_____

_____

2. Which are generally older—the Appalachian Mountains or the Rocky Mountains? Which have been more recently active? Cite evidence from the map for your answer.

_____

_____

_____

_____

_____

_____

_____

LAB ◆ **21.1**   **INVESTIGATION**

Fossilization and Earth's History

Fossils, which are the remains of once-living plants or animals, are important evidence of the physical and environmental history of Earth. Organic remains are preserved by original preservation, permineralization, molds, and casts. Fossils are also sometimes preserved in amber, which formed from the hardened sap of evergreen trees, and by freezing. Some organisms and organism parts have better chances than others of being preserved. Fossil remains that are associated with different geologic time periods provide evidence of how life-forms change over time, as well as information about the location of energy sources such as coal and petroleum.

PREPARATION

PROBLEM
How is evidence of life-forms preserved, and what information is in the fossil record?

OBJECTIVES
- **Construct** models of fossils formed by molding, casting, and original preservation.
- **Compare** the characteristics of different types of fossils.
- **Construct** possible scenarios for fossil formation.
- **Evaluate** the quality of information that comes from the fossil record.

MATERIALS
seashell
petroleum jelly
plaster of Paris
water
2 plastic spoons
food coloring
4 paper cups
2 grapes
marking pen

freezer
dead, unsquashed,
  hard-bodied insect
  (such as a beetle
  or an ant)
waxed paper, about
  10-cm square
liquid glue

SAFETY PRECAUTIONS

- Wear safety goggles and an apron during the lab procedure.
- Wear disposable plastic gloves to protect your hands against the chemicals in the glue.

PROCEDURE

1. Label a paper cup with your names. Fill the cup about two-thirds full of water. Add dry plaster of Paris to the water a little at a time, stirring with a spoon. Stop adding plaster when the mixture is about the consistency of honey.

2. Coat a seashell with a thin layer of petroleum jelly. Press the shell into the surface of the plaster. Allow the plaster to dry overnight.

3. Label two paper cups with your names. Put one grape into each cup. Place one cup in the freezer and one in a warm place where it will not be disturbed. You will examine this experiment in about 1 week.

LAB **21.1** INVESTIGATION

PROCEDURE, *continued*

4. In nature, after sediments cover the shell and are cemented and compacted into rock, the shell will often dissolve. Remove the shell from the plaster of Paris to represent this process.

5. Answer Analyze question 1 and draw and label a diagram of what you observe in the plaster of Paris after the shell is removed.

6. Coat the surface of the plaster of Paris with a thin layer of petroleum jelly.

7. Label a paper cup with your names. Fill it about halfway with water. Mix another batch of plaster of Paris, as you did in step 1. Stir a few drops of food coloring into the fresh plaster. Slowly pour the colored plaster into the cup containing the hardened, white plaster. Allow the plaster to dry overnight.

8. After the plaster has dried, carefully tear away the paper cup. Gently pry apart the colored and uncolored blocks of plaster.

9. Draw and label a diagram of what you observe about the colored block of plaster. Answer questions 2–4.

10. Get a dead, unsquashed, hard-bodied insect, a piece of waxed paper, and liquid glue. Put a drop of liquid glue on the waxed paper, then put the insect on the spot of glue. Cover the insect with more glue, and allow the glue to dry solid. Answer question 5.

11. After the grapes have sat for 1 week, examine them. Answer question 6 and the Conclude and Apply questions.

DATA AND OBSERVATIONS

DIAGRAM

ANALYZE

1. What does the dry plaster of Paris look like?

_____

2. What does the colored plaster represent?

_____

3. Which diagram shows a mold? Which shows a cast?

_____

LAB **21.1** **INVESTIGATION**

ANALYZE, *continued*

4. If the shell had been completely buried in sediments and dissolved after the sediment had turned to rock, what kind of impression would it leave in the rock?

_____

_____

5. The first drop of glue on the waxed paper represents sap oozing from a damaged spot in the bark of a tree. In nature, what things have to happen next to result in a fossilized insect encased in amber?

_____

6. How do the two grapes differ in appearance after 1 week?

_____

_____

_____

CONCLUDE AND APPLY

1. Compare the types of information about fossil organisms that can be provided by casts and molds with that of original preservation.

_____

_____

_____

_____

2. What conditions are necessary for the successful preservation of marine organisms?

_____

_____

3. How do low temperatures affect preservation? Why are mammoth fossils that are found in frozen mud often well-preserved?

_____

_____

_____

_____

LAB 21.1 INVESTIGATION

CONCLUDE AND APPLY, *continued*

4. How much information about vertebrates (such as ourselves) would be preserved in the fossilization process? What kinds of things that we consider important about our bodies would not usually be preserved? Draw a picture of how a researcher would see you if only half of your bones and teeth and none of your soft parts were preserved and found.

_____

_____

5. Many plants and animals never have a chance to be preserved as fossils. For fossils to provide an accurate representation of the living community, where would marine organisms, insects, and plant materials have to be when they died?

_____

_____

_____

6. Think about plants, animals, and humans living today. If future scientists had to depend upon fossils from our age to interpret our physical and environmental history, what conclusions do you think they would come to? Hint: Which organisms would be preserved? How? Would this be an accurate representation of the living community? Why or why not?

_____

_____

_____

_____

_____

 **LAB** **21.2**   **DESIGN YOUR OWN**

Analysis of a Climate-Change Time Line Using Planktonic Foraminifera

Microfossils such as planktonic foraminifera are evidence of how life and environmental conditions have changed during the planet's history. One species of foraminifera, Neogloboquadrina pachyderma, *is an excellent recorder of climatic temperatures through geologic time. When Earth experiences periods of relatively cold temperatures, ocean waters are cooler, and* N. pachyderma *forms a shell that coils to the left. During periods of relatively warm temperatures, when ocean waters are warmer,* N. pachyderma *forms a shell that coils to the right. Populations of these microfossils can be examined and their characteristics used as indicators of climatic change.*

Neogloboquadrina pachyderma
(right-coiling)

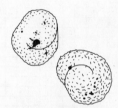

Neogloboquadrina pachyderma
(left-coiling)

PREPARATION

PROBLEM

How can a series of foraminifera samples record climatic temperatures?

OBJECTIVES

- **Identify** right-coiling and left-coiling *Neogloboquadrina pachyderma.*
- **Plan** and **carry out** a study of climatic change using *N. pachyderma* as an indicator of temperature change.
- **Gather** microfossil data and **plot** them on a graph.
- **Interpret** the climatic history of Earth during the last 160 000 years.

HYPOTHESIS

As a group, form a hypothesis about how you could use samples containing planktonic foraminifera populations to put together a record of climatic temperatures over geologic time. Write your hypothesis below.

_____

_____

_____

POSSIBLE MATERIALS

representations of microfossil samples, from the present to 160 000 years ago

calculator

PLAN THE EXPERIMENT

Think about how to determine historical changes in climate using the indicator microfossils. Decide how you will analyze the samples. What data will you collect and how will you organize it? What calculations will you have to carry out?

List the steps that you will take for this study. Prepare a table to record the data from each sample, including the percentage of right-coiling *N. pachyderma* present. Select an appropriate style for graphing your

LAB 21.2 — DESIGN YOUR OWN

PLAN THE EXPERIMENT, *continued*

results. Which variables will the graph illustrate? What scale of measurement will you use? How will the axes be labeled? Have your teacher approve your plan before you begin the study.

_____

_____

_____

DATA AND OBSERVATIONS

LAB **21.2**   DESIGN YOUR OWN

ANALYZE

1. What evidence does the data provide about changes in ocean temperature over the years?

_____

_____

_____

2. Do the data contain exact temperatures? Explain your answer.

_____

_____

_____

3. Can you identify any patterns or cycles in the data?

_____

_____

_____

4. What percentage and time intervals did you use for the axes of your graph?

_____

_____

5. How does your graph help you interpret the climatic history of Earth?

_____

_____

CHECK YOUR HYPOTHESIS

1. Was your **hypothesis** supported by your data? Why or why not?

_____

_____

CONCLUDE AND APPLY

1. Describe your conclusion about the climatic history of Earth during the last 160 000 years.

_____

_____

_____

LAB ◄ **21.2** ►   **DESIGN YOUR OWN**

CONCLUDE AND APPLY, *continued*

2. What evidence do you have for this conclusion?

_____

_____

_____

3. Is there any evidence from the microfossil data about the causes of the temperature change in the climate time line?

_____

4. Where does Earth appear to be in the climate cycle at present?

_____

5. Review news periodicals, radio and television broadcasts, and nature and science magazines, and talk to your parents and grandparents or other older people you know to find forms of evidence of climate change existing today. Describe two types of evidence and their probable causes.

_____

_____

_____

_____

6. Using the information that you have gathered, predict the direction that the climate-change graph might take from the present into the near future. Explain your prediction.

_____

_____

_____

_____

LAB 22.1   **INVESTIGATION**

Sequencing Time

Earth has been in existence for 4.6 billion years—a period of time so long it is difficult to imagine. When we discuss a topic such as the reign of the dinosaurs, it may seem like it occurred in Earth's distant past. It may surprise you to know, however, that dinosaurs walked Earth in relatively recent times, geologically speaking. Earth's long history can be represented visually by the geologic time scale, which divides Earth's period of existence into relatively small units. To better appreciate the history of Earth and the passage of geologic time, you will make a graphic version of the geologic time scale and compare it to a time scale of your own life.

PREPARATION

PROBLEM
How do milestones in the existence of Earth correspond to a human lifespan?

OBJECTIVES
- **Compare** the proportionate length of a human life to that of Earth.
- **Calculate** the scale at which Earth's history can be graphically compared to a human lifetime.

- **Analyze** the timing and scope of the evolution and diversification of life on Earth.

MATERIALS
pencil
2.5-m long roll of paper
calculator
meterstick

PROCEDURE

1. On the left side of the roll of paper, construct the geologic time scale. Make 1 cm on your paper equal 20 million years. Include the eons, eras, and geologic time periods shown in the table in Data and Observations. Begin at the bottom of the paper, with the birth of Earth 4600 million years ago.

2. Now construct a personal time scale. To do this, you will map your life alongside the length of existence of Earth. The scale will be different from the scale you used for the geologic time scale in step 1. Begin by computing the proportionate length of one year of your life.

The formula for this step is shown below.

> Mapped length of one year of life = total geologic time scale (in cm)/number of years in your life (to the closest month; expressed as a decimal)

Recall that mapping the 4600 million years of Earth's existence took 230 cm, so for a person who is 15 years and 8 months old: Mapped length of one year of life = 230 cm/15.75 years = 14.6 cm/year of life

Copyright © Glencoe/McGraw-Hill, a division of the McGraw-Hill Companies, Inc.

LAB **22.1**   **INVESTIGATION**

PROCEDURE, *continued*

3. On the right side of the roll of paper, mark off the years of your life using the scale you computed. Your birth should begin alongside the birth of Earth. The current time in your life should fall alongside the current time in Earth's history noted at the top of the roll of paper.

4. Refer again to the table and in the center of the paper, between the two scales you have drawn, write in important events in the evolution of life on Earth. For example, in the section that corresponds to the Ordovician, write "Fishes," and so on.

DATA AND OBSERVATIONS

Table

Era or Eon	Period	End Date (millions of years ago)	Length (in millions of years)	Life on Earth
Cenozoic	Quaternary	—	2	Humans
	Neogene	1.6	64	Mammals diversify.
	Paleogene	23		Mammals diversify.
Mesozoic	Cretaceous	66	80	Dinosaurs become extinct.
	Jurassic	146	62	Birds
	Triassic	208	37	Dinosaurs, mammals
Paleozoic	Permian	245	45	Seed plants
	Pennsylvanian (Carboniferous)	290	33	Reptiles diversify.
	Mississippian (Carboniferous)	323	39	Reptiles
	Devonian	362	46	Amphibians
	Silurian	408	31	Land invertebrates and plants
	Ordovician	439	71	Fishes
	Cambrian	510	30	Marine invertebrates
Proterozoic Eon (Precambrian)		540	1960	Multicellular organisms
Archean (Precambrian)		2500	2100	Early bacteria
		4600		Birth of Earth

LAB 22.1   **INVESTIGATION**

A N A L Y Z E

1. What was the longest division of time in Earth's history? Approximately what percentage of Earth's history occurred during this division?

_____

_____

_____

_____

2. Relate this long division of Earth's existence to your own life. About how many years of your life is proportional to the longest division of time in Earth's history?

_____

_____

_____

_____

3. About what percentage of the entire existence of Earth have bacteria been alive?

_____

_____

_____

_____

LAB **22.1**   **INVESTIGATION**

CONCLUDE AND APPLY

1. What can you conclude about the rise of living things? Did the rise of new organisms and the diversification of living things occur at an even rate over the entire history of Earth?

   _____

   _____

   _____

   _____

   _____

2. Assuming that humans have been alive for 2 million years, to what length of time in your own life is this proportional?

   _____

   _____

   _____

   _____

   _____

   _____

 **LAB** **22.2**   **MAPPING**

What came first?

Evidence of early life-forms and the planetary conditions that existed during the Precambrian provides us with information that we can use to make inferences about changes in the crust, atmosphere, and oceans throughout Earth's history. These changes contributed to the conditions necessary for the development of more advanced life-forms and the plant and animal life that exists today.

PREPARATION

PROBLEM
How can we illustrate the relationship of Precambrian life-forms to those that exist today?

OBJECTIVES
- **Represent** life-forms that appeared during different periods of Earth's history, beginning with the Precambrian.
- **Relate** time to the number and complexity of organisms on Earth.
- **Describe** how information about the Precambrian can be used to **analyze** planetary materials in the search for life elsewhere in the universe.

MATERIALS
geologic time scale
event card

PROCEDURE

1. Examine the time scale that has been hung the room. Discuss its characteristics with your group members and the class.

2. Pick an event card. Each card represents an event or the first evidence of an organism in the fossil record. You will become that organism or event. (Refer to Table 1 for your approximate geologic

time.) As your approximate age is announced, stand in front of the time scale at the place that represents that age. If your organism becomes extinct, sit on the floor when the Permian Mass Extinction Event or the Cretaceous-Paleogene Mass Extinction Event is announced.

LAB ◁ **22.2** ▷   **MAPPING**

DATA AND OBSERVATIONS

Event or First Evidence in Fossil Record	Approximate Geologic Time
Bacteria	3 b.y.b.p.
Green algae	1 b.y.b.p.
Jellyfish	600 m.y.b.p.
Ediacara organisms	550 m.y.b.p.
Eurypterids*	510 m.y.b.p.
Horn corals*	500 m.y.b.p.
First vertebrates	480 m.y.b.p.
Spiders	400 m.y.b.p.
Sharks	400 m.y.b.p.
First jawed fish*	380 m.y.b.p.
Ferns	350 m.y.b.p.
Earthworms	300 m.y.b.p.
Great Permian Extinction Event	250 m.y.b.p.
Drastic geographic and climatic changes	248 m.y.b.p.
First dinosaurs*	220 m.y.b.p.
First mammals	210 m.y.b.p.
Ginkgo biloba	200 m.y.b.p.
Abundant ammonites*	180 m.y.b.p.
Archaeopteryx	140 m.y.b.p.
First flowering plants	120 m.y.b.p.
Ants	100 m.y.b.p.
Cretaceous-Paleogene Extinction Event	66 m.y.b.p.
Camel	35 m.y.b.p.
Grass	20 m.y.b.p.
Australopithecus afarensis ("Lucy")	4 m.y.b.p.

* = now extinct
b.y.b.p. = billion years before present
m.y.b.p. = million years before present

LAB 22.2   **MAPPING**

ANALYZE

1. List the major divisions of Earth's history that are represented on this time scale.

_____

2. Identify the approximate beginning and ending points of these major divisions on the time scale, in inches.

_____

_____

_____

3. Which of these divisions is the longest? Shortest? Oldest? Most recent?

_____

_____

_____

4. From your observations of the completed time scale, describe two major differences between the Precambrian and the Cenozoic Era. Why do you think these differences exist?

_____

_____

_____

_____

_____

_____

LAB **22.2**

CONCLUDE AND APPLY

1. Evidence from the Precambrian indicates that organisms at that time produced the oxygen that changed the composition of the atmosphere. What effect did this have on the evolution of life-forms?

_____

_____

_____

_____

2. What were the most important overall impressions that you got from observing the construction of the time scale?

_____

_____

_____

_____

3. How might information from the Precambrian be useful in analyzing extraterrestrial material for evidence of life elsewhere in the universe?

_____

_____

_____

_____

LAB 23.1   MAPPING

Water to Land

Early life-forms on Earth developed in the seas. As the climate and the shapes, sizes, and locations of these seas and landforms changed, some life-forms developed adaptations that enabled them to move onto land. Paleontologists are able to reconstruct Earth as it was millions of years ago by studying fossils to infer what environments were present at different times.

PREPARATION

PROBLEM
How can we use representative fossils to infer the type of environment in which organisms once lived?

OBJECTIVES
- **Map** the fossils in a progression of different environments.
- **Categorize** fossils based on adaptations for survival in sea, beach, or land environments.
- **Draw** the boundaries of environments on a fossil map.
- **Defend** interpretations of fossil evidence.

MATERIALS
fossil cards or models
blue, yellow, and green pencils

PROCEDURE

1. Examine a fossil card or model at a station.

2. In the space in Data and Observations that has the same number as the fossil, sketch the fossil and label it. You will have about 2 minutes for this.

3. Move to the next station and repeat steps 1 and 2, until you have sketched all the fossils.

LAB 23.1   **MAPPING**

DATA AND OBSERVATIONS

1	2	3	4	5
6	7	8	9	10
11	12	13	14	15
16	17	18	19	20
21	22	23	24	25
26	27	28	29	30

LAB 23.1   **MAPPING**

ANALYZE

1. What does this fossil evidence indicate about the types of environments in which the organisms might have lived?

_____

_____

_____

2. Examine the distribution of the fossils in Data and Observations. Using dashed lines, indicate where one environment might have ended and another environment might have begun. Describe how the environments are arranged.

_____

_____

_____

_____

_____

CONCLUDE AND APPLY

1. Color your filled-in grids as follows:

   boxes with land fossils = green

   boxes with beach fossils = yellow

   boxes with sea fossils = blue

   What are the major differences among the organisms that lived in these different environments?

   _____

   _____

   _____

   _____

   _____

   _____

2. Because you did not actually observe these organisms while they were living in the three environments, you have inferred their habitats from fossil evidence. List the reasons for your inferences of the evidence.

   _____

   _____

   _____

   _____

   _____

   _____

   _____

   _____

LAB ◆ **23.2**   **INVESTIGATION**

Searching for Oil with Microfossils

Oil accumulates in ancient sedimentary rocks. Beds containing the organic remains of unicellular organisms are the source rock for oil, which travels to and is stored in reservoir rock such as sandstone or porous limestone. Silt and clay sediments with abundant organic material deposited in water depths of greater than 1000 m are good source rocks for oil. Beach sands can become good reservoir rocks. Benthic foraminifera live attached to the sea bottom. Scientists study fossil benthic foraminifera to find water-depth locations where oil-producing organisms may have been deposited during the geologic past.

PREPARATION

PROBLEM
How do benthic foraminifera indicate potentially good reservoir rock and source rock in an ocean basin?

OBJECTIVES
- **Identify** eight species of fossil benthic foraminifera and their preferred ocean habitats.
- **Analyze** diagrams of foraminifera samples for water-depth range.

- **Infer** water depths in the basin.
- **Use** water depth to **predict** where to find potential source rock and reservoir rock.

MATERIALS
2 colored pencils

Figure 1   **Environments of Living Foraminifera in Ancient Oceans**

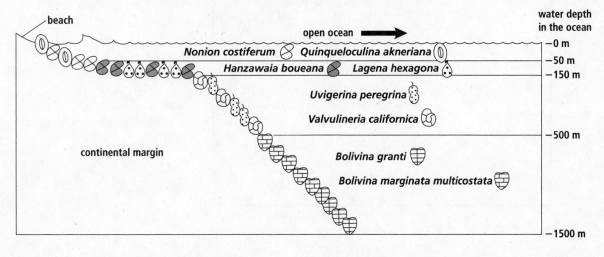

LAB ◀ **23.2** ▶   **INVESTIGATION**

PROCEDURE

1. Examine Figure 1 to identify the habitats of benthic foraminifera during the geologic past. For this exercise, the ancient ocean is divided into four zones based on water depth: 0–50 m, 50–150 m, 150–500 m, and 500–1500 m. The foraminifera that preferred each environment are listed with a schematic drawing for each species. Notice that the seafloor slopes down at the continental margin. Because of this, when foraminifera die, gravity may transport them downslope into deeper water. This would mean, for example, that, although *Hanzawaia boueana* and *Lagena hexagona* live on the seafloor at water depths of 50–150 m, after they die, they might be found in samples representing 350 m or 1500 m. Keep this in mind when you are analyzing the samples. For interpretation of water-depth locations, use only the species in the sample who lived at the lowest depths.

2. Figure 2 is a map of the ocean basin and the sample localities. Mark the ancient water-depth numbers on the map. Sample 2 has already been filled in for you. Review the distribution of water depths on the map.

3. Figure 3 shows samples of benthic foraminifera that were collected from an ocean basin off the west coast of North America. They were collected from ten different locations in the basin. In other parts of the basin, rocks of the same age contain oil reserves. Each box in Figure 3 displays the foraminifera species found in the sample. Compare each sample in Figure 3 with the key to water-depth environments in Figure 1.

4. In the blank for ancient water-depth interpretation under each sample, put a water-depth range implied by your analysis. Sample 2 has been filled in for you.

DATA AND OBSERVATIONS

Figure 2

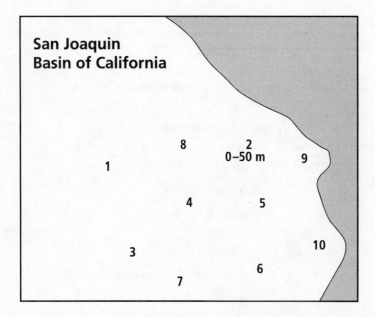

LAB **23.2**   **INVESTIGATION**

DATA AND OBSERVATIONS, *continued*

Figure 3

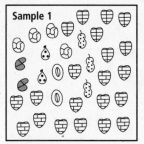

Sample 1

ancient water-depth
interpretation _____

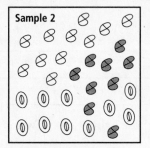

Sample 2

ancient water-depth
interpretation _0 – 50m_

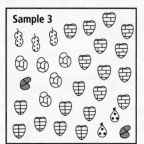

Sample 3

ancient water-depth
interpretation _____

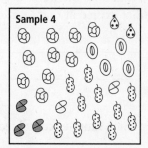

Sample 4

ancient water-depth
interpretation _____

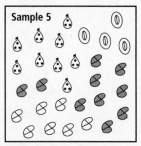

Sample 5

ancient water-depth
interpretation _____

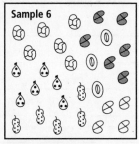

Sample 6

ancient water-depth
interpretation _____

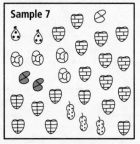

Sample 7

ancient water-depth
interpretation _____

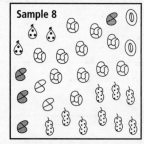

Sample 8

ancient water-depth
interpretation _____

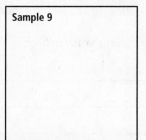

Sample 9

no fossil foraminifera found
in this sample
ancient water-depth
interpretation _____

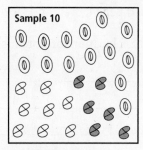

Sample 10

ancient water-depth
interpretation _____

ANALYZE

1. What might be a reason for the absence of benthic foraminifera in sample 9?

_____

_____

_____

2. Which samples contain foraminifera that were transported downslope?

_____

LAB **23.2** **INVESTIGATION**

CONCLUDE AND APPLY

1. What does the water depth and characteristics of sample 9 suggest about the type of habitat that existed at that location?

   _____

   _____

   _____

2. Which samples contained *only* fossil foraminifera whose habitat was at water depths of 0–50 m?

   _____

3. Where was the beach located when these microfossils were living? Explain your answer.

   _____

   _____

   _____

   _____

   _____

4. Using a colored pencil, draw and label on Figure 2 the possible location of the beach (shoreline).

5. What might be a location for potential source rock in this basin? Explain your answer.

   _____

   _____

   _____

6. With a second color, draw and label the area for potential source rock.

7. What is your evaluation of the potential for good reservoir rock and source rock in this part of the basin?

   _____

   _____

   _____

   _____

   _____

Cenozoic Ice Sheets and Plant Distribution

An analysis of pollen grains from the Cenozoic Era can provide evidence of past climatic conditions. Because we know the conditions in which many plant species grow today, changes in ancient climates can be estimated by comparing fossil pollen samples with living relatives and estimating ancient plant distribution from the changing concentrations of pollen remains. Changes in climate can then be inferred from the changes in the distribution of vegetation.

PREPARATION

PROBLEM

How can the relationship between changes in the extent of the Laurentide ice sheet in North America and changes in the distribution of vegetation inform us about climate change during the Cenozoic?

OBJECTIVES

- **Describe** the distribution of different plant groups in North America at different times during the last ice age.
- **Explain** the relationship between changes in plant distribution and the extent of the Laurentian ice sheet.
- **Make inferences** about the relationship between plant distribution and climate change.

PROCEDURE

The maps on the next page show the distribution of pollen in the Eastern United States from the time of the last ice age, the Laurentide, to the present. The label ka means thousands of years ago. Refer to the legend and use the markers to color the North American plant distribution maps as follows:

MATERIALS

fine-point colored markers or
   colored pencils
political map of North America

Plant Group	Color
Ice	White
Tundra	Violet
Forest Tundra	Purple
Boreal Forest (northern forest south of the tundra)	Dark Green
Mixed Forest	Light Green
Deciduous Forest	Orange
Aspen Parkland	Yellow
Prairie	Brown
Southeast Forest	Blue
No Match	Red
No Data	Gray

LAB **24.1**   **MAPPING**

DATA AND OBSERVATIONS

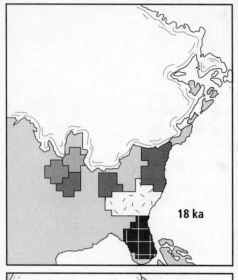

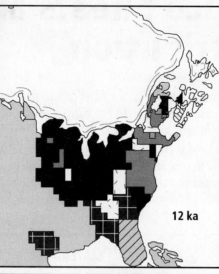

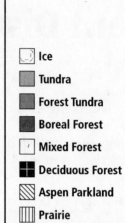

Ice

Tundra

Forest Tundra

Boreal Forest

Mixed Forest

Deciduous Forest

Aspen Parkland

Prairie

Southeast Forest

No Match

No Data

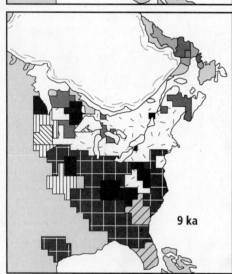

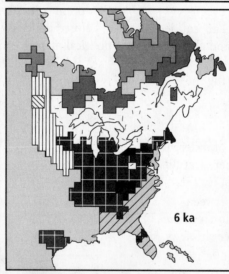

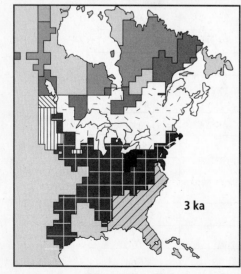

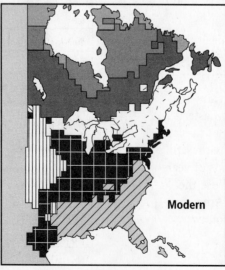

LAB 24.1   **MAPPING**

A N A L Y Z E

1. The extent of the Laurentide ice sheet has varied over the past 18 000 years.

   a. At what time was the Laurentide ice sheet at its greatest extent?

_____

   b. How many plant groups were present at this time? What were they?

_____

_____

   c. By what approximate time was the ice sheet first absent from the North American continent?

_____

   d. How many plant groups were present at this time? What were they?

_____

_____

_____

   e. What information does this change in number and type of plant groups give us about climate?

_____

_____

_____

2. At 18 ka, tundra vegetation was present in the area that today is the Midwest.

   a. By 9 ka, what type of vegetation had replaced the tundra?

_____

   b. What can we infer about climate from this change in vegetation?

_____

_____

3. Tundra now exists in northern Canada, Alaska, and Siberia.

   a. What do we know about today's climate in those areas?

_____

   b. Which states today coincide with the approximate area that was covered by tundra at 18 ka?

_____

LAB **24.1**   **MAPPING**

ANALYZE, *continued*

c. According to the maps, Florida's climate at 18 ka was similar to today's climate in which of today's areas?

_____

_____

CONCLUDE AND APPLY

1. Map B shows the extent of the Laurentide ice sheet at approximately 15 ka. Using what you know about the relationship of climate to plant group, predict the plant group distribution for the western half of North America at that time. Color those areas on the map. Explain your prediction.

_____

_____

_____

_____

_____

_____

LAB ◄ **24.2** ►   **INVESTIGATION**

Index Fossils and Dinosaur Bones

One of the most reliable ways to locate fossils is to use other fossils. Certain widely found fossils represent animals that lived on Earth for a very short time. When these index fossils are found in rock layers in different areas, scientists believe that the layers formed at the same time and correlate with one another. If dinosaur fossils are found in a certain layer in Montana and that same layer is found in western Canada, we would expect to find dinosaur fossils in the Canadian layer.

PREPARATION

PROBLEM
How can dinosaur fossils be traced from one place to another by using index fossils?

OBJECTIVES
• **Develop** a hypothesis about a correlation between rock layers in Montana and western Canada.

• **Identify** rock layers that contain index fossils.

• **Predict** which rock layers in western Canada will contain the same kind of fossils as those in Montana.

MATERIALS
colored pencils
index-fossil chart

PROCEDURE

1. Figure 1 shows two stratigraphic columns, one in Montana and one in western Canada. Without index fossils, this is all the information that scientists would have to correlate layers. Use a colored pencil to correlate the rock layers in Montana with those in western Canada. This correlation is your hypothesis, or best guess, about which layers might contain the same kinds of fossils.

2. Label the layer in western Canada that you predict will contain dinosaur bones that are the same age as the one found in layer D in Montana.

3. Your teacher will distribute a chart of index fossils found in certain

rock layers. Each fossil was found in only one layer in Montana and one layer in western Canada. From this information, you can correlate the layers. In Figure 2, sketch or label the fossils in each layer. (For example, fossil 1 appears in layers B and H.)

4. Use a different colored pencil to correlate the rock layers, using the fossil evidence that you have just drawn. Use the key to determine in what type of rock each fossil might be found.

LAB ◇ **24.2**   **INVESTIGATION**

DATA AND OBSERVATIONS

Key

_____ Sandstone   Shale   Limestone

Figure 1

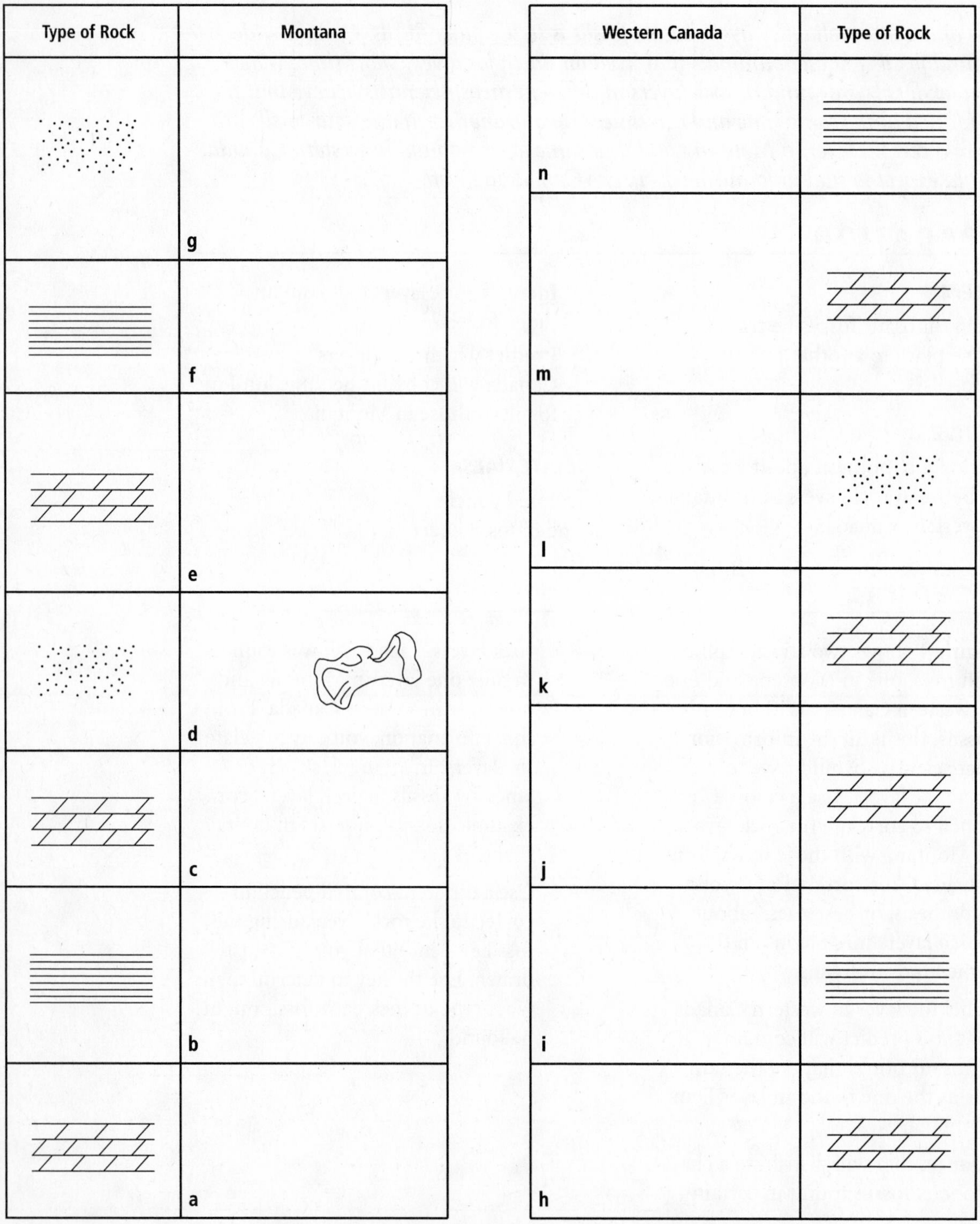

Type of Rock	Montana
	g
	f
	e
	d
	c
	b
	a

Western Canada	Type of Rock
n	
m	
l	
k	
j	
i	
h	

LAB ◆ **24.2**   **INVESTIGATION**

DATA AND OBSERVATIONS, *continued*

Figure 2

Type of Rock	Montana
(dotted pattern)	g
(horizontal lines)	f
(diagonal brick pattern)	e
(dotted pattern)	d (bone illustration)
(diagonal brick pattern)	c
(horizontal lines)	b
(diagonal brick pattern)	a

Western Canada	Type of Rock
n	(horizontal lines)
m	(diagonal brick pattern)
l	(dotted pattern)
k	(diagonal brick pattern)
j	(diagonal brick pattern)
i	(horizontal lines)
h	(diagonal brick pattern)

ANALYZE

1. Compare the connections you made in Figure 1 and Figure 2. Describe the differences between the two correlations.

_____

_____

_____

_____

_____

_____

LAB ⬦ **24.2**   **INVESTIGATION**

ANALYZE, *continued*

2. Which set of correlations do you think is more accurate? Why?

_____

_____

_____

_____

_____

_____

CONCLUDE AND APPLY

1. Which layer in western Canada do you now think contains the dinosaur fossil? Why?

_____

_____

_____

_____

2. Is layer **g** in Montana younger or older than layer **n** in western Canada? Explain your answer.

_____

_____

_____

_____

_____

3. Would you expect to find dinosaur bones in layer **h**? Explain your answer.

_____

_____

_____

_____

_____

LAB ◆ **25.1** **DESIGN YOUR OWN**

Neutralizing Acid Precipitation

*W*hen fossil fuels are burned to power vehicles or to generate electricity, they produce sulfur dioxide and nitrogen oxides in the atmosphere. These pollutants combine with atmospheric moisture to create sulfuric acid and nitric acid. As a result, the precipitation is more acidic than unpolluted forms of precipitation. Acid precipitation can decrease soil productivity and damage buildings, vegetation, and wildlife.

PREPARATION

PROBLEM

How can the acidity of acid precipitation be decreased, or neutralized?

OBJECTIVES

- **Design** an experiment to **test** the pH levels of two solutions.
- **Determine** how to neutralize an acidic solution.
- **Compare** and **contrast** an acidic solution and a neutralized solution.

HYPOTHESIS

As a group, review the pH scale and the characteristics of acidic and basic solutions. Write a hypothesis about how an acidic solution could be neutralized. Write your hypothesis below.

_____

_____

_____

POSSIBLE MATERIALS

500 mL distilled water
230 g powdered limestone
white vinegar
baking soda
250-mL glass beakers (2)
stirring rods
measuring spoons
dropper
marking pen
plastic wrap
pH paper
pH color chart

SAFETY PRECAUTIONS

- Wear safety goggles, gloves, and an apron during the lab procedure.
- If you break any glassware, notify your teacher right away. Do not attempt to clean up broken glass.
- Label all solutions.
- Follow your teacher's suggestions for disposing of lab materials.

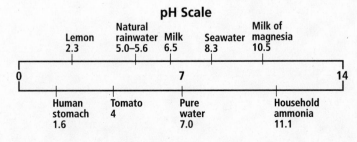

pH Scale

LAB ◆ **25.1**   **DESIGN YOUR OWN**

PLAN THE EXPERIMENT

Review the list of possible materials. Design a plan to slowly decrease, or neutralize, the acidity of a solution over the course of several days. Your experiment should include a control, a way to test pH, and a method to ensure that the solutions do not evaporate. Set up a table to record your results. The pH color chart provided by your teacher and the pH scale will help you interpret your results. Outline your plan and have your teacher approve it before you begin the experiment.

_____

_____

_____

_____

_____

_____

DATA AND OBSERVATIONS

DATA TABLE

LAB **25.1**

DATA AND OBSERVATIONS, *continued*

GRAPH

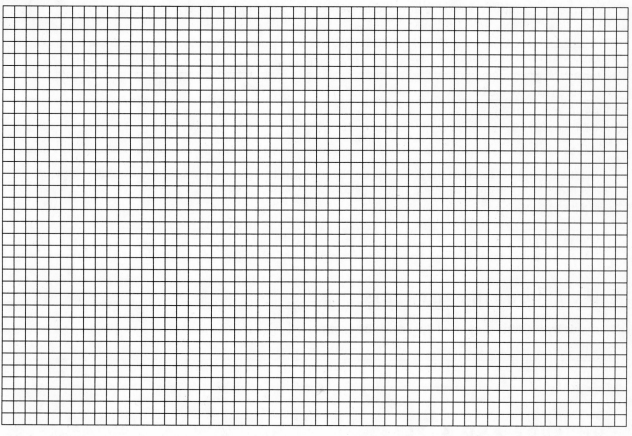

ANALYZE

1. What was your control? What was the independent variable in this experiment?

_____

_____

2. How did you decrease the acidity of your solution? Why was your method effective?

_____

_____

_____

_____

LAB 25.1   DESIGN YOUR OWN

ANALYZE, *continued*

3. Plot the pH levels of the solutions on a graph below your table. Compare and contrast the pH levels of the two solutions. Describe how these levels changed during the experiment.

_____

_____

_____

_____

4. Plot the final pH levels of the solutions on the pH scale in Figure 1. How do these levels compare to those of other items on the scale?

_____

_____

CHECK YOUR HYPOTHESIS

Was your **hypothesis** supported by data? Why or why not?

_____

_____

CONCLUDE AND APPLY

1. Suppose that the pH levels of your solutions represent the pH levels of two separate rainfalls. How might each rainfall affect vegetation and aquatic organisms?

_____

_____

2. Based on your results, describe how acid precipitation can be neutralized in lakes and ponds.

_____

_____

3. Would the method you described in question 2 solve the problem of acid precipitation permanently or temporarily? Explain your answer.

_____

_____

LAB **25.2** **INVESTIGATION**

Water Usage

*A*ccording to the United States Geological Survey (USGS), the government agency that oversees United States water supplies, the United States has abundant freshwater resources. However, many existing sources of groundwater and surface water, such as wells, lakes, and reservoirs, are in danger of being overused, and drought is a problem in some areas. The economic and environmental health of the country—and of the entire planet—depends, in part, on maintaining a balance between water demand and water supply.

PREPARATION

PROBLEM
How has water usage changed in the United States since 1950?

OBJECTIVES
- **Analyze** changing trends in water usage over a 40-year period.

- **Determine** which categories use the most water per day.
- **Discuss** conservation methods that might decrease water use.

MATERIALS
calculator

PROCEDURE

1. Study the bar graph, based on data from the USGS. Look for patterns in water usage. Do certain categories consistently use more water than others? Have some categories increased their water use more quickly than others?

2. Create a data table based on the graph. Place the nine time periods across the top of the table. List the

   five categories on the left side of the table. In the rows, write the total amount of water used per day by each category for the years listed.

3. Calculate the total amount of water used per day by all categories for each year. Add this information to the data table.

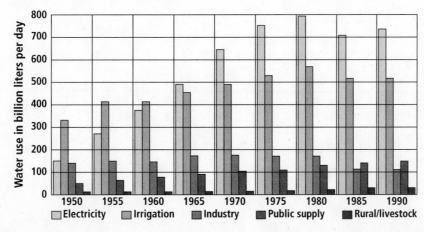

LAB 25.2 **INVESTIGATION**

DATA AND OBSERVATIONS

Data Table

LAB ◇ **25.2**   **INVESTIGATION**

ANALYZE

1. Approximately how many billions of liters of water were used per day in the United States in 1990? How does this amount compare to total water usage in 1950?

_____

_____

2. Which category showed the greatest increase over the course of the 40 years shown in the graph? What might account for the increase?

_____

_____

_____

3. Which category showed a decrease in water use over the course of 40 years? What might account for the decrease?

_____

_____

_____

4. When did water usage peak in the United States for most categories? Which categories continued to show an increase? Make a hypothesis for the reasons behind the increase.

_____

_____

_____

5. Which two categories consistently account for most water usage in the United States? How much water did these categories use in 1980?

_____

_____

6. Describe how water might be used for each category in the graph.

_____

_____

_____

_____

LAB **25.2** **INVESTIGATION**

CONCLUDE AND APPLY

1. The 1990 population of the United States was about 252 million. Use the amount listed in the "Public supply" category for 1990 to calculate the average amount of water each United States citizen used daily.

_____

_____

_____

2. In 1995, total United States water use was about 1520 billion L per day. Add this information to your data table. In your own words, describe the overall trend in water usage in the United States from 1950 to 1995.

_____

_____

_____

_____

_____

3. Think of all the ways that you use water each day. Describe at least three things that you could do as an individual to decrease your daily water use. Identify two things that government or industry could do to decrease water use.

_____

_____

_____

_____

LAB 26.1   **DESIGN YOUR OWN**

Solar Water-Heater

Scientists estimate that, in one hour, enough solar energy reaches Earth to meet global energy needs for an entire year. Solar energy is nonpolluting, renewable, and cost effective. Why isn't it more widely used? Because solar energy is not available at night or on overcast days, it must be stored in some way. Also, many areas do not receive enough sunlight to make solar energy a viable large-scale resource. Technological advances will likely solve these problems in the near future. Meanwhile, there are many small-scale uses for solar energy.

PREPARATION

PROBLEM
What factors must you consider when building a solar water-heater?

OBJECTIVES
- **Design** and **construct** a solar water-heater.
- **Analyze** the efficiency of various solar energy devices and **suggest** improvements to them.
- **Discuss** the advantages and disadvantages of solar energy.

HYPOTHESIS
As a group, discuss how you could use the materials provided by your teacher to design and build a solar water-heater. Form a hypothesis about the factors that might affect the efficiency of your solar energy device.

_____

_____

_____

_____

_____

_____

POSSIBLE MATERIALS
3 L water
3 m black tubing
shallow cardboard box, about
  30 cm × 40 cm
black construction paper
clear plastic wrap
insulating materials
  (cotton, newspaper, cloth, etc.)
tape
scissors
alcohol-based thermometer
clothespin
2 clean plastic 2-L bottles

SAFETY PRECAUTIONS

- Wear safety goggles during the lab procedure.
- If you break a thermometer, notify your teacher right away. Do not attempt to clean up broken glass.
- Use caution when handling sharp objects such as scissors.
- Avoid using mercury-based thermometers. Mercury is toxic.
- Follow your teacher's suggestions for disposing of lab materials.

LAB **26.1** DESIGN YOUR OWN

PLAN THE EXPERIMENT

Review the list of possible materials. Working individually, design a device to warm water by using solar energy. Sketch your design below and label its parts. With your group, decide upon the best design. You may wish to incorporate elements from several designs. Sketch and label the revised design below. Plan how to test the design's effectiveness. How will you ensure that the heater receives enough solar energy? What will you use for insulation? How will you maintain a steady flow of water through the heater? Set up a data table to record your results. Have your teacher approve your plan before you build and test the heater.

DATA AND OBSERVATIONS

DATA TABLE

LAB 26.1   **DESIGN YOUR OWN**

DATA AND OBSERVATIONS, *continued*

GRAPH

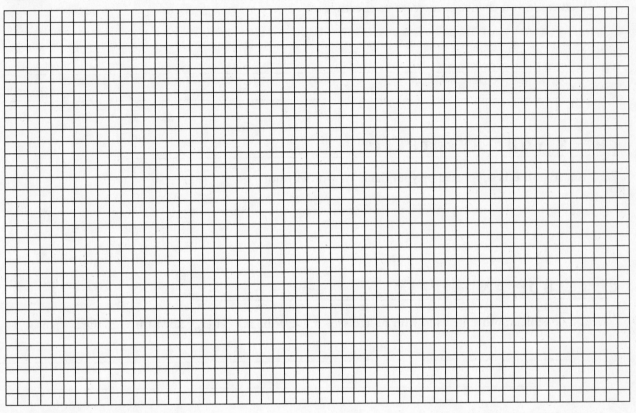

ANALYZE

1. How did you test the effectiveness of your solar water-heater?

_____

_____

_____

2. Graph the data that you gathered as you tested your device.
Describe any patterns that you observe in the data.

_____

_____

_____

3. Did your solar water-heater function as planned? Explain your answer.

_____

_____

LAB ◆ **26.1**   **DESIGN YOUR OWN**

ANALYZE, *continued*

4. Compare your designs to those of other groups. Think about improvements to your design. What could you change to increase its effectiveness?

_____

_____

_____

CHECK YOUR HYPOTHESIS

Was your **hypothesis** supported by your data? Why or why not?

_____

_____

CONCLUDE AND APPLY

1. Add possible improvements to your design sketch. Describe how energy flows through the system.

_____

_____

_____

2. Review your results and those of other groups. Which factors appear to affect the efficiency of solar water-heaters?

_____

_____

_____

3. Based on what you have learned in this activity and on your previous knowledge of solar energy, identify two advantages and two disadvantages of solar energy.

_____

_____

_____

LAB 26.2

Assessing Wind Energy

Humans have used energy from the wind for thousands of years to pump water and grind corn. Experts estimate that this nonpolluting source of energy may provide up to 10 percent of electricity needs worldwide within the next 50 years. Wind energy is generally produced at wind farms that use wind turbines to turn generators and create electricity. Currently, however, electricity from wind energy is difficult to store and to transport long distances. Until technology improves, wind energy is largely limited to areas with steady, strong winds.

PREPARATION

PROBLEM
Is wind energy a viable energy resource for your area?

OBJECTIVES
- **Construct** a tool to measure wind speed.
- **Observe** and **record** wind speeds at different locations.
- **Determine** if local wind speeds are high enough to generate electricity.
- **Consider** the advantages and disadvantages of wind energy.

MATERIALS
small plastic ball
white paper
tape
cardboard, 10 cm × 16 cm
scissors
marking pen
heavy-duty sewing needle
heavy thread, 30 cm
calculator

SAFETY PRECAUTIONS

- Wear safety goggles during the lab procedure.
- Be careful not to stab yourself when punching a hole with the needle.
- Use caution when handling sharp objects such as scissors.

PROCEDURE

1. Use white paper and a pencil to trace Figure 1. Cut out the paper protractor and tape it to the cardboard.

2. Trace the outline of the paper protractor on the cardboard, and cut it out. Mark the angles of the protractor, as shown in Figure 1.

3. Thread the sewing needle with heavy thread. Carefully use the threaded needle to punch a hole through the center of a small plastic ball. The needle should go completely through the ball. Unthread the needle and tie a knot in the thread so the ball will not slide off the end.

LAB ◄ **26.2** ►   **INVESTIGATION** 🔍

PROCEDURE, *continued*

Figure 1

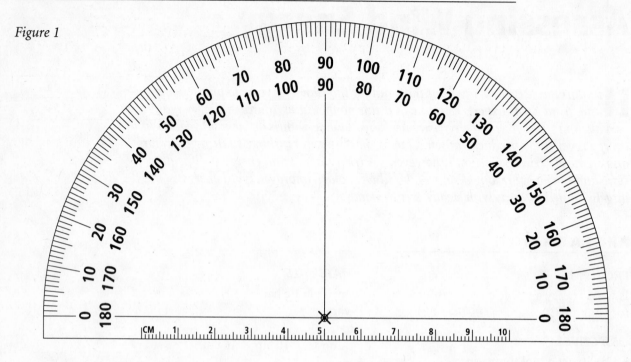

4. Tape the other end of the thread to the cardboard protractor. The *X* on the protractor in Figure 1 indicates where to tape the thread.

5. Go outside and choose three sites near your school that are relatively open. Stand with your back to the wind and hold the protractor level with the straight edge up so that the thread with the ball hangs down parallel to the 90° mark. Hold the protractor in front of you so that you do not completely block the wind. The thread with the ball should be able to move freely along the face of the protractor.

6. Measure the angle of the thread on the protractor (see Figure 2). Record the angle in Table 2. Use Table 1 to convert your measurements into actual wind speeds.

7. Measure and record wind speeds at the other two sites. Collect data at each site daily for 5 days.

Figure 2

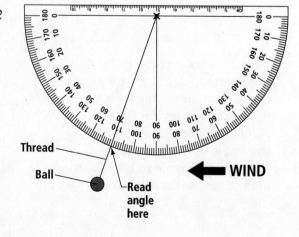

LAB 26.2   **INVESTIGATION**

DATA AND OBSERVATIONS

Table 1

Angle (°)	Approximate Wind Speed (km/h)	Angle (°)	Approximate Wind Speed (km/h)	Angle (°)	Approximate Wind Speed (km/h)	Angle (°)	Approximate Wind Speed (km/h)
90	0	70	12	50	18	30	26
85	6	65	13	45	20	25	29
80	8	60	15	40	21	20	33
75	10	55	16	35	23		

Table 2

	Day	Site 1	Site 2	Site 3
Angle	1			
Wind speed	1			
Angle	2			
Wind speed	2			
Angle	3			
Wind speed	3			
Angle	4			
Wind speed	4			
Angle	5			
Wind speed	5			

ANALYZE

1. Calculate the average wind speed at each site. Compare your averages to those of other groups. Did wind speeds vary widely or were they relatively constant for all groups? Give reasons for the similarity or variation.

_____

_____

_____

_____

2. Where were the greatest wind speeds measured? Describe the layout of those areas.

_____

_____

LAB **26.2** **INVESTIGATION**

ANALYZE, continued

3. Use the space below to plot your average wind speeds. Describe any daily variations in the plotted values. How might these variations affect the reliability of wind as an energy resource?

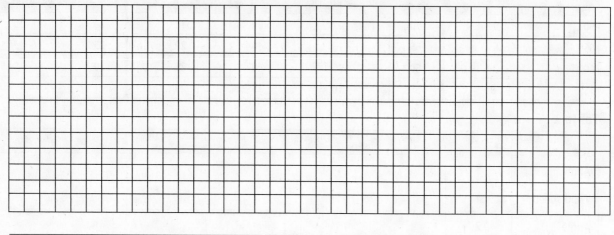

_____

_____

_____

4. To generate electricity from wind efficiently, average wind speeds must be at least 21 km/h. How do your average values compare to this value?

_____

_____

CONCLUDE AND APPLY

1. Wind energy increases with the cube of the wind speed. If local average wind speed was 10 km/h, how much of an increase in wind speed would be necessary to double local energy output?

_____

_____

2. An area that experiences weak winds is not suitable to generate electricity by wind. An area that experiences very strong winds is also not suitable to generate electricity by wind. Why?

_____

_____

3. Based on your measurements of wind speed, would your area be a suitable place for the production of electricity by wind energy? Explain your answer.

_____

_____

 **LAB 27.1** **DESIGN YOUR OWN**

Cleaning Up Oil Spills

Extracting fossil fuels such as coal from Earth's crust often results in pollution of land or water resources. Pollution may also occur during transport of fossil fuels. Oil spills caused by tanker collisions or leaks at offshore oil wells may form thick layers of crude oil on the water's surface, which can interfere with marine organisms' ability to feed, breathe, move, and reproduce. Major oil spills like the one from the Exxon Valdez in Prince William Sound have disrupted food webs and devastated marine ecosystems.

PREPARATION

PROBLEM
Which materials are most effective in cleaning up an oil spill?

OBJECTIVES
- **Develop** criteria to **determine** the effectiveness of different materials in cleaning up oil spills.
- **Model** a cleanup of an oil spill.
- **Compare** and **contrast** the effectiveness of different materials as cleaning agents for oil spills.

HYPOTHESIS
As a group, decide how various materials could be used to clean up an oil spill. Form a hypothesis about which material will be the most effective cleaning agent. Write your hypothesis below.

_____

_____

_____

POSSIBLE MATERIALS
olive oil
shallow pan
paper towels
water
toothpicks
feathers
string
cotton balls
cardboard
dropper
liquid detergent
gravel
sponge

SAFETY PRECAUTIONS

- Wear safety goggles, an apron, and gloves during the lab procedure.
- Dispose of oil-soaked materials as directed by your teacher.

LAB **27.1**   DESIGN YOUR OWN

PLAN THE EXPERIMENT

As a group, discuss and agree upon a plan stating how you could clean up an oil spill using the materials provided. Write down your plan. Be specific about how you will use the gravel and the pan to model a rocky beach. How will you model the oil spill? You will need to design and conduct several tests to determine the most effective cleaning agents. In your plan, explain how you will separate and control variables, so that you test only one variable at a time. Set up a table to record your results. Have your teacher approve your plan before you begin the experiments.

_____
_____
_____
_____
_____
_____
_____
_____
_____

DATA AND OBSERVATIONS

DATA TABLE

LAB **27.1** **DESIGN YOUR OWN**

ANALYZE

1. Which materials were most effective in absorbing the oil from the water's surface?
Which materials were least effective?

_____

_____

2. What criteria did you use to judge how well the materials cleaned up the oil spill?

_____

_____

3. The water in the pan represented the open ocean, and the gravel represented a rocky shore.
Did the cleaning agents perform equally well in both locations? Why or why not?

_____

_____

_____

_____

4. Identify some disadvantages that may be associated with your cleaning materials. For instance,
are any of your cleaning methods harmful to marine organisms?

_____

_____

_____

5. Based on your results, would you recommend a combination of cleaning methods or one
method alone? Explain your answer.

_____

_____

_____

LAB **27.1**

DESIGN YOUR OWN

CHECK YOUR HYPOTHESIS

Was your **hypothesis** supported by your data? Why or why not?

_____

_____

CONCLUDE AND APPLY

1. Describe the appearance of the feathers after they were dipped in the oil. Based on your observations, predict how an actual oil spill might affect a seabird.

_____

_____

_____

2. Oceans are in constant motion. Describe some of these movements. Would the motion of the water help or hinder efforts to clean up an oil spill?

_____

_____

_____

 **LAB** **27.2** **INVESTIGATION**

Algal Blooms

Farmers commonly add fertilizers containing nitrogen, potassium, and phosphorus to their fields to increase crop production. These chemicals can leach into the soil and run off into nearby ponds, streams, and lakes. When an excessive amount of fertilizer enters freshwater, algae and aquatic plants can experience population explosions. If the algal population explodes and covers the surface of the pond, it is called an algal bloom.

PREPARATION

PROBLEM
Under what conditions do algae grow best?

OBJECTIVES
- **Observe** the growth of algae in two controlled experiments.
- **Discover** what makes algae thrive.
- **Recognize** that excessive growth of algae may be linked to human activities.

MATERIALS
2 L distilled water
2 L liquid fertilizer
1 L pond water
1-L glass jars with lids (4)
100-mL graduated cylinder
marking pen
microscope
microscope slides
coverslips
dropper

SAFETY PRECAUTIONS

- Wear splash-resistant safety goggles, gloves, and an apron during the lab procedure.
- If you break any glassware, notify your teacher right away. Do not attempt to clean up broken glass.
- Follow your teacher's suggestions for disposing of lab materials.

PROCEDURE

1. Use a marking pen to label four jars from 1 to 4.

2. Measure 475 mL of distilled water into each jar. Add 250 mL of pond water to each jar.

3. Carefully measure 5 mL of liquid fertilizer into jar 2 and into jar 4. Screw the lids on all four jars.

4. Place jars 1 and 2 (experiment A) on a sunny windowsill. Place jars 3 and 4 (experiment B) in a cool, shady area of the lab where they will not be disturbed.

5. Each day for 10 days, observe any changes in the water in the jars. Record your observations in the table provided.

6. On the last day of the experiments, put a drop of water from jar 1 on a microscope slide and cover it with a coverslip. Look at the slide under a microscope. Record your observations. Observe water from the other three jars as well.

LAB 27.2   **INVESTIGATION**

DATA AND OBSERVATIONS

	Observations			
	Experiment A		**Experiment B**	
Day	**Jar 1**	**Jar 2**	**Jar 3**	**Jar 4**
1				
2				
3				
4				
5				
6				
7				
8				
9				
10				

ANALYZE

1. What was the independent variable for experiment A? What was the independent variable for experiment B? Identify the control in both experiments. How did experiment A differ from experiment B?

_____

_____

_____

_____

_____

2. Describe any changes that occurred in the water in the jars. Did the color of the water change in all four jars? What did you observe under the microscope?

_____

_____

_____

_____

_____

ANALYZE, *continued*

3. Which jar showed the greatest algal growth? Which jar showed the least growth? Explain why.

_____

_____

_____

_____

_____

4. Explain why the pond water was a crucial component of this lab.

_____

_____

_____

_____

5. Based on your observations, under which conditions would algae grow best?

_____

_____

_____

_____

_____

LAB 27.2 INVESTIGATION

CONCLUDE AND APPLY

1. Algae use oxygen during respiration and decomposition. That means a large population of algae can deplete the oxygen in a body of water. How might this affect fish and other aquatic life in the water?

_____

_____

_____

_____

2. Fertilizers sometimes run off into ponds and cause algal blooms. Describe how a farmer could try to lessen this problem.

_____

_____

_____

_____

3. Based on what you have learned about algal growth, why do algal blooms sometimes occur near power plants and factories that release hot water into a river or lake?

_____

_____

_____

_____

LAB 28.1   **INVESTIGATION**

Make Your Own Telescope

The earliest telescopes were refracting telescopes, which have two lenses. The large one at the front is the objective, and the small one that you look through is the eyepiece. Lenses have two main properties—size and power. The size of a lens is its diameter. The power of a lens depends on its focal length. When you use a lens to project an image on a screen, the focal length is the distance of the image from the lens.

PREPARATION

PROBLEM

Which combination of lenses will make the best refracting telescope?

OBJECTIVES

- **Measure** the diameter and focal length of lenses.
- **Find** the ideal telescope length, given a pair of lenses whose focal lengths are known.
- **Examine** the magnification properties of various pairs of lenses.
- **Construct** a telescope.

MATERIALS

set of 3 lenses with long focal lengths (set A: A1 has the shortest focal length of the set; A3 has the longest; and A2 is in between)

set of 3 lenses with short focal lengths (set B: B1 has the shortest focal length of the set; B3 has the longest; and B2 is in between)

set of 3 lenses of identical focal length and different diameters (set C)
ring stand
burette clamp
meterstick
2 lens holders
screen
screen holder
2 nested cardboard tubes (combined length 1 m)
2 foam lens holders

SAFETY PRECAUTIONS

- Under no circumstances should you look at the Sun through a telescope; it could cause permanent damage. Do not project images of the Sun through a lens. Wear goggles to help decrease any glare.
- Be careful when handling glass lenses. Watch out for sharp edges.

PROCEDURE

1. Measure and record in Table 1 the diameter of each lens to the nearest tenth of a centimeter.

2. Use a burette clamp to attach a meterstick to a ring stand. The meterstick should be horizontal.

This arrangement is known as an optical bench. Mount the lenses and screen on the optical bench with the appropriate holders. See Figure 1.

PROCEDURE, *continued*

Figure 1

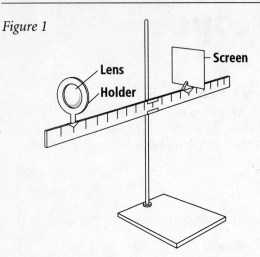

Lens
Holder
Screen

3. Point the meterstick of the optical bench at a window. Mount a lens on the end of the optical bench that is closer to the window. If the classroom does not have windows, a lamp will work. **CAUTION:** *Do not project images of the Sun.* Mount the screen on the optical bench next to the lens, on the side that is farther from the window.

4. Slide the screen along the optical bench until an image of a distant object forms. For this, you must make sure that the lenses are both precisely perpendicular to the meterstick.

5. When you have the best-focused image, read the distance between the screen and the lens. This is the focal length. Record this data for each lens.

6. Choose one lens from set A and one from set B. Mount the lenses next to each other on the window end of the optical bench.

7. Slide the lens that is farther from the window away from the other lens until you get a clear image of distant objects. Make sure the lenses are aligned perpendicular to the meterstick. When you have the best focus, the distance between the lenses is the telescope length. Record this length in Table 2.

8. You should see a relationship between the telescope length and the sum of the focal lengths of the two lenses. This is the telescope length relation. Confirm your telescope length relation, using a different pair of lenses.

9. Choose a lens from set A, and place it at the window end of the optical bench. This is your objective lens.

10. Choose a lens from set B, and use your telescope length relation to place it on the optical bench as an eyepiece. Adjust the lens to get a sharp image of distant objects.

11. In quick succession, look at a particular distant object, first through the telescope, then directly. Estimate the ratio of the size of telescope image to the size of the image when viewed directly. This is the magnification of the telescope. Record your estimate of the magnification in Table 3.

12. Record the ratio of the focal length of the objective lens to that of the eyepiece lens.

13. Repeat steps 9–12, trying all combinations of lenses from sets A and B. You may get magnifications of 1 or even less than 1 when you use lenses from set B as objective lenses.

14. Repeat steps 9–12, using set C as objective lenses and set B as eyepieces. Record your data in Table 4.

15. Select an objective lens and eyepiece to make a telescope, using two tubes and two foam lens holders. See Figure 2.

Figure 2

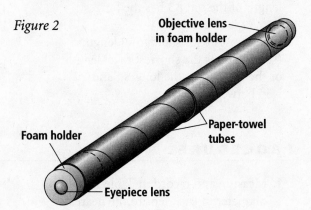

Objective lens in foam holder
Paper-towel tubes
Foam holder
Eyepiece lens

LAB **28.1**   **INVESTIGATION**

DATA AND OBSERVATIONS

Use all of the lenses from sets A (A1, A2, A3), B (B1, B2, B3), and C (C1, C2, C3) to complete the tables below.

Table 1

Lens ID	A1	A2	A3	B1	B2	B3	C1	C2	C3
Diameter (cm)									
Focal length (cm)									

Table 2

Objective ID	Focal Length of Objective	Eyepiece ID	Focal Length of Eyepiece	Sum of Focal Lengths	Telescope Length

Table 3

Objective ID	A1	A1	A1	A2	A2	A2	A3	A3	A3
Eyepiece ID	B1	B2	B3	B1	B2	B3	B1	B2	B3
Ratio of focal lengths									
Magnification									

Objective ID	B1	B1	B1	B2	B2	B2	B3	B3	B3
Eyepiece ID	A1	A2	A3	A1	A2	A3	A1	A2	A3
Ratio of focal lengths									
Magnification									

Objective ID	C1	C2	C3	C1	C2	C3	C1	C2	C3
Eyepiece ID	B1	B1	B1	B2	B2	B2	B3	B3	B3
Ratio of focal lengths									
Magnification									

LAB 28.1   **INVESTIGATION**

ANALYZE

1. Look at your data in Table 2. Compare the sum of the focal lengths to the telescope lengths. Summarize your comparison in one sentence. This is your telescope length relation.

_____

_____

2. Look at your data in Table 3. Compare the ratio of focal lengths to your estimated magnifications. Summarize this comparison in one sentence. This is your telescope magnification relation.

_____

_____

3. Use your telescope magnification relation and your measurements of focal length to predict the magnification that you would get using C2 as an objective lens with B2 as an eyepiece.

_____

4. Is your answer to question 4 greater or less than the magnification you measured using A3 as an objective lens with B2 as an eyepiece?

_____

CONCLUDE AND APPLY

1. What did you notice about the effect of changing the diameter of the objective lens?

_____

_____

2. Which pair of lenses do you think would make the best telescope? Specify which lens would be the objective and which the eyepiece. Give reasons for your choice.

_____

_____

_____

LAB 28.2 DESIGN YOUR OWN

Observing the Moon

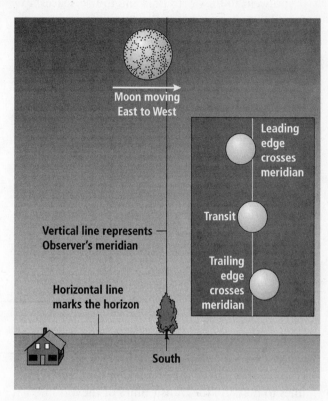

Moon moving East to West

Leading edge crosses meridian

Transit

Trailing edge crosses meridian

Vertical line represents Observer's meridian

Horizontal line marks the horizon

South

You can estimate the phase of the Moon by observing how much of it is lit. However, a much more accurate method involves timing the precise moment when the Moon is directly south. This moment is the transit time of the Moon. Here is how it works.

For an observer in the northern hemisphere, the Sun is always in the south at noon. That is when the Sun is highest in the sky. Similarly, the southerly stars, the planets, and the Moon are all highest in the sky when they cross an imaginary line that passes through the zenith (the point straight up) and the southernmost point on the horizon. This line is called the observer's meridian. The transit time of a celestial object is when it crosses the meridian. For example, the Sun always transits near midday. When the Moon is full, it is exactly on the opposite side of Earth from the Sun. Because Earth spins once in 24 hours, the Moon transits 12 hours later than the Sun, at midnight. The quarter moon transits at 6:00 P.M. and 6:00 A.M., depending on whether it is at first quarter or third quarter. If you measure the transit time of the Moon a few times, you can predict quite accurately when the next full moon will be, or the precise length of the month.

Astronomers measure transit times with a transit telescope. They point it south, and it is free to move only up and down, perpendicular to the horizon. These telescopes have eyepieces with crosshairs so that the observer can accurately determine the transit crossing time of an object. With large objects like the Sun and Moon, the transit crossing time is when the midpoint of the object is exactly south. That moment is halfway between when the leading edge and the trailing edge of the object are exactly south.

PREPARATION

PROBLEM
How can you determine observationally the Moon's location at a particular time and the period of its motion?

OBJECTIVES
• **Measure** the transit time of the Moon for 1 week.
• **Predict** the times of the next full moon and quarter moon.
• **Determine** the exact length of the month.

LAB 28.2   **DESIGN YOUR OWN**

PREPARATION, *continued*

HYPOTHESIS

If you went to the north pole and took a spaceship directly up, you could see Earth spinning counterclockwise. This is why the Sun rises in the east. Hypothesize the direction that the Moon is orbiting Earth—clockwise or counterclockwise. Depending on your hypothesis, will the Moon transit earlier each day or later?

_____

_____

_____

_____

POSSIBLE MATERIALS

accurate watch
2 plumb lines (2 or 3 m) with weights
2 stepladders
simple ladder
rope
map compass with crosshairs
calculator

SAFETY PRECAUTIONS

- Under no circumstances should you look directly at the Sun, especially through a telescope or binoculars; it could cause permanent damage. Wear goggles to help decrease any glare.
- Do not climb on any of the ladders during this lab.

PLAN THE EXPERIMENT

As a class, design an apparatus that uses two plumb lines to measure the transit times of the Moon. Because the Sun transits an hour earlier on the eastern edge of a time zone than it does on the western edge, you cannot be sure that the Sun is directly south at noon. For this reason, you should keep track of the Sun's transit as well as observe the Moon's transit. Obtaining information about the Sun's transit from a web site will likely yield the most current data. Do not attempt to observe the Sun yourself. Decide how you will measure the Moon's transits for several consecutive days. How will you record your data? What calculations do you need to do to find the exact transit time? You should use 24-hour notation (hours:minutes:seconds, so noon is 12:00:00). Outline your method below, and draw your apparatus. Have your teacher approve your plan before you start collecting data.

_____

_____

_____

_____

_____

LAB 28.2   **DESIGN YOUR OWN**

DATA AND OBSERVATIONS

DATA TABLES

ANALYZE

1. Did the Moon transit earlier each day or later? By how many minutes?

_____

2. Do the data support or refute your hypothesis? Which way does the Moon orbit (clockwise or counterclockwise) when viewed from above the north pole?

_____

3. Use your data to complete Table 1. Time in seconds = (hours × 3600) + (minutes × 60) + seconds. Phase in degrees = (phase in seconds) ÷ (86 400 seconds per day) × (360 degrees).

Date	Time of Sun Transit (s)	Time of Moon Transit (s)	Phase (s) (difference between times of Moon and Sun transits)	Phase (degrees)

4. Draw a circle to represent the path of the Moon's orbit. Mark a point on the circle to represent the direction of the Sun. This point is zero degrees of phase. Mark points on your circle corresponding to the phase data in degrees. These points are the positions of the Moon at the times of your measurements.

LAB ◇ **28.2** ◇   **DESIGN YOUR OWN**

CHECK YOUR HYPOTHESIS

Was your **hypothesis** supported by your data? Why or why not?

_____

_____

CONCLUDE AND APPLY

1. How many seconds passed between the first transit of the Moon you observed and the last one?

   _____

2. Through how many degrees did the Moon move between the first and last timings of the Moon?

   _____

3. Using the answers to questions 1 and 2, how many seconds does it take the Moon to move through one degree?

   _____

4. How much time would it take the Moon to move through 360°? Express your answer in seconds. Then express your answer in days, hours, minutes, and seconds. This calculation shows the length of a month. Does it make sense?

   _____

   _____

5. When will the next full moon be? Compare your prediction with the time stated in a calendar or on a web site. What about the next quarter moon and new moon? How good are your predictions?

   _____

   _____

   _____

   _____

LAB ◆ **29.1**   **INVESTIGATION**

Your Age and Weight on Other Planets

What could be more down-to-earth than a person's age and weight? Yet both are controlled by astronomical forces. The Sun swings Earth around once, and we say that another year has gone by. But how many birthdays would you have had if you had been living on Mercury? The pull between Earth and a human body leads us to declare that a person weighs some amount. How heavy would you be if you lived on Venus? You can use Kepler's third law and Newton's law of universal gravitation to answer these questions.

PREPARATION

PROBLEM
What would your age and weight be if you lived on another planet?

OBJECTIVES
- **Calculate** your age on the other eight planets of the solar system.
- **Calculate** your weight on each planet.

MATERIALS
calculator
scale

PROCEDURE

1. Kepler's third law states that the orbital radius (a) of a solar system planet relates to its orbital period (P) in this formula if P and a are expressed in solar system units: $P^2 = a^3$. In solar system units, the unit of time is the year, the unit of length is the astronomical unit (AU), and the unit of mass is the mass of the Sun. Use this relation and the data in Table 1 to find out the length of the planet's year in Earth years.

2. You now have the number of Earth years per planet year, but what you want is the number of planet years per Earth year. So calculate the reciprocal.

3. Multiply the number of planet years per Earth year by your age to obtain your age on the planet. Record your results, to three decimal places, in Table 2.

LAB 29.1   **INVESTIGATION**

PROCEDURE, *continued*

4. To calculate your weight on another planet, use Newton's law of universal gravitation.

$$F = G\frac{m_1 m_2}{r^2}$$

F is the force between two bodies, which in this case is your weight on the planet; G is the universal constant of gravitation; m_1 is the mass of the planet; m_2 is your own mass; and r is the distance between the centers of the two bodies, which in this case is the radius of the planet. Notice that even though your weight is different from planet to planet, your mass remains the same.

5. Using the scale, weigh yourself to find your weight in pounds. Convert your weight from pounds (lb) to kilograms (kg). Use the following formula to make your calculations. 1 lb = .455 kg

6. Using Table 1, and Newton's law of universal gravitation in step 4, calculate your weight on each planet. m_1 is your mass, which you calculated in step 5. m_2 is the mass of the planet. $G = 6.6726 \times 10^{-11}$ m^3/kg•s^2.

7. Record your results in Table 2.

Name _____ Class _____ Date _____

DATA AND OBSERVATIONS

Table 1

Planet	Orbital Radius, a (AU)	Planetary Radius, r (km)	Planetary Mass, m (10^{24} kg)
Mercury	0.387	2439.7	0.3302
Venus	0.723	6051.8	4.8685
Earth	1.0	6378.1	5.9736
Mars	1.524	3397	0.64185
Jupiter	5.204	71 492	1898.6
Saturn	9.582	60 268	.568.46
Uranus	19.201	25 559	86.832
Neptune	30.047	24 764	102.43
Pluto	39.236	1195	0.0125

Table 2

Planet	Your Age in Planet Years	Planet Mass/ Earth Mass (kg)	Earth Radius/ Planet Radius (km)	Square of Radius Ratio (km)	Your Weight on Planet (N)
Mercury					
Venus					
Earth					
Mars					
Jupiter					
Saturn					
Uranus					
Neptune					
Pluto					

LAB **29.1** **INVESTIGATION**

ANALYZE

1. In the years of which planets are you oldest and youngest? Is this surprising? Why or why not?

_____

_____

_____

2. On which planet would you be heaviest?

_____

CONCLUDE AND APPLY

1. What is the weight of the heaviest thing you can lift? If an object weighed that much on the planet on which you are heaviest, how much would it weigh on Earth? Name an object that weighs this much.

_____

_____

_____

_____

2. What would be the heaviest object you could lift on Pluto?

_____

_____

_____

_____

LAB ◇ **29.2** **DESIGN YOUR OWN**

Relating Gravitational Force and Orbits

*I*n *the seventeenth century, Kepler noticed that the planets' periods of revolution are related to their orbital distances in a special way. His observation later became known as his third law: $P^2 = a^3$. Would this relation be true if the Sun were twice as massive as it is? Or half as massive? Does the orbital period depend, not only on the distance at which the planet orbits, but on the mass of the central body? We can use a model to investigate these questions.*

PREPARATION

PROBLEM
How do the orbital periods of the planets relate to the mass of the Sun?

OBJECTIVES
- **Construct** a simple model of planetary motion.
- **Check** the model to see how well it follows Kepler's third law.
- **Use** the model to find out if orbital period depends on the mass of the central body.
- **Estimate** the mass of Earth.

HYPOTHESIS
With your group, form a hypothesis about whether changes in the central mass affect Kepler's third law.

_____

_____

_____

_____

POSSIBLE MATERIALS
glass tube, 15 cm, fire polished
   and taped
scissors
duct tape
fishing line
plastic-foam ball, 10 cm
paper clips
40 metal washers
metric ruler
stopwatch
marking pen
calculator

SAFETY PRECAUTIONS

Be careful when handling scissors.
Never point sharp objects at anyone.

LAB 〈 **29.2** 〉   **DESIGN YOUR OWN**

PLAN THE EXPERIMENT

Design an experiment to study the effect of varying the central mass, using a small-scale model. The figure below shows a suggestion for a model. How will you show whether the model follows Kepler's third law? What will your independent and dependent variables be? What measurements and data do you need to gather? How will you test the effect of different mass on the relationship? Outline your experiment. Design a table to record your data. Have your teacher approve your plan before you start the experiment.

_____

_____

_____

_____

_____

_____

_____

_____

_____

_____

_____

_____

_____

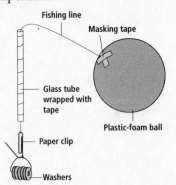

Fishing line

Masking tape

Glass tube wrapped with tape

Plastic-foam ball

Paper clip

Washers

DATA AND OBSERVATIONS

Sample Data Table

Radius (cm)	Swings	Total time (s)	Period (s)	p^2/a^3 ($\times 10^{-15}$)

LAB **29.2** **DESIGN YOUR OWN**

DATA AND OBSERVATIONS, *continued*

DATA TABLES

LAB ◈ **29.2**   **DESIGN YOUR OWN**

ANALYZE

1. Does the period increase, decrease, or stay the same as you increase the radius of revolution with the central mass fixed?

_____

2. With the radius fixed, does the period increase, decrease, or stay the same as you increase the number of weights?

_____

_____

3. Did your results meet your expectations? Explain your answer.

_____

_____

CHECK YOUR HYPOTHESIS

Was your **hypothesis** supported by your data? Why or why not?

_____

_____

CONCLUDE AND APPLY

1. How well do you think your model performed? Would you draw strong conclusions from this model? Explain your answer.

_____

_____

_____

_____

2. Assuming a is constant, what happens to the square of the period (P^2) when you double the number of weights? Does it triple, double, stay the same, half, or third?

_____

_____

3. Assuming a is constant, how long do you think an Earth year would last if the Sun were twice as massive as it is?

_____

_____

LAB **30.1**   **INVESTIGATION**

Diameter and Rotation of the Sun

Although the Sun is a fairly typical star, it is very special to us because it is much closer to Earth than any other star. That makes it the easiest star to study. With simple equipment, you can measure the diameter and rotation of the Sun.

PREPARATION

PROBLEM
What are the diameter and rotation rate of the Sun?

OBJECTIVES
• **Measure** the diameter of the Sun.
• **Measure** the rotational rate of the Sun.
• **Estimate** the size of sunspots.

MATERIALS
meterstick
2 index cards
scissors
tape
aluminum foil, 4 cm square
straight pin

single-edge razor blade
unlined white paper
clipboard
small telescope
small telescope stand

SAFETY PRECAUTIONS

• Wear safety goggles during the lab procedure to help eliminate glare.

• Never look at the Sun through a telescope or directly at the Sun; it could blind you.

• Use caution when handling pins, scissors, or razor blades. Be careful not to puncture or cut your skin.

PROCEDURE

1. With a razor blade, make three slits in the shape of a capital I in two index cards so that they can be mounted snugly on a meterstick.

2. Draw a pair of fine parallel lines on one of the index cards, exactly 0.8 cm apart. You will project an image of the Sun onto this screen.

3. Cut a 1-cm × 1-cm-square hole in the other index card and tape aluminum foil over it. Use a pin to punch a small, clean hole in the center of the aluminum foil.

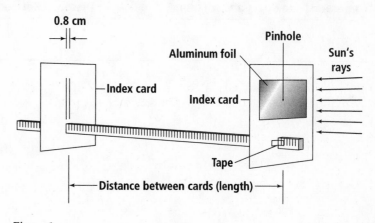

Figure 1

PROCEDURE, *continued*

4. Assemble the pinhole camera as shown in Figure 1. Make sure that the cards fit tightly on the meterstick and that they are perpendicular to it.

5. Point the pinhole at the Sun so that an image of the Sun projects onto the screen.

6. Move the screen along the meterstick until the circular image of the Sun has a diameter of exactly 0.8 cm.

7. Measure the distance between the pinhole and the image. If the cards are perpendicular to the meterstick, this will be the distance between the cards. Record this distance and the diameter of the Sun's image in the table provided.

8. Fit the telescope with a low-power eyepiece if possible. Make sure the lens cap is on it.

9. With the lens cap *on* the telescope, mount the telescope on its stand. Point the telescope at the Sun. In order to avoid looking directly at the Sun, the telescope's shadow can be used to fine-tune the pointing.

10. Make a screen by putting a piece of unlined paper on a clipboard. Place the screen next to the eyepiece and carefully remove the lens cap.

Adjust the alignment until the projection is visible.

11. Move the screen away from the eyepiece until the image of the Sun is almost as wide as the paper. You may need to adjust the alignment and focus of the telescope for this. The screen may be several meters from the telescope at this point, depending on the power of the telescope.

12. Focus the telescope until you have a sharp image of the Sun. You should see clusters of sunspots. Trace the outline of the Sun directly onto the screen paper. Trace the sunspots, making a careful record of their locations and sizes. The image will tend to drift across the screen because Earth is rotating.

13. Draw an arrow to show which direction the image is drifting. Record on the drawing the date and time. Write down any interesting observations.

14. Repeat steps 8–13 at the same time of day for 4 or 5 days, drawing on separate sheets of paper. Try to make the size of the Sun's image the same in each drawing.

DATA AND OBSERVATIONS

Table

Diameter of the Sun's Image (cm)	Distance Between Pinhole and Screen (cm)

LAB ◆ **30.1**   **INVESTIGATION**

ANALYZE

1. Figure 2 has two similar triangles. Similar geometric shapes have proportional sides, so the diameter of the Sun (km)/distance to the Sun (km) = diameter of the Sun's image (cm)/distance from the pinhole to the screen (cm). The distance to the Sun is about 1.5×10^8 km. Calculate the diameter of the Sun.

_____

_____

Figure 2

2. Do you think the orientation of the Sun is the same in each of your drawings? Give reasons for your answer.

_____

_____

_____

3. Choose an individual sunspot near the center of one of your drawings. What is its diameter, in centimeters? What is the diameter of the Sun, in centimeters? What is the ratio of the diameter of the sunspot to that of the Sun?

_____

_____

4. Multiply the ratio of the diameter of the sunspot to that of the Sun by the actual diameter of the Sun to determine the actual size of the sunspot, in kilometers. Compare this to the size of Earth.

_____

_____

_____

LAB **30.1** **INVESTIGATION**

CONCLUDE AND APPLY

1. Would sunspots appear to move in circles or along straight lines if we were viewing the Sun from directly above its equator? How about if we were viewing from directly above one of the Sun's poles?

   _____

   _____

2. Do the sunspots in your sequence of drawings appear to move in circles or in straight lines? Do you think we are viewing the Sun from above its equator or from above one of its poles?

   _____

   _____

   _____

3. Choose a sunspot that appears in all your drawings. Bearing in mind that the Sun is more or less spherical, estimate the angle, in degrees, that the sunspot moved through between the first drawing and the last drawing. How much time elapsed between the drawings? How long would it take for the sunspot to move through 360°?

   _____

   _____

   _____

LAB ◁ 30.2 ▷   **MAPPING**

Constellations and the Seasons

Even in a city, where lights make many stars invisible, you can see a few hundred stars in various constellations at night. Star charts identify many well-known stars and constellations, even as they move across the sky in an evening and from season to season.

PREPARATION

PROBLEM
How do stars appear to move in the sky?

OBJECTIVES
- **Identify** several stars and constellations in the night sky.
- **Understand** how stars move during a night.
- **Understand** why different constellations are visible during a year.
- **Measure** the latitude of your city or town.

MATERIALS
protractor with hole at origin
stiff, thin wire, 10 cm
small weight
tracing paper
binoculars

SAFETY PRECAUTIONS

- Use caution when handling wire. Be careful not to puncture or cut your skin.
- Wear safety goggles during the lab procedure.

PROCEDURE

1. Make a plumb line by attaching a weight to a wire.

2. Thread the free end of the wire through the hole at the origin of a protractor. Bend the wire over. If you hold the protractor with the flat edge at the top, the plumb line should hang free, allowing you to read angles on the protractor scale.

3. Take your protractor and plumb line outside shortly after sunset. Use the star charts in this lab to find the pointers of the Big Dipper (Ursa Major). These help you locate Polaris (the North Star).

4. Sight along the flat edge of the protractor toward Polaris. Read the altitude of Polaris (the angle of Polaris above the horizon) from

the protractor scale. Record in Table 1 the altitude of Polaris, and note a feature on the horizon that is below Polaris.

5. A position angle is the angle that the line joining two points makes with the vertical. For example, the position angle of a clock's hour hand at three o'clock is 90°. At eight o'clock, the position angle is 240°. Use the protractor with the scale facing you. Measure the position angle of the pointers in the Big Dipper. Record this angle and the time.

6. Repeat steps 3–5 after 2 hours, after 4 hours, and after 6 hours if it is practical.

PROCEDURE, *continued*

7. On the next day in class, answer Analyze questions 1–4.

8. Use the star charts to identify the compass direction of each constellation in Table 2 in each season.

9. Using tracing paper, draw the circular outline of the autumn map and mark the compass directions on it. Label this "Map 1: Seasonal Motion of Gemini." Trace the constellation Gemini on the map and label it "Autumn." Place the tracing paper on the winter map, lining it up with the compass directions, and trace Gemini again, labeling it "Winter." Repeat for "Spring." (Note that Gemini does not appear on the summer map.)

10. Draw arrows between the seasonal locations of Gemini. Answer Analyze question 5.

11. The three stars Vega, Deneb, and Altair constitute the summer triangle. Label a piece of tracing paper "Map 2: Seasonal Motion of Summer Triangle." Use the method in step 9 to trace the seasonal locations of the summer triangle.

12. Label a piece of tracing paper "Map 3: Seasonal Motion Around Polaris." Using the spring map, trace the positions of Polaris and Cassiopeia. Label them "Position 1." Repeat this, using the winter map and labeling them "Position 2." Draw an arrow showing the direction of motion from Position 1 to Position 2.

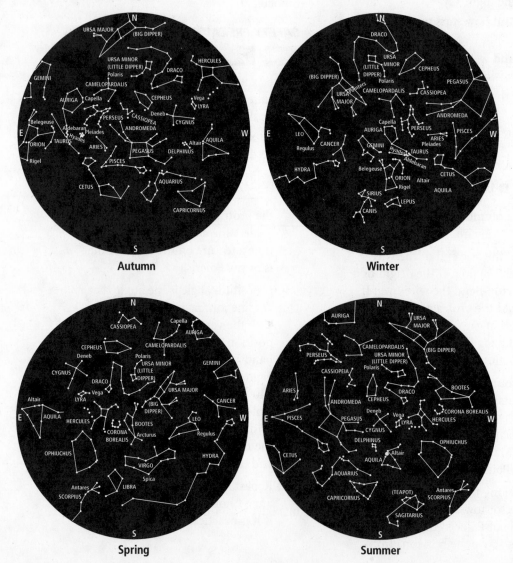

Autumn   Winter

Spring   Summer

LAB **30.2** **MAPPING**

DATA AND OBSERVATIONS

Table 1

Time	Altitude of Polaris	Horizon Feature Below Polaris	Position Angle of Pointers

Table 2

Constellation	Autumn	Winter	Spring	Summer
Bootes				
Lyra				
Orion				
Pegasus				

ANALYZE

1. What is remarkable about the position of Polaris?

_____

2. Does the Big Dipper move clockwise or counterclockwise around Polaris?

_____

_____

3. Use the elapsed time between your first and last measurement of the position angle of the Pointers and the angle that the Pointers moved through during that time to calculate how much time it takes for the Pointers to move through 1°.

_____

4. How much time does it take for the Pointers to move through 360°? What is the significance of this answer?

_____

_____

_____

5. In what direction does Gemini move throughout the seasons?

_____

LAB ⟨ 30.2 ⟩   **MAPPING** 🌐

CONCLUDE AND APPLY

1. Use a local map to find out the latitude from which you observed Polaris. Compare the latitude to your measurement of the altitude of Polaris. What do you conclude about the relationship between the latitude of the observer and the altitude of Polaris?

   _____

   _____

   _____

2. Based on the path of Gemini in Map 1, where would Gemini be in summer? Explain why Gemini does not appear on the summer map.

   _____

   _____

   _____

   _____

3. In what season does the summer triangle appear in view? In what direction does it move across the sky? In what season does it disappear from view?

   _____

   _____

   _____

4. Map 3 shows the positions of Cassiopeia at two times of the year. Cassiopeia also passes through these positions at different times of day. Suppose Cassiopeia was at Position 1 at 6:00 P.M. At what time would it be at Position 2?

   _____

LAB   **31.1**   **INVESTIGATION**

Modeling Spiral Galaxies

Galaxies come in all shapes and sizes. Some, like the Milky Way Galaxy, have a broken spiral-arm pattern. Astronomers theorize that the arms in this type of galaxy continually form and re-form in response to supernovae explosions and other disturbances in space. Other galaxies have distinctive two-arm spiral patterns that appear to be permanent features. Scientists hypothesize that these arms may be maintained by spiral density waves that rotate through interstellar gas and dust in rigid patterns.

Barred spiral galaxy

Normal spiral galaxy

PREPARATION

PROBLEM

How do the arms of spiral galaxies form?

OBJECTIVES

- **Model** spiral galaxies.
- **Compare** and **contrast** scientific theories about the formation of spiral arms.
- **Describe** the characteristics of spiral galaxies.

MATERIALS

water
oil
teaspoon
nondairy powdered creamer
250-mL beaker
several rocks
bucket

SAFETY PRECAUTIONS

Wear safety goggles and an apron during the lab.

PROCEDURE

1. Working with a partner, pour 200 mL of water at room temperature into the beaker.

2. Add a teaspoon of oil to the water. Then carefully add a teaspoon of powdered creamer to the mixture.

3. Use the teaspoon to slowly stir the mixture in a clockwise direction. Observe what happens to the creamer. While you are stirring, your partner should sketch your observations in the box labeled Sketch 1 in Data and Observations.

4. Stop stirring the mixture. Observe what happens to the creamer. Sketch your observations in the box labeled Sketch 2 in Data and Observations.

5. Next, fill a bucket with water. Drop a rock into the water, then sketch your observations in the box labeled Sketch 3 in Data and Observations.

DATA AND OBSERVATIONS

Sketch 1

Sketch 2

Sketch 3

LAB 31.1 INVESTIGATION

ANALYZE

1. Describe your observations of the mixture. What happened to the creamer when you stirred the mixture? What happened when you stopped stirring?

   _____

   _____

   _____

2. What did you observe when the rock was dropped into the bucket of water? What astronomical event did the rock model? Explain your answer.

   _____

   _____

   _____

3. Explain how your observations after stirring the mixture resemble a spiral galaxy. How do your observations differ from a spiral galaxy?

   _____

   _____

   _____

   _____

4. Identify the parts of a spiral arm galaxy and state where each part is located. Where would globular clusters be found?

   _____

   _____

   _____

   _____

LAB ⟨**31.1**⟩ INVESTIGATION

CONCLUDE AND APPLY

1. Which theory of spiral arm formation does your observations from the procedure support? Explain.

_____

_____

_____

_____

2. Use your observations of the rock and the bucket of water to form a hypothesis about what would happen to interstellar dust and gas following a supernovae.

_____

_____

_____

3. Where would young stars be located in your model galaxy? Where would old stars be?

_____

_____

_____

4. An irregular galaxy has no distinct shape. How could you model an irregular galaxy?

_____

_____

_____

Name ___ Class ___ Date ___

LAB 31.2 MAPPING

Three-Dimensional Map of the Local Group

*T*he Milky Way Galaxy is just one of a number of galaxies in our cosmic neighborhood, which are collectively known as the Local Group. The galaxies of the Local Group are believed to be gravitationally bound together, so they perform a complicated orbit around one another. By far, the biggest two galaxies in the Local Group are the Milky Way and M31, the Andromeda Galaxy, which is about 2 million ly away.

The locations of the galaxies of the Local Group are in the table in Data and Observations. The x, y, and z coordinates are given for each galaxy in units of 100 000 ly. Earth is at the origin of the coordinate system. The z-axis points north. The x-axis points in the direction of the Sun, as viewed from Earth on the vernal equinox (March 21).

PREPARATION

PROBLEM
What does the Local Group of galaxies look like?

OBJECTIVES
- **Map** the Local Group from three viewpoints.
- **Construct** a scale model showing the locations of the galaxies of the Local Group.

MATERIALS
cardboard, 30 cm × 20 cm
fishing line or thread, 4 m
metric ruler
scissors
heavy needle
modeling clay

SAFETY PRECAUTIONS

Be careful when using sharp objects to make holes in the cardboard. Pointed objects can puncture skin.

PROCEDURE

1. Look at the three blank maps in Analyze. Each map will represent a view of the Local Group along one of the axes. On the map labeled "*xy* projection," plot the position of the Milky Way Galaxy and M31, using the x and y coordinates in Table 1.

2. Plot the positions of the Milky Way and M31 on the *yz* projection map using the values for y and z for each galaxy and on the *xz* projection map using the values for x and z for each galaxy. Have your teacher check your graphs.

3. Mark the Milky Way and M31 Galaxies in a bright color. Plot the locations of all the other galaxies on all three projections.

Copyright © Glencoe/McGraw-Hill, a division of the McGraw-Hill Companies, Inc.

Laboratory Manual   Chapter 31 *Earth Science: Geology, the Environment, and the Universe* **245**

LAB 31.2

  MAPPING

PROCEDURE, *continued*

4. Draw a scale copy of the *xy* projection on a piece of cardboard. Use a scale of 0.3 cm/ 100 000 ly. Cross-check your copy with your original map of the *xy* projection. When you are satisfied that the locations are correct, push a hole through each point with a needle.

5. The cardboard sheet will be the top of your model of the Local Group. You will suspend the galaxies on threads from the horizontal cardboard sheet. For each galaxy, the length of its suspending thread should be $(40 - z) \times 0.3$ cm, where z is the coordinate of the galaxy

in units of 100 000 ly. This assumes that you are using a scale of 0.3 cm/100 000 ly. Cut each thread a little longer than this length. Make a knot at one end of the thread and pass the thread through the appropriate hole in the cardboard sheet. Trim the thread to the correct length and fix a clay "galaxy" to the lower end of the thread.

6. When all the "galaxies" are in place, make four extra holes in the cardboard, one in each corner, and use these to suspend the model with four pieces of thread.

DATA AND OBSERVATIONS

Galaxy Name	Distance in 100 000 ly		
	x	*y*	*z*
WLM	19.27	0.17	−5.33
IC 10	20.33	1.81	34.4
NGC 147	14.42	2.1	16.48
Andromeda III	17.47	2.71	13.09
NGC 185	14.42	2.47	16.43
NGC 205	16.18	2.87	14.63
M32	16.35	3.08	14.39
M31	16.25	3.06	14.51
Andromeda I	16.99	3.43	13.54
SMC	0.86	0.20	−2.87
Sculptor	1.61	0.43	−1.11
Pisces	26.74	7.63	11.26
IC 1613	23.99	6.98	0.92
Andromeda II	17.35	6	12.12
M33	19.73	8.57	12.74
Fornax	3.16	2.64	−2.83

Galaxy Name	Distance in 100 000 ly		
	x	*y*	*z*
LMC	0.11	0.68	−1.88
Leo A	−37.16	21.58	25.56
Carina	−0.34	1.86	−2.33
Leo I	−5.18	2.74	1.28
Sextans I	−2.68	1.35	−0.09
Leo II	−5.44	1.12	2.26
GR8	−37.5	−9.91	9.78
Ursa Minor	−0.79	−0.86	2.76
Draco	−0.28	−1.57	2.54
Milky Way	−0.02	−0.26	−0.15
SagDIG	14.58	−35.21	−12.15
NGC 6822	7.26	−14.75	−4.33
DDO 210	19.48	−21.82	−6.67
IC 5152	10.91	−6.12	−15.6
Pegasus	47.90	−6.60	12.74

ANALYZE

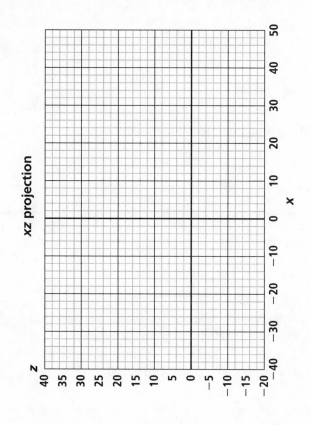

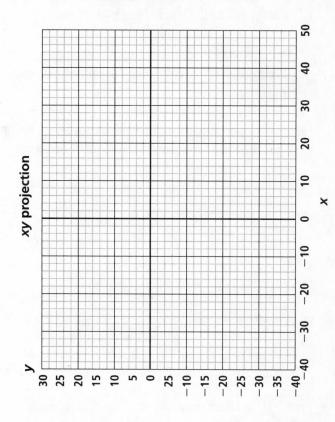

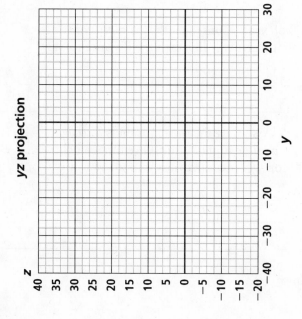

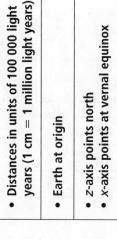

- **Distances in units of 100 000 light years (1 cm = 1 million light years)**
- **Earth at origin**
- **z-axis points north**
- **x-axis points at vernal equinox**

ANALYZE, *continued*

1. The three pairs of axes in the figure on page 247 define a rectangular box. What are the dimensions of the box in light years?

_____

2. What is the volume of the box in cubic light years?

_____

3. There are two main clumps of galaxies in the Local Group, one centered on the Milky Way, one on M31. How many galaxies are in each clump?

_____

_____

_____

CONCLUDE AND APPLY

1. The diameter of M31 is about 200 000 ly. The Milky Way's diameter is about 130 000 ly. The rest of the Local Group galaxies have diameters between 200 ly and 20 000 ly. Thus, the combined volume of the Local Group galaxies is on the order of 5×10^{15} ly^3. Divide this volume by the box volume from Analyze question 2 to find the percentage of space that is filled with galaxies.

_____

_____

2. The age of the universe is estimated to be about 15 billion years. Consequently, the radius of the observable universe is about 15 billion ly. How many times farther is this than the distance to M31?

_____

_____

3. M31 is moving toward the Milky Way at about 100 km/s. Assuming that this motion is *directly* toward the Milky Way, the two galaxies will collide at some time in the future. Given that a light year is equal to about 10^{13} km, estimate when the collision will occur. Express your answer in seconds and in years.

_____

_____

TEACHER GUIDE
Laboratory Manual

1.1 ▪ Investigation
Observing and Analyzing Stream Flow

OBJECTIVES
- Observe a model of natural phenomena.
- Communicate observations clearly and accurately.
- Choose criteria to classify observed phenomena.

PROCESS SKILLS
observe, classify, communicate

TIME ALLOTMENT
1 class period

MATERIALS
pens or pencils (30)

Figures 2–7 in lab manual

PREPARATION
Students should work individually.

PROCEDURE
Teaching Strategies

Tell students that they can use simple terminology as long as the terms bear a meaningful relationship to the features shown in the figures and are used consistently.

Troubleshooting

If you want to provide stream terminology, define and explain the following terms: headwaters, channels, tributaries, meanders, meander migration, banks, cutbanks, delta, and floodplain.

DATA AND OBSERVATIONS
- In Figure 2, two branches flow into the stream, which follows a slightly curving course. Steep, low banks have formed on the outside of the meanders. A wedge-shaped sand deposit has begun to form at the end of the stream, with most of the water flowing on the right side.
- In Figure 3, the curve of the model stream has increased slightly. Steep, slightly higher banks have formed on the outside of the meanders. The upper right bank has a gentler slope with a shallow ridge. The wedge-shaped sand deposit at the end of the stream is larger than in Figure 2, and the water flow has shifted to the left side of the stream table.
- In Figure 4, the left bank of the left-hand branch is steep; sand deposits slope where they meet the right-hand branch. The right-hand branch is straighter than the left-hand branch. The gentler slope with the shallow ridge that was the upper right bank has disappeared. The right bank is steep and drops straight into the water. The wedge-shaped sand deposit at the end

of the stream is again larger, and the water flow has shifted back to the right side.
- In Figure 5, the left-hand branch at the top of the stream table has disappeared, and the steep slope where it met the right-hand branch has flattened out. The right-hand branch is still straight. A gentle slope has reappeared under the steep slope on the upper right bank. The wedge-shaped sand deposit at the end of the stream is even larger, and the water flow has shifted slightly to the left.
- In Figure 6, the meanders in the stream are sharper, and the banks are high and steep. Between the first and second meanders, there is a low, triangular mound of sand in the middle of the streambed. The wedge-shaped sand deposit at the end of the stream extends the width of the table. On each side, a wide, gently sloping bank has formed. The water flow in the wedge-shaped area has several irregular branches.
- In Figure 7, the meander nearest the beginning of the stream is very sharp, and near this bend the water flows in crisscrossing channels. The wedge-shaped sand deposit at the end of the stream still extends the width of the table. On each side of the model stream, a wide, gently sloping bank is still present. The water flow in the wedge-shaped area still has several irregular branches, but they have changed shape and position somewhat.

ANALYZE
1. Answers may vary. Students may classify the figures together as showing stream development. Or, they may group them according to time, as early, middle, and late stages of stream development. They may focus more on the shape or size of the physical features, such as bank height, sharpness of the bends, number of tributaries, and so forth.

CONCLUDE AND APPLY
1. Answers may vary, but should include a discussion of the following points. A stream begins when water flows toward lower ground along the same path. The course of the water flow changes. Curves (meanders) change positions, banks form and are eroded, and channels form and are abandoned. When the stream flows into another body of water, it drops its load and a wedge-shaped deposit can form over time.
2. Answers may vary and may include modifications such as using a different kind of material (sediment); reducing or increasing the slope of the stream table at the beginning of the experiment; adding barriers to water flow, such as large rocks or dams; using a faster flow; or allowing water to flow from more than one spigot.

1.2 ▪ Design Your Own
Formulating a Hypothesis

OBJECTIVES
- Design a hidden phenomenon in a box.
- Use various observational methods to examine the unknown phenomenon.
- Write a hypothesis to explain or describe the phenomenon.

PROCESS SKILLS
observe, infer, form hypotheses

TIME ALLOTMENT
1 class period

POSSIBLE MATERIALS

boxes (5)	tape (5 rolls)
small objects (35)	magnets (5)
modeling clay (1 container)	balances or scales (5)
string (1 spool)	measuring tapes (5)
bubble wrap (1 roll)	scissors (5)
newspapers (5)	

SAFETY PRECAUTIONS
- Remind students that any objects with sharp points or edges could puncture their skin.
- If you supply any edible objects in the collections, warn students not to put these into their mouths.

PREPARATION
- Students should work in groups of six.
- All groups should have identical boxes and different collections of items.
- Collect a large number of small items of various shapes, densities, and materials. At least some of the items should be observable with more than one sense. Divide the objects among five collections. The following collections are suggested:
  1. metal key, wooden building block, cork stopper, cotton balls, ball bearings, chocolates, small sealed jar of liquid
  2. cloth swatch, billiard ball, coins, pins or needles, peppermints, bell, dried beans
  3. incense, empty pill or spice bottle, large plastic beads, large iron nail, battery, metal bottle caps, small bell
  4. small toy car, marble, small sack of sand, plain round key rings, several toothpicks, scented dryer sheet, lump of lead
  5. cinnamon stick, irregular piece of wood, rock, empty candy tin, seashell, buttons, golf ball

PLAN THE EXPERIMENT
Have the groups number themselves and their boxes from 1 to 5. Give one empty box and a collection of items to each group. Remind students not to share the contents of their boxes with other groups.

Possible Procedures

Arrange a few items from the collection inside the box. Write a brief description of the contents and how they are arranged. Close the box, seal it with tape, and write the group number on the box.

Exchange boxes and record observations. Form a hypothesis about the contents of the box and how they are arranged. Then open the boxes and compare the hypotheses with the actual contents and how they are arranged.

DATA AND OBSERVATIONS
Students may shake the box, smell it, weigh it, or determine its mass. They may use the magnet to detect whether there are any magnetic items inside the box.

ANALYZE
1. Answers will vary. Sample answer: We listened to sounds made by objects in the box as we moved the box around.
2. Answers will vary. Students should have used more than one sense to try to figure out the contents of the box.

CONCLUDE AND APPLY
1. Answers will vary but should include a guess about the type and number of objects in the box as well as some attempt to describe the arrangement of items.
2. Answers will vary. Sample answer: Yes, because we used modeling clay to restrict the movements of objects inside the box, we inferred that the box of unknown contents might be constructed similarly.
3. Answers will vary but should suggest ways to modify the observations such as by using different senses, making more acute observations, and so forth.
4. When formulating hypotheses, scientists often combine prior knowledge of natural phenomena with data compiled through observation and experimentation. When examining an unknown phenomenon, scientists may use visual observation to collect data that can form the basis for a hypothesis. Unlike the investigators in this lab, scientists often have sophisticated tools and techniques available to make observations of unknown phenomena.

2.1 ▪ Mapping
Modeling Topographic Maps

OBJECTIVES

- Construct a model of a mountain with a minimum of two different elevations.
- Use contour lines on the model to represent changes in elevation.
- Model a topographic map by transferring the contour lines to a flat surface.
- Interpret a map constructed by another student to identify the appropriate model mountain.

PROCESS SKILLS

observe, infer, recognize and use spatial relationships, measure, interpret data, formulate models

TIME ALLOTMENT

3 class periods (1 to prepare the tank and make the model; 1 to draw the contour lines and make the map; and 1 to interpret maps and identify models)

MATERIALS

5-gallon aquarium tanks (10)
modeling clay (10 containers)
waterproof black markers (10)
metric rulers or metersticks (10)
masking tape (1 roll)
grease pencils (10)
turkey basters (10)
transparency paper (30 sheets)
black yarn (2 skeins)
water
aprons (30)
safety goggles (30)

SAFETY PRECAUTIONS

- Students can wear gloves, if they choose, to protect their hands when working with clay.
- Use only low voc (volatile organic compound) markers. Consult your MSDS.
- Students should wipe up any spills immediately.
- Instruct students to wear safety goggles and aprons during the lab procedure.

PREPARATION

- Students should work in groups of three.
- Have examples of topographic maps available in the classroom.

PROCEDURE

- Review the uses of topographic maps and methods of marking directions on maps.
- Have students identify their maps with some type of code. Collect the maps after they have dried and redistribute them at the beginning of the next class period. Each student or group should have a map other than their own with which to identify a model.

DATA AND OBSERVATIONS

The mountain profiles will vary, but should demonstrate use of the transect line method illustrated in the students' Conclude and Apply section. (Not every students will need to draw a mountain profile on the graph paper, but encourage all students to try it.)

ANALYZE

1. Answers will vary.
2. Answers will vary.
3. Sample answer: In the steeper areas, the contour lines will be closer together. In gently sloping and flat areas, the contour lines will be farther apart.

CONCLUDE AND APPLY

1. Sketches will vary, but should reflect the shapes of the contour lines. (See the Data and Observations section.)
2. Answers will vary.
3. Answers will vary. If the student or group does not identify the correct model, review the method illustrated in the diagram for translating contour lines into a profile.

2.2 ▪ Investigation
Interpreting Political and Landform Maps

OBJECTIVES

- Draw a political map and a landform map of a single location in or near students' school or home.
- Describe the strengths and limitations of each map.
- Compare the information provided by political, topographic, and physical maps.

PROCESS SKILLS

observe, infer, recognize and use spatial relationships, measure, predict, use numbers, interpret data, formulate models

TIME ALLOTMENT

2 class periods for drawing the maps; 1 class period for analysis, conclusion, and discussion

MATERIALS

calculators (30)
pencils (30)

PREPARATION

- Students should work in pairs.
- Demonstrate measuring by pacing, and have students practice pacing around the classroom.
- Have multiple copies of full-size political, topographical, and physical maps in the classroom for students to examine.

PROCEDURE

Review map directions and drawing to scale.

DATA AND OBSERVATIONS

Maps will vary. Maps 1 and 2 should show defining features of a political map and a physical map, respectively.

ANALYZE

1. Answers will vary but students should note that the political map shows a flat surface with features described in lines and words, while the physical map shows features in relief.
2. The political map; it shows streets and highways, and their names and direction.
3. The physical map; it shows objects and buildings that might be in the way of a cross-town hike.

CONCLUDE AND APPLY

1. marked trails that show the locations of fences and gates
2. Map C is physical, Map A is political, and Map B is topographic.
3. Answers will vary. Sample answer: Take route 119 because there are more places to stop for lodging and food.
4. Answers will vary. Students may note that the topographic map would give them a better idea of elevation, and thus their routes might differ.

3.1 ▪ Design Your Own
Changes in State

OBJECTIVES
- Describe methods of measuring the boiling and freezing points of liquids.
- Plan and carry out a demonstration of changes in state of liquids and solids.
- Generalize your results to the scale of the hydrologic, lithospheric, and atmospheric systems of Earth.
- Predict the variables involved in further investigation of changes in state.

PROCESS SKILLS
observe, measure, form hypotheses, interpret data

TIME ALLOTMENT
1 class period to design and plan the experiment; 1 class period to complete the experiment; 1 class period to graph, analyze, and interpret the data

POSSIBLE MATERIALS
hot plates (10)
ring stands (10)
test-tube clamps (10)
beakers (10)
flasks (10)
clear plastic tubing or distillation apparatus
test-tube corks or stoppers (20)
water

test tubes (20)
carnauba wax (available in hardware stores)
thermometers, alcohol-based (10)
graph paper (30 sheets)
aprons (30)
safety goggles (30)
thermal mitts (30 pairs)

SAFETY PRECAUTIONS
- Instruct students to wear thermal mitts when handling hot plates, boiling water, or melted wax.
- Avoid using mercury-based thermometers. Mercury is toxic.

PREPARATION
Students should work in groups of three.

Possible Hypothesis
Students may plan methods of measuring boiling and freezing points of matter in degrees centigrade, using available laboratory equipment. Data tables may contain entries for time, temperature, and observations. Graphs may consist of axes for time and temperature measurements.

PLAN THE EXPERIMENT
Teaching Strategies
Review safety procedures for working with heat and hot liquids.

Possible Procedures
Students might use a ring-stand apparatus with hot plate, beaker, test tube, and clamp. They might measure

temperature in degrees Centigrade at 1-minute intervals until the melting or freezing points have been reached, and then for five 1-minute intervals after that point.

DATA AND OBSERVATIONS
Answers will vary, but the boiling point for water should be near 100°C, and the freezing and melting points for the wax should be 86–88°C. When the water is heated, it begins to evaporate at the surface. When water reaches the boiling point, bubbles of water vapor form within the liquid and rise to the surface, where they escape into the air. When the wax is heated, it reaches a melting point and liquifies; as the wax cools, it solidifies at the "freezing" point.

ANALYZE
1. Answers will vary.
2. Answers will vary; they should address any problems identified in question 1.
3. Time intervals should be in equal segments, thus providing data in the form appropriate for line graphs.
4. The temperatures of water and wax rise as they absorb thermal energy and fall as they release thermal energy.

CHECK YOUR HYPOTHESIS
Answers will vary depending on students' hypotheses.

CONCLUDE AND APPLY
1. Answers will vary. They should address the boiling point of water, the melting and freezing points of wax, and the state of the substances at different temperatures.
2. The graphs cross at a point between 86 and 88 degrees Centigrade. The freezing point and melting point of the wax are the same.
3.

Form of Matter	State of Matter #1	Change in Thermal Energy (absorbed or released)	State of Matter #2
Ice	Solid	Absorbed	Water
Water	Liquid	Absorbed	Steam
Water	Liquid	Released	Ice
Glue stick	Solid	Absorbed	Liquid glue
Liquid glue	Liquid	Released	Bonded glue
Gasoline	Liquid	Absorbed	Gaseous gasoline
Stick of butter	Solid	Absorbed at room temperature	Soft butter
Stick of butter	Solid	Absorbed when heated	Liquid butter
Melted chocolate	Liquid	Released	Solid chocolate
Kerosene	Liquid	Absorbed	Gaseous kerosene
Magma	Liquid	Released	Solid rock

3.2 ▪ Investigation
Rates of Chemical Reactions

OBJECTIVES

- Observe and record the results of chemical reactions.
- Use collision theory to interpret reaction data.
- Illustrate the dynamics of chemical reactions in the context of collision theory.
- Describe the relationship between the rate of chemical reactions and surface area, concentration, and temperature.

PROCESS SKILLS

experiment, observe, interpret data, communicate, infer

TIME ALLOTMENT

1 class period for setup, performing experiment, and recording data; 1 class period for analyzing data

MATERIALS

forceps (10)
test tubes (60)
test-tube racks (10)
glass markers (10)
large pieces of
  granulated zinc (60)
small pieces of
  granulated zinc (240)
HCl solution A
  (2 moles/liter)

HCl solution B
  (1 mole/liter)
thermometers,
  alcohol-based (10)
beakers (10)
water
hot plates (10)
thermal mitts (30 pairs)
aprons (30)
safety goggles (30)

SAFETY PRECAUTIONS

- Eye wash should be made available to all students.
- Instruct students to wear thermal mitts when handling hot glassware.
- Avoid using mercury-based thermometers. Mercury is toxic.

PREPARATION

- Students should work in groups of three.
- Prepare HCl solution B by diluting solution A (purchased as "dilute" HCl: 2 moles per liter) with an equal amount of water.
- Prepare one 16-oz dispenser bottle of each solution for each student group.
- Prepare a supply of large and small pieces of granulated zinc.

PROCEDURE

Teaching Strategies
Review procedures for working with acid and heat.

Troubleshooting
Plan the allocation of tasks: monitoring hot plate, reading the temperatures, labeling test tubes, obtaining supplies, adding reactants to thermometer, cleaning up.

DATA AND OBSERVATIONS

Reactants	Bubbles Faster	Bubbles Slower	Cause of Higher Rate of Reaction Surface area, concentration, or temperature
Tube "A" large zinc + dilute HCL	✓		Concentration of acid
Tube "B" large zinc + $\frac{1}{2}$ dilute HCl		✓	
Tube "L" large zinc + dilute HCl		✓	
Tube "S" small zinc + dilute HCl	✓		Surface area of zinc
Tube "R" zinc + HCl room temperature		✓	
Tube "H" zinc + HCl heated	✓		Temperature of the solution

ANALYZE

Diagrams will vary, but should reflect the condition that reaction rates are affected more, or speed up, when temperatures are higher and there is more surface area.

CONCLUDE AND APPLY

1. Iron plus oxygen yields iron oxide.
2. Surface area
3. See table below.

Reaction	Rate Reduced or Increased	Factor Involved
Rusting of metal	Reduced by painting	Surface area
Skin burned by acid	Reduced by rinsing	Concentration
Spoilage of food	Reduced by refrigeration (Answers will vary.)	Temperature (Answers will vary.)
Cut-up apples turning brown	Reduced by wrapping in plastic (Answers will vary.)	Surface area (Answers will vary.)
Brewing of coffee	(1) Increased by grinding beans (2) Increased by heating	(1) Surface area (2) Temperature
Dissolving of limestone formations producing caves (Hint: Where are limestone caves found?) In areas which have or have had average or above average rainfall	Increased by contact with groundwater (rainwater with dissolved carbon dioxide (= carbonic acid), which has percolated through the soil and absorbed complex organic acids	Surface area and concentration
Answers will vary.	Answers will vary.	Answers will vary.

4.1 • Investigation
Growing Crystals

OBJECTIVES

- Form crystals by evaporating solutions.
- Identify several of the major crystal systems.

PROCESS SKILLS

observe, classify, communicate, formulate models

TIME ALLOTMENT

2 class periods

MATERIALS

solutions A–D (20 test tubes full of each solution)
solutes A–D (50 grams of each solute)

test tubes (40)	pipettes (10)
test-tube racks (10)	microscope slides (40)
glass markers (10)	table lamps (10)
small petri dishes (40)	compound microscopes (30)
metal spatulas (10)	thermal mitts (30 pairs)
Bunsen burners (10)	gloves (30 pairs)
lighters (10)	aprons (30)
test-tube tongs (10)	safety goggles (30 pairs)

SAFETY PRECAUTIONS

- Have students wear safety goggles, gloves, and an apron during the lab procedure. Tell students to tie back long hair and keep loose clothing out of the Bunsen burner.
- Some of the solutions are toxic; remind students to wash their hands at the end of lab.
- Instruct students to wear thermal mitts when handling hot objects.
- Circuits must be protected by a GFI (ground fault interruptor) when electricity is used near a water source.
- Warn students not to inhale any powder or fumes; chemicals can be toxic if inhaled.

DISPOSAL

- Designate a box or waste basket for used slides.
- Refer to an MSDS (Material Safety Data Sheet) for proper disposal techniques for hazardous chemicals. The MSDS must be available at all times during the use of chemicals.

PREPARATION

- Students should work in groups of three.
- Each group will need half a test tube of each solution and several grams of each solute. Prepare four saturated solutions, using the directions in the table. Put them in large beakers labeled A–D. Put each powdered solute in small beakers labeled A–D.

Solution	Formula	Recipe
A. Alum	$AlK(SO_4)_2 \cdot 12H_2O$	20 g per 100 mL hot water
B. Rochelle salt	$KNaC_4H_4O_6 \cdot 4H_2O$	130 g per 100 mL hot water
C. Copper acetate monohydrate	$Cu(CH_3COO)_2 \cdot H_2O$	10 g per 100 mL hot water
D. Calcium copper acetate hexahydrate	$CaCu(CH_3COO)_4 \cdot 6H_2O$	Add 22.5 g powdered calcium oxide to 200 mL water. Pour glacial acetic acid into the solution until it is clear. Dissolve separately 20 g copper acetate monohydrate in 150 mL water. Mix the two solutions and let cool.

Alternative Materials

If you have hot plates that have a very low setting that will not burn your hand, you can use them instead of table lamps. Droppers can be used instead of pipettes. Dissecting microscopes do not work for this lab. Other solutions will grow good crystals, such as sodium chlorate, potassium ferricyanide, and nickel sulfate hexahydrate; but these solutions have not been included in this lab due to safety concerns and levels of toxicity.

PROCEDURE

Review the major crystal systems in Table 4-1 in the textbook.

DATA AND OBSERVATIONS

Small crystals form at different locations in the solution. The crystals grow and become more numerous. The droplet dries out from the edges inward, forming a polycrystalline mass. The predominant form of the crystals will vary in different solutions, as will the distribution of crystal size.

ANALYZE

1. At first, the crystals are small and scattered. At midstage (about 20 minutes), an array of large crystals appears. In the final stage, crystals with irregular treelike shapes grow rapidly from the edges of the drop inward. These are like frost on a windowpane.

CONCLUDE AND APPLY

1.

Solution	Crystal System	Color
A. Alum	cubic	none
B. Rochelle salt	orthorhombic	none
C. Copper acetate monohydrate	monoclinic	blue-green
D. Calcium copper acetate hexahydrate	tetragonal	blue

2. Answers will vary. Sample answer: The model crystals form faster than crystals in nature form. The crystal shapes are similar in both.

4.2 ▪ Design Your Own
Rockhounding

OBJECTIVES

- Identify a local spot of geologic interest.
- Plan a field trip to collect samples of rocks and minerals.
- Collect samples of different rocks and minerals.
- Identify rocks and minerals.

PROCESS SKILLS

observe, classify, communicate, interpret data

TIME ALLOTMENT

1 class period to plan a field trip; a half-day or longer for the trip; 1 class period to identify and display samples

MATERIALS

resources on local geology
small backpacks (30)
chisel-edged hammers (30)
short pry bars (30)
cloth or leather gloves
    (30 pairs)
newspapers
bags for samples (30)
notebooks (30)
masking tape (2 rolls)
markers (30)
hand lenses (30)

field guide to rocks and
    minerals
food
water
sunscreen (1 large bottle)
porcelain tiles (30)
hardness testing kit
dilute hydrochloric acid
safety goggles (30)
long-sleeved shirts or
    jackets (30)

SAFETY PRECAUTIONS

- If you have not been to the selected site, visit it or check with someone who has so that you have a good idea of possible hazards, such as treacherous terrain, tides, and poisonous plants and animals.
- Discuss what to wear and what to bring for a safe and comfortable outing. Students should wear long pants, gloves, long-sleeved shirts or jackets, and boots or heavy sneakers. They may wish to bring a spare set of clothes.
- Warn students to wear safety goggles when they are hammering stones or near someone who is.
- Remind students to keep hydrochloric acid away from their eyes and skin. It is toxic.

PREPARATION

- Students should work together as a class.
- Gather materials about local geologic hot spots that are accessible. Check with local experts to see if you need permission to visit and collect on a site.

Possible Hypothesis

Students may come up with several possible sites. It might be wise to check out some sites before the actual field trip, so you can offer information about them.

PLAN THE EXPERIMENT

- Have extras of absolute essentials for the field trip (water, paper, pencils, safety goggles).
- Provide hardness-testing equipment, dilute hydrochloric acid, and other materials for identification in the lab.
- Plan where you want to exhibit the collection of samples and whether you want to invite other classes to see it.
- Encourage students to discuss specimens while they survey the class's exhibit.

Possible Procedures

The Internet has many fine resources about the geology of most localities. Many places have an amateur geology society that might publish pamphlets on the area. Groups will propose locations, after which the whole class will discuss the proposals until they reach a consensus, moderated by the teacher. It may take a few days to get permission to visit a site.

DATA AND OBSERVATIONS

The field-identification table might include the name of the rock or mineral, ways to identify it in the field, its rarity, and likely places to find it.

ANALYZE

1. Answer will vary. The table should include sample number, field identification, test results, and final identification.
2. Answers will vary, but should include numbers and names of samples, and should perhaps note commonest or rarest finds.
3. Answers will vary. Students should write labels that include where the sample was found (possibly with a sketch), its identity, some notes on whether it is in typical condition, and so on.

CHECK YOUR HYPOTHESIS

Answers will vary depending on students' hypotheses.

CONCLUDE AND APPLY

1. Answers will vary, but should reflect efforts to compare and evaluate specimens.
2. Answers will vary, but should reflect the class table and field experience.
3. Answer will vary, but should point out discrepancies between hypothesis and the field experience.

5.1 ▪ Investigation
Comparing Lunar Rocks to Earth Rocks

OBJECTIVES
- Estimate mineral percentages in igneous rock samples.
- Identify types of igneous rocks.
- Compare lunar rocks to Earth rocks.

PROCESS SKILLS
observe, classify, infer

TIME ALLOTMENT
1 class period

MATERIALS
igneous rocks from Earth (15 sets of 4 rocks)
igneous-rock key
pictures of lunar rocks

SAFETY PRECAUTIONS
Warn students that rocks may have sharp edges that may cut their skin.

PREPARATION
- Students should work in pairs.
- Each pair of students will need a set of numbered rocks. Number the igneous rocks with tape: 1, granite; 2, basalt; 3, rhyolite; 4, gabbro.
- If possible, obtain pictures of lunar rocks and maps and photos of where they were collected.

PROCEDURE
Teaching Strategies
- Discuss igneous activity on the Moon. Tell students that numerous lavaflows have erupted on the Moon. The last flows may have erupted millions of years ago. The lava flow from these eruptions created many of the rocks found on the Moon's surface.
- Moon rocks were collected by American astronauts during the Apollo missions to the Moon. The rocks were collected in order to help determine the origin and structure of the Moon. How old is the Moon? How was the Moon formed? Could or did the Moon support life? These are some of the questions the rocks could help answer.

DATA AND OBSERVATIONS
Every rock has its own characteristic physical properties. Some of these physical properties include the color, mineral composition, and texture of the rock. Using igneous-rock key, students should identify the rock samples to complete the table.

Table

Rock Sample	Texture	Estimated % of Dark Minerals	Felsic, Mafic, or Intermediate	Type of Feldspar	Estimated % of Quartz	Name of Rock
1	coarse	0–20	felsic	potassium	15–60	granite
2	fine	50–80	mafic	plagioclase	0	basalt
3	fine	0–20	felsic	potassium	15–60	rhyolite
4	coarse	50–80	mafic	plagioclase	0	gabbro

ANALYZE
1. The dark color of lunar rocks indicates that magnesium and iron are prevalent.
2. Lunar rocks appear most like gabbro and basalt from Earth.
3. Answers may vary. Sample answer: Some elements are similar, such as magnesium and iron, and some are different. Lunar rocks have very little feldspar and quartz.

CONCLUDE AND APPLY
1. Igneous rocks are abundant on the Moon, which suggests lavaflows and igneous activity were common.
2. When the lunar flows were active, the lava flowed out of vents and down to the bottom of the crater. Eventually, the lava collected in the crater and solidified into mafic rocks. These areas are darker than the surface of the Moon because mafic rock is very dark.
3. The fine texture of the lunar rocks suggests that the magma cooled quickly.

5.2 ▪ Mapping
Locating Igneous Rocks on Earth

OBJECTIVES
- Classify igneous rocks based on texture and color.
- Recognize that the characteristics of rocks are linked to their formation conditions and origins.
- Plot the location of igneous rocks on a map.

PROCESS SKILLS
observe, classify, communicate, interpret scientific illustrations, compare and contrast

TIME ALLOTMENT
1 class period

MATERIALS
igneous rocks (15 sets of 9 rocks)

SAFETY PRECAUTIONS
Warn students that rocks may have sharp edges that may cut their skin.

PREPARATION
- Students should work in pairs.
- Each pair of students will need a set of numbered rocks. Number the igneous rocks with tape: 1, pumice; 2, obsidian; 3, scoria; 4, rhyolite; 5, andesite; 6, basalt; 7, granite; 8, diorite; 9, gabbro.

PROCEDURE
Teaching Strategies
- Do not give students any information about the rocks until the lab is complete.
- Emphasize that the texture and color of a rock helps scientists determine the conditions under which the rock formed.

Troubleshooting
Review mapping skills if students are having trouble mapping coordinates. Tell students that cartographers use a grid system to locate places on Earth. The grid system consists of lines of latitude and longitude. Latitude refers to distance in degrees north or south of the equator. Longitude refers to distance in degrees east or west of the prime meridian.

DATA AND OBSERVATIONS

Rock/ Location	Color(s)	Felsic, Mafic, or Intermediate	Texture (glassy, fine-grained, coarse-grained, or porphyritic)	Intrusive or Extrusive
1/C, F, or G	light gray	felsic	glassy	extrusive
2/D, A, or B	black/gray	intermediate	glassy	extrusive
3/E, H, or I	black	mafic	glassy	extrusive
4/F, C, or G	gray	felsic	fine	extrusive
5/A, B, or D	gray	intermediate	fine	extrusive
6/H, E, or I	gray	mafic	fine	extrusive
7/G, C, or F	tan, black, and pink	felsic	coarse	intrusive
8/B, A, or D	gray, green	intermediate	coarse	intrusive
9/I, E, or H	dark green/ black	mafic	coarse	intrusive

ANALYZE
1. Felsic rocks are generally found in large landmasses.
2. Mafic rocks are found in ocean areas, and may form underwater, underground, or on the surface of land.
3. Intermediate rocks are found where landmasses meet oceans.

CONCLUDE AND APPLY
1. Felsic rocks are primarily light colors, such as white, tan, gray, pink, and red. Mafic rocks are primarily dark colors, such as dark green, dark gray, and black. Intermediate rocks are colors such as green and gray.
2. Coarse-grained rocks cooled slowly underground. Fine-grained rocks cooled quickly at Earth's surface, in air or water. Glassy rocks cooled very quickly.
3. Hawaii is in a mafic region on the map, and Texas is in the felsic region. The rocks that originated in these separate areas eventually eroded and became the sand that formed these beaches. Mafic rocks will erode into the black sand found in Hawaii. The felsic rocks will erode into the white sand found in Texas.
4. Glassy rocks form when lava cools very quickly. These rocks have microscopic crystals. Fine-grained rocks contain small crystals and form when lava cools quickly on Earth's surface. Porphyritic rocks form when cooling conditions change. These rocks usually contain large crystals, indicating a period of slow cooling, surrounded by small crystals, indicating a period of quick cooling.

6.1 ▪ Investigation
Comparing Chemical Sedimentary Rocks and Modeling Their Formation

OBJECTIVES
- Differentiate among several types of chemical sedimentary rocks.
- Simulate the formation of chemical sedimentary rocks.

PROCESS SKILLS
classify, observe, communicate

TIME ALLOTMENT
1 class period

MATERIALS
chemical sedimentary rocks
  (45; 15 samples for each of the 3 rock types)
sodium chloride solution (30 test tubes full)
silver nitrate solution (1 test tube full)
water (5.7 liters)
test tubes (30)
test-tube racks (15)
test-tube holders (30)
500-mL beakers (15)
hot plates (15)
droppers (15)
thermal mitts (30 pairs)
gloves (30 pairs)
aprons (30)
safety goggles (30)

SAFETY PRECAUTIONS
- Warn students not to handle hot glassware without protection. Instruct them to wear thermal mitts if needed.
- Silver nitrate may stain skin and clothes. It is a highly toxic chemical.
- Remind students to wear safety goggles, gloves, and aprons during the lab procedure.

PREPARATION
- Students should work in pairs.
- Prepare 450 mL of saturated sodium chloride solution (enough for four classes of 30 students).
- Dissolve 4 g silver nitrate in 250 mL of water (enough for four classes of 30 students).

PROCEDURE
Give each pair of students a sample of each of the three types of chemical sedimentary rocks listed in Table 1. Number each set of samples 1 to 3.

DATA AND OBSERVATIONS
In Table 2, results will vary, depending on the samples. Salt crystals form in test tube 1 as the water evaporates. In test tube 2, a white precipitate forms as the silver nitrate solution mixes with the salt solution.

ANALYZE
1. The identification of the samples in Table 3 should match your labeling of the samples.
2. The salt crystals form as water evaporates from the saturated sodium chloride solution.
3. A cloudy precipitate formed, indicating a chemical reaction.

CONCLUDE AND APPLY
1. Sodium and chloride make up table salt and halite.
2. Answers may vary. Sample answer: Sedimentary rock is horizontally deposited, layered, clastic, and composed of some form of sediment.
3. Answers may vary. Sample answer: In areas that are or once were covered with shallow seawater; the salts would precipitate as the seawater evaporated and could later turn to rock.

6.2 ▪ Mapping
Grand Canyon Formations

OBJECTIVES

- Interpret information about rock layers in the Grand Canyon.
- Create a geologic cross section.
- Hypothesize about how rock layers formed.

PROCESS SKILLS

communicate, infer, recognize and use spatial relationships, form hypotheses

TIME ALLOTMENT

1 class period

MATERIALS

colored pencils (300)

PREPARATION

- Students should work individually.
- It would be helpful to have pictures of the Grand Canyon available, especially good photographs of the canyon walls.

DATA AND OBSERVATIONS

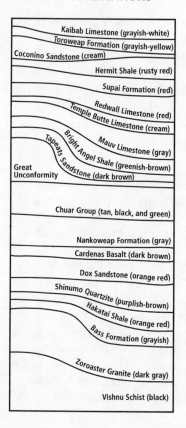

- Students should have background on sedimentary, metamorphic, and igneous rock.

PROCEDURE

Troubleshooting

Students may need help interpreting the geologic time scale and reconstructing the geologic cross section.

ANALYZE

1. Answers will vary. Students' answers should include the fact that cross sections will vary in different areas, and that rock layers will vary in thicknesses.
2. The Vishnu Schist is a metamorphic rock, formed as a result of pressure and high temperature from overlying layers of sedimentary rock. It forms from shale. Quartzite is a metamorphic rock composed of quartz which has metamorphosed from sandstone.

CONCLUDE AND APPLY

1. The mountains eroded.
2. Answers may vary. A lowering of sea level would have exposed the sediments to erosion. A rising sea level would have cause erosion of the shoreline as the waves moved inland.
3. The environment was probably a beach. The sand, dune, and tracks and burrows suggest this hypothesis.
4. The environment was probably a muddy, moist area, as indicated by the fern fossils and amphibian and reptile tracks.
5. Granite forms from magma that is beneath Earth's surface. Organic materials cannot survive at the high temperatures of magma.

7.1 ▪ Investigation
Chemical Weathering and Temperature

OBJECTIVES
- Determine the effect of an acid on limestone.
- Model the effect of temperature on the chemical weathering of limestone.
- Calculate the relationship between temperature increase and chemical breakdown.

PROCESS SKILLS
observe, communicate, measure, interpret data

TIME ALLOTMENT
2 class periods

MATERIALS
pea-sized limestone
  chips (1500 g)
balances (15)
paper towels (2 rolls)
glass markers (15)
200-mL beakers (30)
500-mL beakers (30)
vinegar (6 L)
100-mL graduated
  cylinders (15)

ice
aluminum foil (1 roll)
alcohol-based
  thermometers (15)
hot water
plastic spoons (30)
gloves (30 pairs)
aprons (30)
safety goggles (30)

SAFETY PRECAUTIONS
- Instruct students to wash their hands after handling the limestone chips and vinegar.
- Avoid using mercury-based thermometers. Mercury is toxic.
- Eye wash should be made available to all students.
- Make sure all solutions are labeled.

DISPOSAL
Weathered limestone can be rinsed off, dried, and reused.

PREPARATION
- Students should work in pairs.
- Use pea-sized limestone. Put 100 g of limestone in a container of water per pair of students.
- Use *fresh* apple cider or white vinegar. Two gallons should be plenty for a class of 30 students.

Alternative Materials
Plastic drink containers may be used instead of beakers.

PROCEDURE
Teaching Strategies
- If the vinegar is very warm to begin with, students will see bubbles form after it is added to limestone.
- Students should weigh limestone to the nearest 0.1 g.

- Keep the vinegar in beaker W as warm as possible during the first day and overnight. Keep the vinegar in beaker C as cool as possible; refrigerate it overnight.
- If possible, stir the limestone and vinegar several times during the day.

DATA AND OBSERVATIONS
Answers may vary somewhat.

		Beaker C	Beaker W
	Mass before weathering	52.0 g	51.3 g
	Mass after weathering	52.0 g	51.2 g
Day 1	Temperature of vinegar	10°C	50°C
	Change in mass	0 g	0.1 g
	Percentage change in mass	0%	0.19%
	Mass before weathering	52 g	51.2 g
	Mass after weathering	52 g	50.4 g
Day 2	Temperature of vinegar	10°C	30°C
	Change in mass	0 g	0.8 g
	Percentage change in mass	0%	1.6%

ANALYZE
1. Bubbles came from the rock.
2. The limestone in the warm vinegar lost more mass than did the limestone in the cold vinegar. The warm vinegar may have turned darker.
3. The higher temperature caused more weathering.
4. Answers may vary. Sample answer: The change could be expressed as a loss of the mass of limestone. The loss could be expressed as a percentage of the original mass of the chips.

CONCLUDE AND APPLY
1. Answers may vary. Sample answer: The data suggest that an increase in the temperature of an acid speeds up the chemical weathering of limestone, as evidenced by its greater loss of mass. A warmer, wetter climate generally produces a faster rate of chemical weathering than a colder climate does.
2. Answers may vary. Sample answer: You could run the experiment longer, use finely ground limestone or a stronger acid, or increase the temperature.
3. Answers may vary. Sample answer: In a rainy northern valley; acid wouldn't weather the limestone without water to dissolve it, so limestone in a desert wouldn't weather as fast. Also, freeze-thaw cycles break up rock, producing more surface area for the acid to attack.

7.2 ▪ Mapping
Global Soils and Climate

OBJECTIVES
- Use maps to compare climate and soils in different regions.
- Relate regional soil types to temperature and rainfall.

PROCESS SKILLS
interpret data, observe, infer, predict

TIME ALLOTMENT
1 class period

MATERIALS
rulers (30)

PREPARATION
Students should work individually.

PROCEDURE
Teaching Strategies
Students should review the development of soil and soil types in Chapter 7.

DATA AND OBSERVATIONS

Table 1

Soil Type	Range of Latitudes
Polar	45°–70°N
Tropical	30° N to 30°S
Northern temperate	10°–60°N

Table 2

City	Range of Rainfall
Perth	60–90 cm
Cook	0–60 cm
Darwin	>120 cm
	Range of Temperature
Sierra Leone	21°–27°C
Aswan	>27°C
Cape Town	16°–20°C

ANALYZE
1. The deserts of the world are found around latitudes 30°N and 30°S.
2. In the United States, the high altitude of the Rocky Mountains and other ranges causes the temperature and rainfall to be similar to more northern latitudes.
3. The soil types correspond to rainfall. The interior is dry, with desert soil. The exterior has more rainfall, with tropical soils in the warmer parts of the continent and temperate soils in the cooler parts.
4. Answers may vary. Sample answer: The soil types correspond somewhat to temperatures in Africa. Desert soil is in the hotter areas, and tropical and temperate soils are in regions with more moderate temperatures. Southern Africa, however, has desert soils and moderate temperatures.

CONCLUDE AND APPLY
1. The soil types are related to climate. Tropical soils are found more or less around the equator where the climate is warm; polar soils are found where the climate is cold. Desert soils are related to both temperature and rainfall. Temperate soils seem to be related to more mild temperatures. In some cases, factors other than latitude affect soil distribution; for example, in the mountainous areas of the United States, polar soils are found next to the desert.
2. Answers may vary. Sample answer: Soil types seem to be related more closely to rainfall than to temperature.
3. temperature, rainfall, elevation, and type of bedrock

8.1 ▪ Investigation
How Does Wind Erosion Take Place?

OBJECTIVES
- Observe and compare the effects of moving air on different particle sizes.
- Observe some features of wind deposits.

PROCESS SKILLS
formulate models, interpret data, infer, communicate, observe

TIME ALLOTMENT
1 class period

MATERIALS
hair dryer with cool heat setting
boxes, cardboard (approximately
  30 cm wide, 60 cm long, 10 cm high) (10)
samples of sand and gravel (1 bag)
400-mL beakers (10)
twigs with a number of branches, (40)

candles (10)   paper clips (10)
matches (10)   tape (1 roll)
rocks or rubber stoppers   thermal mitts (30 pairs)
  of various sizes (30)   gloves (30 pairs)
protractors (10)   aprons (30)
cardboard strips   safety goggles (30)
  (15 cm × 5 cm) (10)
20-cm thin string (10 pieces)

SAFETY PRECAUTIONS
- If possible, plug the hair dryer into a ground fault interrupter (GFI) outlet. Warn students not to get the hair dryer wet or use it with wet hands. Tell students not to stick metal objects into the hair dryer.
- The heat switch on the hair dryer can be taped in the off position to remind students not to inadvertently turn it on. Students may also wear thermal mitts if the hair dryer becomes hot to the touch.
- Caution students not to blow sand at other students because it can cause eye and skin irritation.
- If fine-grained sand is used, the experiment should be conducted under a hood or outdoors.

DISPOSAL
All sand should be retuned to a central storage location. Wet sand should be kept separate from dry sand.

PREPARATION
- Students should work in groups of three.
- A shoe box can be used as the box for the sand.
- Silica sand and pebbles can be purchased beforehand at a hardware or nursery. You'll need about 40 pounds of sand and 5 pounds of pea-sized pebbles.

- Be sure the sand is dry before starting the experiment.

Alternative Materials
- Steel wool, slightly pulled apart, can substitute for twigs.
- Dried sandbox sand can be used in place of silica sand.

PROCEDURE
Teaching Strategies
- You may cut away a portion of the front of the box so that the air from the hair dryer blows more parallel to the surface of the sand.
- Use a pencil to anchor the steel wool.

DATA AND OBSERVATIONS
Sample Data

	Observations
Procedure 4	The sand jumps along and is not suspended in the air.
Procedure 6	Windward side = 30°; Leeward side = 45°
Procedure 7	The twigs keep some of the sand from blowing away.
Procedure 8	The candle was blown out when it was moved far enough behind the beaker, instead of directly behind it.
Procedure 9	There was no sand directly behind the beaker. The sand was deposited at a distance behind the beaker that is approximately the same as the distance at which the candle was blown out.
Procedure 10	The air from the dryer diverted the sand toward the end of the box, but the sand still continued toward the bottom of the box
Procedure 11	The sand blew away and left the pebbles behind.
Procedure 12	The sand particles do not move.

ANALYZE
1. The dune formed in front of the obstacle.
2. The leeward side was steeper. Sand particles were eroded from the gently sloping windward side and deposited on the more steeply sloping leeward side.
3. The plants prevented the wind from eroding the surface as much as it eroded without plants. Some sand particles were stopped by the plants.
4. The candle burned when it was behind the beaker. As the candle moved far enough away from the beaker, the flame was blown out.

CONCLUDE AND APPLY
1. The force of wind and the deposition behind an obstruction are less directly behind an obstruction, and increase as you move further downwind from the obstruction.
2. An obstruction such as shrubs, bushes, trees, or a fence would slow the movement.
3. The sand did not remain in suspension, but rather fell to the bottom of the box.

8.2 ▪ Design Your Own
Analysis of Glacial Till

OBJECTIVES

- Determine the particle sizes in samples of glacial till and outwash.
- Measure the relative amounts of each particle size.
- Compare the particle sizes and relative amounts of each size in glacial till and outwash.

PROCESS SKILLS

form hypothesis, interpret data, classify, communicate, measure

TIME ALLOTMENT

1 class period

POSSIBLE MATERIALS

unknown glacial till and/or outwash
pan sets (10)
balances (10)
beakers (10)
screening sieves (40; 10 sets of 4 various sizes)
filter paper (10 filters)

SAFETY PRECAUTIONS

Avoid breathing the dust from the samples. Avoid vigorously shaking the samples.

DISPOSAL

Set aside a waste basket designated only for the disposal of glacial till and/or outwash.

PREPARATION

Students should work in groups of three.

Possible Hypothesis

Make a hypothesis about how the range of particle sizes might vary as you dig deeper in the glacial till.

Alternative Materials

You can make your own till by mixing together known amounts and various sizes of sand, clay, and pebbles.

PLAN THE EXPERIMENT

Possible Procedures

Determine the mass of the empty beaker and record the value. Determine the masses of each of the empty sieves and the pan. Fill the beaker about two-thirds full of the glacial sediment. Record the total mass of the beaker with the glacial sediment. To find the mass of the sediment alone, subtract the mass of the empty beaker from the mass of the beaker plus sediment. Record this value. Stack the sieves and the pan in the correct order of their screen sizes, so that the smallest mesh is on the bottom and the largest mesh is on the top. Pour the glacial sediment onto the top screen. Place the sieve cover on the top. Shake the sieves to sift the sample. Carefully separate

each sieve from the one below it. Determine the mass of each sieve or pan together with the sediment it contains. Record each value. Find the total mass of sediment by subtracting the mass of each empty sieve or pan from the mass of the container plus the sediment. The total mass of the sediment should equal the total mass of the original sediment sample obtained in Procedure 4. To find the percentage of the total mass, divide the mass of sediment retained on each screen or pan by the total mass of the original sediment sample. Multiply each of these answers by 100 to change to a percentage. Record this information.

DATA AND OBSERVATIONS

Object	Mass of Empty Container (g)	Mass of Container plus Sediment (g)	Total Mass of Sediment (g)	Percent of Total Mass of Sediment
beaker	143.3	582.2	439.9	100
top screen	180.8	222.9	42.1	9.6
second screen from top	165.9	282.9	117.0	26.7
third screen from top	159.4	383.2	223.8	51.0
bottom screen	149.3	200.1	50.8	11.6
pan	123.0	128.1	5.1	1.2

ANALYZE

1. Answers may vary. Students should have used a screening material to separate till or outwash.
2. Answers may vary according to how many screens were used.
3. Answers will vary according to type of material used and sizes of screening material.
4. Answers will vary according to type of material and sizes of screening.

CHECK YOUR HYPOTHESIS

Answers will vary depending on students' hypotheses.

CONCLUDE AND APPLY

1. Answers will vary according to type of material used. Typically, till will have more or less equal amounts of material in each sorted group. Outwash usually has a preponderance of one size material.

2.

0.01(size in mm)			0.0625	0.125	0.25	0.5	1.0	2.0	4.0	8.0
Fine Silt	Medium Silt	Coarse Silt	Very Fine Sand	Fine Sand	Medium Sand	Coarse Sand	Very Coarse Sand	Granules	Small Pebbles	
Pan		Screen 4		Screen 3		Screen 2		Screen 1		

3. Answers may vary. Students may want to use more sieve screens and measure various samples from the area. They might also be more careful in their sorting.

9.1 ▪ Investigation
Analyzing Watersheds

OBJECTIVES

- Examine maps showing condition and vulnerability indicators.
- Analyze maps and establish a watershed health report.
- Develop a list of goals aimed at reversing damage and improving the health of the watershed.

PROCESS SKILLS

interpret data, predict, communicate

TIME ALLOTMENT

1 class period

MATERIALS

rulers (30)
colored markers (60)

PREPARATION

- Students should work individually.
- Locate a topographic map of your area and mark your local watershed.

PROCEDURE

- Visit sites on the Glencoe Science Web Site for information about your local watershed. The figures in this lab are dated 1997. The Glencoe Science Web Site can provide updated information about the area pictured. In addition, students can access information about EPA-sponsored programs, such as *Adopt Your Watershed*, to learn about recent efforts and progress made in specific watershed areas.

ANALYZE

1. Answers will vary. Many watersheds have problems with chemicals in the groundwater, toxins in the water, contaminated sediments, and wetland loss. There are also fish-consumption advisories.
2. Answers will vary. Most of the watersheds have atmospheric deposition, pesticide runoff, and moderate-to-high risk of nitrates.
3. Answers will vary. Sample answer: Yes; the conditions affecting the selected watershed are so widespread that they also affect surrounding areas.

CONCLUDE AND APPLY

1. Answers will vary. Sample answer: The condition of the watershed will continue to deteriorate until some of the water becomes undrinkable, wetlands disappear, and there is not enough water to supply the population.
2. Most of the watersheds have some serious problems. The vulnerability indicators show that the conditions will get worse at an increasing rate if changes are not made.
3. Answers may vary. Samples answer: Controlling the release of chemicals, legislating water-use controls, cleaning contaminated sediments, looking for safer pesticides, and protecting wetlands.

DATA AND OBSERVATIONS

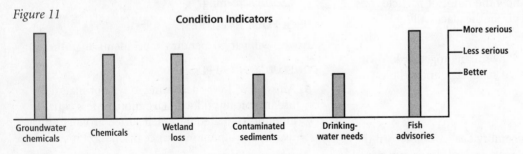

Figure 11   **Condition Indicators**

More serious — Less serious — Better

Groundwater chemicals | Chemicals | Wetland loss | Contaminated sediments | Drinking-water needs | Fish advisories

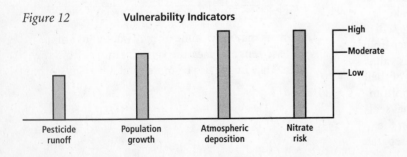

Figure 12   **Vulnerability Indicators**

High — Moderate — Low

Pesticide runoff | Population growth | Atmospheric deposition | Nitrate risk

9.2 ▪ Mapping
Interpreting a River's Habits

OBJECTIVES
Use a topographic map to answer questions about a river and its valley.

PROCESS SKILLS
interpret data, observe, infer, predict

TIME ALLOTMENT
1 class period

MATERIALS
rulers (30)

PREPARATION
- Students should work individually.
- Visit sites listed on the Glencoe Science Web Site to view two-dimensional and three-dimensional versions of a topographic map. Viewing both maps side by side can help students visualize a two-dimensional topographic map.
- Offer extra credit to students who make a three-dimensional clay model of the Souris River valley.
- Ask students to contact North Dakota schools via E-mail for photographs or descriptions of the Souris River.

DATA AND OBSERVATIONS
Table

1. 110 feet
2. 17 000 feet
3. 54 000 feet
4. The river has a very gradual gradient.
5. 2 feet ÷ 54 000 feet = 0.0037 feet/100 feet
6. 0.029 feet/mile
7. very slowly
8. 3000 feet
9. An oxbow lake formed.
10. yes, in sections 4 and 5
11. kettle lakes
12. yes (The contours show steep, serrated rocks, which usually indicate water erosion has taken place.)
13. yes (in the lower left portion of section 8)

ANALYZE
1. Sediment blocks the stream from entering a meander; the meander becomes an oxbow lake.
2. The flat land could have been the floodplain of an earlier river that was filled in by the glacier. Another origin of the flat land may be downcutting, resulting in the Souris River's current level.

CONCLUDE AND APPLY
1. The Souris River is slow-moving with many meanders. There has been some downcutting into the bedrock, as evidenced from the differences in elevation between the riverbed and the highest bluffs.
2. The area is relatively flat, with some bluffs of about 100 feet. There is water erosion north of the river, with some evidence of a previous river's floodplain or a higher level of the Souris River prior to downcutting.
3. Sample answer: The overall rain pattern is likely to be little to moderate, given the small differences in elevation and the meandering nature of the river.

10.1 ▪ Investigation
Measuring Permeability Rate

OBJECTIVES
- Measure the water permeability of various types of soil.
- Compare and contrast the permeability of pure and mixed materials.

PROCESS SKILLS
observe, infer, communicate, predict, experiment

TIME ALLOTMENT
1 class period

MATERIALS
hand lenses (10)
sand (1 bag)
pebbles
potter's clay (5 containers)
unsorted soil (1 bag)
100-mL graduated
  cylinders (10)
water

stopwatches (10)
rubber bands (40)
cheesecloth squares (40)
large funnels (40)
500–1000-mL beakers (40)
aprons (30)
safety goggles (30)

SAFETY PRECAUTIONS
- Potter's clay irritates eyes and nose. Have students wear goggles while handling dry clay.
- Tell students to wipe up any spills immediately.

DISPOSAL
Designate a bucket for the wet soil. The materials can be dug into the soil outdoors at the end of the lab.

PREPARATION
- Students should work in groups of three.
- Mix up one part sand, one part pebbles, and one part clay for the unsorted material.
- You could add another setup with soil from students' yards.
- The size of the beaker will depend on the size of the funnel. The rim of the beaker has to support the funnel above the bottom of the beaker.

Alternative Materials
- Any sorted clay will work.
- The inverted top half of a plastic, 1-L bottle can be used instead of a funnel.
- A wall clock with a second hand may be used instead of a stopwatch.

PROCEDURE
- Students might find it easier to observe the soils against a white paper.
- Be sure students wet all of the soil in the funnels before they start to measure volume of water.

Troubleshooting
Students should keep the water level below the top of the funnel to prevent overflowing.

DATA AND OBSERVATIONS
The sand particles are crystalline-looking, sharp-edged, and similar in size. The pebbles are similar in size and more rounded. The clay is hard to see, but looks similar in size with some rounded and some sharp-edged particles. The unsorted soil has various sizes and shapes.

	Sand	Pebbles	Clay	Unsorted
Time for draining (s)	214	100	>300	>300
Drained water (mL)	98	98	67	56
Estimated permeability rate (mL/s)	0	0	0	0.5
Calculated permeability rate (mL/s)	0.46	0.98	<0.22	<0.19

ANALYZE
1.

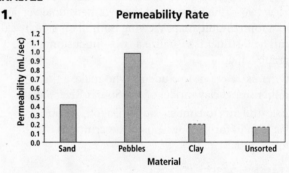

2. The permeability rate of pebbles was the fastest, sand second, clay third, and the unsorted material the slowest.

3. Answers may vary. Sample answer: I predicted 0.5 mL/s, and the actual rate was less than half that.

CONCLUDE AND APPLY
1. The samples with the largest particle sizes had the greatest permeability, and the mixed sample had the slowest permeability. The larger particle sizes have greater pore spaces than the unsorted particles. The smaller pieces in the unsorted sample fill in the spaces between the larger particle pieces, decreasing the pore size and the permeability. The sand and clay have smaller particle sizes than the pebbles, and thus less pore space between the individual pieces.

2. Sorting of material increases the permeability because of the larger pore spaces.

3. A well dug in pebbles would have the greatest amount of water available for drinking because the pore size of pebbles is bigger and the permeability rate is faster than for the other materials.

10.2 ▪ Design Your Own
Analysis of Drinking Water

OBJECTIVES
- Examine test results for well water.
- Interpret the test results and assess health risks.
- Write a report describing test results, listing health risks, and making recommendations.

PROCESS SKILLS
infer, communicate, interpret data

TIME ALLOTMENT
1 class period

POSSIBLE MATERIALS
paper (60 sheets)
computer

PREPARATION
- Students should work individually.
- You could plan to give students time to use a computer to create their reports.

Possible Hypothesis

The test results, when compared to the EPA standard, will tell whether the wells can supply safe drinking water.

PLAN THE EXPERIMENT
Ask students to limit the report to one page. This limit will help them to prioritize the information.

Possible Procedures

Sample report

Analytical Laboratory Report

Client: James J.	Collected by: Renee S.
Project: Analytical water testing	Analyzed by: Maria T.
Date collected: 9/1/2001	Time collected: 9:30 A.M.
Sample identification: kitchen tap	Lab number: 0120

Contaminant	Amount (mg/L)	Maximum Contamination Level
Arsenic	0.045	0.05
Cadmium	0.007	0.005
2-4 D	0.01	0.07
Lead	0.017	0.015
Methoxychlor	0.04	0.04
Nitrate	0.05	10
Picloram	0.000	0.5
Thallium	0.000	0.002

Based on the test results, this water sample does not meet EPA drinking water standards in the following areas:
- High cadmium level
- High lead level

The methoxychlor level is borderline.

Recommendations
- Monitor cadmium, lead, and methoxychlor levels.
- Monitor arsenic and nitrate levels.
- Test water for cyanide.
- Use activated charcoal and reverse osmosis to treat drinking water.
- Contact a physician to determine your family's cadmium, lead, and methoxychlor blood levels.

Submitted by: Ginnie B.
Laboratory Manager

ANALYZE
1. Answers may vary. Minimum information should be the test results and the unacceptable levels of contaminants. Other information for the report would include health risks, additional tests, and ways to clean up the water.
2. Answers may vary. Sample answer: If the measured level is higher than the MCL, warn the client. For measured levels that are close to the MCL, ask the client to monitor them closely.
3. Answers may vary. Sample answer: Yes; Table 1 shows that contaminants in this water may come from fertilizers, mines, and industrial sites. It would be prudent to test for other contaminants that might come from these sources.
4. Answers will vary. Sample answer: reverse osmosis and activated charcoal, to remove the cadmium and lead from the water

CHECK YOUR HYPOTHESIS
Answers will vary depending on students' hypotheses.

CONCLUDE AND APPLY
1. The water from wells 1 and 2 is definitely contaminated. Well 1 has high levels of cadmium, lead, and methoxychlor. Well 2 has high levels of arsenic and barium.
2. Answers may vary. Students may want to put health information, diagrams, background information, and suggestions for retesting.
3. Answers may vary. Sample answer: People need to be educated about water safety via television, newspapers, mailings, and local meetings. It should be mandatory to have wells tested.

11.1 ▪ Investigation
Temperature Inversion

OBJECTIVES
- Graph temperature data for the atmosphere.
- Describe how a temperature inversion affects ground-level pollution.

PROCESS SKILLS
infer, communicate, use numbers, interpret data

TIME ALLOTMENT
1 class period

MATERIALS
rulers (30)

calculators (30)

PREPARATION
- Students should work individually.
- Contact a local weather station for information about recent occurrences of temperature inversions.

PROCEDURE
- Check that students construct their graphs with titles, labels, and appropriately scaled axes.
- The calculated density should always be less than 1 kg/m^3.

Troubleshooting

Because the computed densities are close to 1, they must include at least three decimal places.

DATA AND OBSERVATIONS

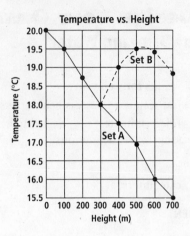

Temperature vs. Height

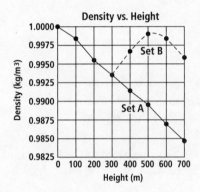

Density vs. Height

Height (m)	Set A		Set B	
	Absolute Temperature (K)	Density (kg/m^3)	Absolute Temperature (K)	Density (kg/m^3)
0	293.15	1.0000	293.15	1.0000
100	292.65	0.9983	292.45	0.9976
200	291.85	0.9956	291.95	0.9959
300	291.15	0.9932	291.15	0.9932
400	290.65	0.9915	292.15	0.9966
500	290.05	0.9894	292.65	0.9983
600	289.15	0.9864	292.55	0.9980
700	288.65	0.9846	291.95	0.9959

ANALYZE
1. Temperature decreases with height; temperature first changes by 1°C at about 170 m/°C.
2. The two lines intersect at 300 m.
3. Temperature rises between 300 m and 500 m. Above 500 m, it starts falling again.
4. Set A shows normal conditions; set B shows a temperature inversion.
5. The density in these two regions is similar.

CONCLUDE AND APPLY
1. At 300 m, where air density starts to increase, pollutants stop rising.
2. 300 m
3. Pollutants rise and are trapped by air. Then they cool, become more dense, and sink back to the ground within a short distance from their origin.

11.2 ▪ Design Your Own
What is in the air?

OBJECTIVES
- Observe how the daily weather affects the number and type of particulates in the air.
- Research the number and type of particulates in the air around the school.

PROCESS SKILLS
observe, classify, measure, form hypotheses, interpret data

TIME ALLOTMENT
1 class period to plan experiment; 30 minutes a day for 5 consecutive days to measure and record data; 1 class period to analyze data

POSSIBLE MATERIALS
coffee filters (5)
rubber bands (5)
thermometer
microscopes (5)
vacuum cleaner with intake hose
outdoor extension cord
masking tape (1 roll)
microscope slides (25)
petroleum jelly (1 container)
petri dishes with lids (25)
aprons (30)
safety goggles (30)

SAFETY PRECAUTIONS
- Select a place for students to gather data outdoors, where the electrical supply to the vacuum cleaner cannot get wet.
- Instruct students to wear safety goggles and aprons during the lab procedure.

PREPARATION
- Students should work with microscopes in groups of six.
- Ask any students who have allergies if they would like to tell the class what they know about local variations in the particulate content of the air.

Possible Hypotheses

High wind, high temperature, and low humidity are likely conditions for high concentrations of airborne particulates. Low outdoor particle counts have little influence in dusty rooms, but do affect counts near exterior doorways. Conversely, high outdoor particle counts may not affect indoor counts if windows and doors are closed.

PLAN THE EXPERIMENT
- Suggest that students count the number of particles in one field of view of the microscope. Separate counts can be made for different types of particulate.
- Weather data such as humidity can usually be found on the Internet.

Possible Procedures

Put a coffee filter over the intake hose of a vacuum cleaner and hold it there with a rubber band. At a suitable outdoor location, turn on the vacuum for 30 minutes on 5 consecutive days to collect airborne particles. Also get a temperature reading there. Examine the exposed filters under a microscope. Count the number of particles in one field of view. On the same days, leave microscope slides smeared with petroleum jelly at five indoor sites for 24 hours. Examine the slides with a microscope and count the number of particles. Collect other weather information from a daily newspaper.

DATA AND OBSERVATIONS
All these data depend on local conditions at the time of the experiment. The data should reflect the general trends mentioned in the possible hypotheses.

ANALYZE
1. Answers may vary. Sample answer: classroom high; kitchen low.
2. Answers may vary, but should include dust, pollen, and soot.
3. wind, humidity, temperature
4. Answers may vary. A slide near the vacuum site or an exterior door should show a correlation.
5. Answers may vary. The indoor measurements may differ from the outdoor measurements if the pollen count outside was high.

CHECK YOUR HYPOTHESIS
Answers will vary depending on students' hypotheses.

CONCLUDE AND APPLY
1. Answers may vary. A wood shop or small classroom with a chalkboard may have more particulates in the air than the outdoors.
2. Answers may vary, but should draw on results of this lab.

12.1 ▪ Investigation
Modeling the Coriolis Effect

OBJECTIVES

- Model the Coriolis effect in the northern and southern hemispheres.
- Sketch various movements caused by the Coriolis effect.
- Infer how the Coriolis effect influences global wind patterns and ocean currents.

PROCESS SKILLS

infer, formulate models, interpret data

TIME ALLOTMENT

1 class period

MATERIALS

globes (15)

red, blue, yellow, and green chalk
(15 pieces of each color)

SAFETY PRECAUTIONS

Have students wash their hands after completing this lab.

PREPARATION

- Students should work in pairs.
- Have a globe available for each pair of students.

Alternative Materials

Washable markers can be used in place of chalk.

PROCEDURE

Encourage students to take turns rotating the globe and drawing the lines.

Troubleshooting

- Have students practice drawing lines from the equator to the north pole as their partners rotate the globes. Stress that the lines should be as steady as possible and should head in a northerly direction. Students should erase their practice lines before beginning the lab.
- Students could use colored pencils to sketch their lines, corresponding to the colors of the chalk used to draw the lines on the globe.

DATA AND OBSERVATIONS

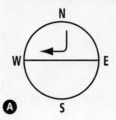

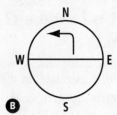

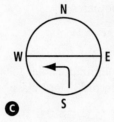

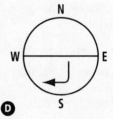

ANALYZE

1. Answers will vary. Sample answer: Sketches A and D, which both show southerly movement, are similar. Sketches B and C, which both show northerly movement, are similar.
2. That is the direction of Earth's rotation.
3. In sketch A, the wind system originated at the north pole and was deflected west as it moved south. In sketch B, the wind system originated at the equator and was deflected west as it moved north. In sketch C, the wind system originated at the south pole and was deflected west as it moved north. In sketch D, the wind system originated at the equator and was deflected west as it moved south.
4. In the northern hemisphere, currents move in a clockwise direction. In the southern hemisphere, currents move in a counterclockwise direction.

CONCLUDE AND APPLY

1. Freestanding objects that move from the north pole to the equator are deflected to the right. Those that move from the south pole to the equator are deflected to the left. In both cases, the objects move in a westerly direction.
2. Answers will vary. Sample answer: Objects would move in a straight north-south direction if the Coriolis effect did not exist.

12.2 ▪ Design Your Own
Predicting the Weather

OBJECTIVES
- Analyze and interpret weather data from a variety of sources.
- Measure and record weather conditions.
- Predict the weather.
- Determine the accuracy of weather forecasts.

PROCESS SKILLS
observe, communicate, interpret data, predict

TIME ALLOTMENT
15 minutes a day for 5 days to gather and record weather data; 1 class period to analyze results

POSSIBLE MATERIALS
weather maps (2)
alcohol-based thermometers (5)
barometer
anemometer
wind vane
rain gauge

SAFETY PRECAUTIONS
- Do not let students gather data outside in dangerous or threatening weather or if a thunderstorm is approaching.
- Warn students about the dangers of broken glass. Tell them not to attempt to clean up broken glass themselves.
- Avoid using mercury-based thermometers. Mercury is toxic.
- Tell students to beware of possible sharp metal edges on instruments.

PREPARATION
Students should work in groups of six.

Possible Hypothesis

Students may hypothesize that a low-pressure system west of their location will bring precipitation and cloudy conditions over the next few days.

PLAN THE EXPERIMENT
Have current issues of local newspapers available. Make copies of the weather maps in the newspapers and distribute a copy to each group.

Troubleshooting

- Review the use of weather instruments before beginning the lab. Let students practice measuring and recording data from each instrument.

- Review the relationships between certain weather elements and actual weather conditions. For example, high air pressure is usually associated with fair weather.

Possible Procedures

Students will likely use the Internet, newspapers, radio, or television reports to make their weather forecasts. Students may use these sources to record actual weather conditions or they may gather their own data. Each group should assign one member to each measuring instrument and collect data on weather conditions for 5 days.

DATA AND OBSERVATIONS
The accuracy of the weather forecasts will vary. In general, short-term weather forecasts will be more accurate than long-term weather forecasts.

ANALYZE
1. Answers will vary, but students should list details such as the name and date of the newspaper.
2. Answers will vary. Sample answer: The presence of high- and low-pressure systems was most helpful in making a forecast. Wind speed and direction were least helpful.
3. Answers will vary, but predictions for precipitation and cloud cover are most likely to be accurate because these weather conditions are relatively easy to interpret.
4. Forecasts from the Internet, newspapers, radio, and television should have approximately the same level of accuracy. Forecasts based on weather observations taken by students are likely to be less accurate.

CHECK YOUR HYPOTHESIS
Answers will vary depending on students' hypotheses.

CONCLUDE AND APPLY
1. Students should find that their weather predictions for the next day were most accurate. Accuracy decreases with time.
2. Answers will vary. Sample answer: More advanced weather instruments would increase the accuracy of forecasts, as would more wide-ranging data.
3. Answers will vary. Sample answer: A wide variety of factors influence weather, and changes in these factors become more difficult to predict over time.

Copyright © Glencoe/McGraw-Hill, a division of the McGraw-Hill Companies, Inc.

13.1 ▪ Investigation
Observing Flood Damage

OBJECTIVES
- Model different types of floods.
- Observe and record rates of erosion.
- Determine how floods affect local communities.
- Discuss ways to reduce flood damage.

PROCESS SKILLS
observe, infer, interpret data, formulate models, predict

TIME ALLOTMENT
1 class period

MATERIALS
stream table
sand (1 large bag)
water source
hose
metric ruler
wooden stick
large sheet of plastic
safety goggles (30)
aprons (30)

SAFETY PRECAUTIONS
- Caution students to be careful when turning on the hose. Make sure students do not use the hose near an electrical receptacle. Tell them beforehand that they are not to turn the hose on one another.
- Wipe up spills immediately.
- Instruct students to wear safety goggles and aprons during the lab procedure.

PREPARATION
- Students should work together as a class.
- If weather permits, conduct this lab outside to prevent spills in the classroom.

Alternative Materials

If a hose cannot be attached to your water source, use a bucket in place of the hose. Large plastic containers can be substituted for stream tables.

PROCEDURE
- Show students photographs of flood damage. Have them discuss any patterns that they observe. For example, where does most damage occur?
- Have students draw diagrams illustrating the erosion patterns around the wooden sticks.

DATA AND OBSERVATIONS
Students will observe that erosion occurs around objects in a stream because of changes in water depth and velocity. Most erosion will occur when the water flows fastest.

ANALYZE
1. Students should note that the water flowed slowest in steps 2 and 3, and fastest in step 4. The water was not absorbed by the sand in step 5 and flowed over the plastic.
2. The water flowed fastest in front of and behind the wooden stick and slowest to the sides of it.
3. Most erosion occurred during step 4. The sand was displaced in front of and behind the stick, and deposited to the sides of the stick.
4. Answers may vary. Sample answer: Increase the amount of time that the water flows from the hose.
5. Step 4 modeled a flash flood; the water flowed very quickly during this step. Step 5 modeled a flood in an urban area; the plastic sheet represented a surface that could not easily absorb water.

CONCLUDE AND APPLY
1. The ground around the supports erodes. Eventually, the supports fall over.
2. Answers may vary. Sample answer: A sudden, violent flood could significantly damage or even destroy houses along a riverbank.
3. Answers may vary. Sample answer: The houses could be built on stilts or constructed farther from the riverbank. Accept all reasonable suggestions.

13.2 • Design Your Own
Building Hurricane-Proof Homes

OBJECTIVES

• Design and construct a model home using an assortment of building materials.

• Test the strength of the structure in a model hurricane.

• Analyze different structural designs and infer which would best withstand severe storm conditions.

PROCESS SKILLS

observe, infer, interpret data, form hypotheses, experiment, formulate models

TIME ALLOTMENT

2 class periods

POSSIBLE MATERIALS

wooden sticks (60)
toothpicks (3 boxes)
cardboard squares of
  various sizes (15 sets)
modeling clay
  (10 containers)
marshmallows (5 bags)

scissors (15 pairs)
tape (15 rolls)
glue (15 small bottles)
fan with variable
  speeds (15)
safety goggles (30)
aprons (30)

SAFETY PRECAUTIONS

• Students should use glue with low voc's (volatile organic compounds).

• Check that the protective screen over the fan is securely in place; students should not put their hands or any other objects near the fan when it is plugged in or turned on.

• Instruct students to use caution when handling sharp objects such as scissors.

DISPOSAL

When the experiment is complete, throw out model homes and marshmallows. Store remaining materials for later labs.

PREPARATION

• Students should work in pairs.

• Have students bring in cardboard boxes and bags of marshmallows the week before this lab. Cut the cardboard into different-sized squares before the lab.

Possible Hypothesis

Students may hypothesize that the ability of the model homes to withstand hurricane winds depends largely on the sturdiness of the walls, or the construction method, and the strength of the wind.

Alternative Materials

Pipe cleaners, straws, foam, and plastic interlocking blocks can be used as substitute building materials.

PLAN THE EXPERIMENT

• Obtain a fan for each group of students. Fans with variable speeds work best.

• Discuss the concept of air pressure with students before beginning the lab. Lead students to understand that decreases in air pressure inside the structure will help the structure withstand high winds.

Troubleshooting

Make sure the tables are cleared of lightweight, small objects before students turn the fan to high speed.

Possible Procedures

One possible design could use tape, glue, toothpicks, and craft sticks. The sticks would make up the bulk of the house, and the toothpicks could be used to create open areas in the walls. Each structure should have a base, four walls, and a roof. Students should use the fan at different speeds and distances to model different wind speeds.

DATA AND OBSERVATIONS

Results will vary, but students should find that open areas in walls help relieve the air pressure that pushes on the structure.

ANALYZE

1. Answers will vary. Sketches should be labeled. Accept all reasonable descriptions and sketches.

2. Students likely used fans to model high winds of varying intensities. The strength of the building was determined by its ability to withstand the winds.

3. Answers will vary. Students should clearly explain how the design did or did not hold up to the winds.

4. Students may note that designs with several open areas in the walls were strongest. Modeling clay and craft sticks usually are sturdier materials than marshmallows or cardboard. Accept all reasonable ideas for improving strength.

CHECK YOUR HYPOTHESIS

Answers will vary depending on students' hypotheses.

CONCLUDE AND APPLY

1. Answers will vary. The revised designs should be labeled with explanations of how the improvements would increase strength.

2. Answers will vary. Students may note that the materials used and the presence of open areas in the walls greatly affected the strength of the models. The intensity of the wind affected model stability.

3. Open walls held up better because they had less surface area exposed to the wind, and thus less air pressure pushing on the walls.

4. Such a design relieves pressure on exterior walls.

14.1 ▪ Investigation
Heat Absorption over Land and Water

OBJECTIVES

- Model rates of heat absorption and heat release by land and water.
- Measure and record different rates of heat absorption and heat release in the air over land and water.
- Analyze the effects of heat absorption and heat release on climate.

PROCESS SKILLS

observe, infer, communicate, interpret data, predict, formulate models

TIME ALLOTMENT

1 class period

MATERIALS

clear plastic boxes (10)
alcohol-based thermometers (20)
masking tape (1 roll)
water
soil (1 large bag)
ring stands (5)
overhead lights with reflectors (5)
watches (5)
colored pencils (20; 5 sets of 4 different colors)
metric rulers (30)
thermal mitts (30 pairs)
aprons (30)
safety goggles (30)

SAFETY PRECAUTIONS

- Tell students to notify you if a thermometer breaks.
- Avoid using mercury-based thermometers. Mercury is toxic.
- Have students wear safety goggles and an apron during the lab procedure. Students should wear thermal mitts when handling hot items.
- Check that electric cords do not touch the water.

PREPARATION

- Students should work in groups of six.
- Get enough potting soil to cover the containers to a depth of 5 cm. Let water stand in containers to reach room temperature before the lab.
- Caution students to avoid exposure to mercury. It is toxic.
- If possible, have students use a ground fault interruptor protected circuit (GFI) to prevent shock.

Alternative Materials

Gooseneck lamps can be used in place of ring stands and overhead lights.

PROCEDURE

Tell students that water and soil absorb heat at different rates because they have different specific heat capacities. Specific heat is the quantity of heat required to raise the temperature of a substance by 1 K. It takes more heat to raise the temperature of water than it does to raise the temperature of soil.

Troubleshooting

Remind students to graph the data for each thermometer with a different-colored pencil.

DATA AND OBSERVATIONS

Students will observe that, when the light is on, soil (and the air above it) heats up faster than water (and the air above it). When the light is off, soil loses heat faster than does water.

ANALYZE

1. Answers may vary. Sample answer: the temperature of water rises and falls more slowly than that of soil.
2. The soil; air over the soil heated up faster than did air over the water.
3. The soil; air over the soil lost heat faster than did air over the water.

CONCLUDE AND APPLY

1. In general, the soil and the air above it heated up and cooled down more quickly than the water and the air above the water.
2. During summer, an air mass over land might be warmer in the day and cooler at night than an air mass over the water.
3. City A is probably closer to the coast. It has a warmer winter temperature; thus, its climate may be moderated by the water.
4. The water does not absorb heat very fast, so during the day it feels cool compared to the sun-warmed air. At night, the water does not lose much heat, so it feels warm compared to the night air.

14.2 ▪ Mapping
Classifying Climates

OBJECTIVES
- Interpret climatic data on a world map.
- Compare and contrast different climates.
- Analyze the factors that make climates different.

PROCESS SKILLS
classify, infer, interpret data

TIME ALLOTMENT
1 class period

MATERIALS
world map or globe

PREPARATION
- Students should work individually.
- Review the concepts of latitude and longitude before the lab. Latitude refers to distance in degrees north and south of the equator. Longitude refers to distance in degrees east and west of the prime meridian.

PROCEDURE
Have students look for patterns on the map. For example, they may note that warm summers, cool summers, and subarctic climates exist only in latitudes north of 30°N.

Troubleshooting
Students may need help distinguishing the different climates on the map. They could color the different climate types, using a different color for each climate. Have students make a key that shows how the colors correspond to the climate types.

DATA AND OBSERVATIONS
Students will use world maps to compare different climates and answer questions.

ANALYZE
1. Answers will vary. Sample answer: Southern California has a mediterranean climate with warm summers, mild winters, and moderate precipitation.
2. Libya; it has an arid climate with very scarce vegetation and very little precipitation.
3. Most tropical wet climates are between 30°N and 30°S.
4. proximity to oceans
5. The east coast of Nicaragua has a tropical wet and dry climate with high temperatures year-round, wet summers, and dry winters. The west coast has a tropical wet climate with high temperatures year-round and high rates of precipitation.
6. Continental climates; they experience the most variation in temperature throughout the year.

CONCLUDE AND APPLY
1. On the windward (west) side of the Rocky Mountains, the climates are marine west coast and mediterranean. On the leeward (east) side, the climates are semiarid and arid. The mountains cause moist climates on their windward sides and dry climates on their leeward sides.
2. The southeastern coast; that area has a marine west coast climate.
3. Parts of South America and Africa have high-elevation climates, which are variations of polar climates.

15.1 ▪ Mapping
Ocean Surface Temperatures

OBJECTIVES

- Interpret a world map of ocean surface temperatures.
- Compare the surface temperatures of different oceans.
- Analyze why ocean surface temperatures vary.

PROCESS SKILLS

infer, predict, interpret data

TIME ALLOTMENT

1 class period

MATERIALS

globe

PREPARATION

- Students should work individually.
- Review the concepts of latitude and longitude with students before the lab. Latitude refers to distance in degrees north and south of the equator. Longitude refers to distance in degrees east and west of the prime meridian.

Alternative Materials

You can substitute world maps for globes. If you do not have enough maps or globes for each student, have students work in groups.

PROCEDURE

- Review the formula for converting degrees Celsius to Fahrenheit. To convert from Celsius to Fahrenheit, multiply the degrees Celsius by 1.8 and add 32.
- To decrease chances of error, make sure that students properly label all oceans and continents.

DATA AND OBSERVATIONS

Students analyze a map of ocean surface temperatures, looking for patterns and differences.

ANALYZE

1. 0°C to 32°C
2. Answers will vary. The temperature range between 22°C and 28°C appears to be most common.
3. Answers will vary, but should include degrees Celsius and Fahrenheit.
4. Surface temperatures are roughly 2°C in the northern Pacific Ocean. Moving southward, temperatures increase to a maximum of 30°C around the equator, then decrease steadily to 0°C at Antarctica.

CONCLUDE AND APPLY

1. The coldest temperatures are found near the north and south poles. The warmest temperatures are found along the equator. Latitude accounts for the variations in temperature.
2. Answers will vary. Scientists could compare maps of ocean surface temperatures for several years. That way they could analyze how temperatures have changed over time. Other uses for the map might be to track ocean currents or marine organisms that can survive only within a certain range of temperatures.
3. The range of cold temperatures would increase during February and decrease during July.

15.2 ▪ Investigation
Making Waves

OBJECTIVES
- Model the movement of waves.
- Measure and record differences in wave heights.
- Infer what factors affect the heights of waves.

PROCESS SKILLS
observe, infer, measure, predict, interpret data, formulate models

TIME ALLOTMENT
1 class period

MATERIALS
electric fan with variable speed

overhead light with reflector

ring stands (30)

white paper (30 sheets)

timers (30)

clear, shallow, rectangular containers (30)

water

metric rulers (30)

safety goggles (30)

SAFETY PRECAUTIONS
- Wipe up spills immediately to prevent slips and falls.
- Make sure that electric cords do not touch the water.
- The light will get hot; caution students not to touch it.
- Instruct students to wear safety goggles during the lab procedure.
- Tell students not to stick their fingers or other objects in the fan blades.
- If students are using any electrical outlets near water, GFI (ground fault interruptor) protection is required.

PREPARATION
- Students should work individually.
- Have a fan and light available for each group of students.

Alternative Materials

A gooseneck lamp can be used instead of the overhead light and ring stand. A clock or watch are good substitutes for the timer.

PROCEDURE
- Review the movement of waves before beginning this lab. Make sure students understand that the water in a wave moves up and down in a circular motion, but does not move forward. Only the energy of the wave moves forward.
- While the fan is blowing during the 3-minute and 5-minute intervals, have students sketch the waves they observe. Students should label the parts of the waves, including wavelengths, wave heights, crests, and troughs.

Troubleshooting

To help prevent spills, have students set up their containers in an open area on the floor. Be sure that the containers are in place before they are filled with water.

DATA AND OBSERVATIONS
Wind speed and wind duration affect the height of the model waves. The distance over which the wind blows, which is called the fetch, also affects wave height.

ANALYZE
1. The heights of the waves steadily increased as the speed of the fan increased.
2. Yes; wave heights at 5 minutes were higher than those at 3 minutes.
3. The shadows moved closer together and were more visible when fan speed increased.
4. The waves gradually stopped.

CONCLUDE AND APPLY
1. Wind speed and wind duration affect wave height.
2. Wave height would increase as the distance over which the fan blows increased. Wave height would increase if the container was deeper because the water would encounter less friction with the bottom of the container.
3. Answers will vary. Sample answer: High waves might be generated by a strong storm with intense winds blowing over a large expanse of deep water. Low waves might be generated during a calm, windless day or when the wind blows over a limited expanse of shallow water.

16.1 ▪ Mapping
Changes in Sea Level

OBJECTIVES
- Observe and measure changes in coastlines.
- Describe changes in sea level over geologic time.
- Predict the impact of rising sea level on coastal regions.

PROCESS SKILLS
interpret data, communicate, infer, measure, predict

TIME ALLOTMENT
1 class period

MATERIALS
rulers (30)
string (1 large spool)

PREPARATION
- Students should work individually.
- Review the concept of map scales before beginning the lab.
- Have removable tape on hand. See Troubleshooting strategies.

PROCEDURE
To increase proficiency in measuring distances, have students convert their answers from SI units to English units.

Troubleshooting
- If students have trouble measuring the coastline with the string, have them use removable tape to secure the string to the map.
- Students may measure changes in coastlines and assume that sea level has risen by a comparable amount. Although coastlines may have retreated by nearly 300 km in 20 000 years, sea level did not rise 300 km in 20 000 years. Make sure that students understand that small changes in sea level can greatly affect the advance or retreat of coastlines and that other forces, such as tectonic activity, also affect coastline location.

DATA AND OBSERVATIONS
Students measure changes in coastlines over geologic time and link these changes to rising sea level.

ANALYZE
1. The coastline 5 million years ago was farther inland than at present. The coastline extended farther into the Atlantic Ocean 20 000 years ago than it does now.
2. The South Carolina coastline extended roughly 280 km into the Atlantic Ocean 20 000 years ago. It was about 80 km inland 5 million years ago.
3. Answers will vary. Sample answer: The current coastline measures about 3300 km and the past coastline about 3600 km. The coastline does not extend as far into the ocean as it did 20 000 years ago. Increasing sea level and tectonic forces probably caused much of the change.
4. Sea level has risen over the last 20 000 years. Melting glaciers accounted for much of this rise.

CONCLUDE AND APPLY
1. Small rises in sea level cause large changes in coastlines.
2. The Great Lakes and Hudson Bay regions; the rising land probably lowers water levels.
3. Answers will vary. Students should choose areas that are close to the ocean and thus would be affected most by rising sea level.
4. Answers will vary. Sample answer: Coastal ecosystems would be adversely affected by rising sea level. Towns and cities along the coast could experience flooding and property damage. Beach erosion would increase.

16.2 ▪ Investigation
Observing Brine Shrimp

OBJECTIVES
- Culture brine shrimp.
- Observe and record data about the structure and behavior of a crustacean.
- Analyze the effects of different salt concentrations on an aquatic organism.

PROCESS SKILLS
observe, infer, interpret data, experiment

TIME ALLOTMENT
1 class period to set up the experiment; 15 minutes each day for 4 days to record observations of brine shrimp; 1 class period to analyze results

MATERIALS
500-mL beakers (20)
glass markers (5)
100-mL graduated cylinders (5)
room-temperature water (12 L)
alcohol-based thermometers (5)
noniodized salt (450 g)
balances (15)
stirring rods (20)
wooden sticks (5)
brine-shrimp eggs (approximately 60)
plastic wrap (1 roll)
droppers (20)
petri dishes (20)
microscopes (5)
safety goggles (30)

SAFETY PRECAUTIONS
- If a thermometer or beaker breaks, students should notify you instead of cleaning up the broken glass.
- Avoid using mercury-based thermometers. Mercury is toxic.
- Tell students to wipe up any spills immediately.
- Instruct students to wear safety goggles during the lab procedure. Salt water can irritate eyes.

PREPARATION
- Students should work in groups of six.
- Brine shrimp eggs are available at pet stores or biological supply houses.
- Start this lab on a Monday.

Alternative Materials

Sea salt can be used instead of noniodized table salt. Flat-ended toothpicks can be used instead of wooden sticks. Hand lenses will allow students to see and count the brine shrimp if microscopes are not available.

PROCEDURE
Assign each student in the group a task. For example, one student can prepare the salt solutions, another can count the eggs to make sure that each solution has roughly the same number of eggs, and a third can transfer the eggs to the solutions. During the course of the experiment, encourage students to take turns observing the brine shrimp.

Troubleshooting
- Do not use iodized salt.
- Make sure students do not inadvertently taint the various solutions when stirring or measuring temperature. Students should use clean, dry instruments for each beaker.

DATA AND OBSERVATIONS
Students should find that brine shrimp hatch best in a 1–4 percent salt solution (beakers B and C).

ANALYZE
1. Answers may vary. It should take 2–3 days for the brine shrimp to hatch. Very few brine shrimp will hatch in beakers A and D.
2. Answers may vary. Beakers B and C should have the largest number of brine shrimp. Beakers A and D probably will have few brine shrimp or none at all.
3. Beaker A = 0 percent salt solution. Beaker B = 5 g salt ÷ 500 mL water = 0.01 g/mL, or 1 percent salt solution. Beaker C = 20 g salt ÷ 500 mL water = 0.04 g/mL, or 4 percent salt solution. Beaker D = 50 g ÷ 500 mL water = 0.1 g/mL, or 10 percent salt solution.
4. Answers may vary. The hatched brine shrimp are nearly transparent and have interesting appendages.
5. Answers may vary. The brine shrimp move rapidly by waving their limbs.

CONCLUDE AND APPLY
1. Answers may vary. The brine shrimp should thrive best in salt solutions of 1–4 percent.
2. Answers may vary. Students should realize that the brine shrimp would likely die if salinity levels increased or decreased beyond the optimal range.
3. Answers may vary. Sample answer: The brine shrimp live in the upper layer of the water, where light penetrates. They probably eat photosynthetic organisms.

17.1 ▪ Design Your Own
Magnetism and Ocean Ridges

OBJECTIVES
- Investigate the mechanism of magnetization.
- Model how magnetic patterns preserved in seafloor rocks arise.

PROCESS SKILLS
infer, interpret data, experiment, formulate models

TIME ALLOTMENT
1 class period

POSSIBLE MATERIALS
test tubes (10)
test-tube stoppers (10)
iron filings
bar magnets (10)
small plotting compasses (10)
metersticks (10)
safety goggles (30)
aprons (30)

PREPARATION
- Students should work in groups of three.
- At the "turning point," Earth's magnetic field is the same as that of the bar magnet. Make sure that students recognize this point and include a way to measure it in their plans.

Possible Hypothesis
Magma and lava crystallize at an ocean ridge, where iron domains in the newly-formed rock are magnetized in Earth's magnetic field at the time. The rock moves away from the ridge at essentially the same rate as the result of seafloor spreading. The magnetism fluctuates because the polarity of Earth's magnetic field changes over time.

PLAN THE EXPERIMENT
Students should use their models to answer Conclude and Apply question 3.

Possible Procedures
- Figure 2 shows a possible procedure. The compass needle must point south in step 3.
- The "turning point," illustrated in step 4 of Figure 2, is the point at which the compass needle shifts from south to north.

DATA AND OBSERVATIONS
When the magnet is close to the compass, the needle turns quickly. Magnetized iron filings produce a weaker (slower) response.

ANALYZE
1. bar magnet, iron filings, Earth's surface, seafloor
2. Answers will vary. Sample answer: At 6 cm (the turning point), the compass reversed direction.
3. The combined field would be weaker than Earth's field because a reversed bar magnet counteracts it.
4. Iron filings have a weaker magnetic field than the bar magnet.

CHECK YOUR HYPOTHESIS
Answers will vary depending on students' hypotheses.

CONCLUDE AND APPLY
1. The rocks record reversed polarity, but this field is overshadowed by Earth's current magnetic field. Normal polarity adds to current (normal) field, giving a stronger reading, whereas reverse polarity subtracts from current field, giving a weaker reading.
2. Plates on either side of the boundary move apart at essentially the same rate and are composed of rocks that formed during a particular magnetic event.
3. Yes; the magnetization of seafloor rocks depends only on Earth's magnetic field during a given time, not on the direction of spreading.
4. In about 0.7 million years; average duration of an epoch = (5 millions years − 0.7 million years) ÷ 3 = 1.43 million years; and about 0.7 million years of the Brunhes epoch has already passed.

Figure 2

① Use a compass to identify north.	② Draw the north-south line.	③ Place a magnet north of the compass, so that the needle turns.
④ Move the compass away from the magnet. Mark the turning point. Leave the compass just outside the turning point.	⑤ Magnetize iron filings at the south end of the magnet.	⑥ Move iron filings toward the compass until the needle turns. Measure the distance between the test tube and the compass.
⑦ Reverse the magnet and magnetize iron filings at the south end.	⑧ Replace the magnet and repeat steps 3 and 4, leaving the compass just inside the turning point.	⑨ Move the compass along the line until the needle turns. Measure the distance between the test tube and the compass.

17.2 ▪ Investigation
Earthquakes and Subduction Zones

OBJECTIVES

- State a hypothesis about the relative ages of the crust at two convergent boundaries.
- Use earthquake data to construct profiles of two convergent boundaries
- Compare the behavior of two subducting plates.

PROCESS SKILLS

communicate, use numbers, interpret data, form hypotheses

TIME ALLOTMENT

1 class

MATERIALS

calculators (30)

PREPARATION

- Students should work individually.
- If students are unfamiliar with best-fit curves, demonstrate how to draw a straight line through a set of scattered points to make the trend clear. Point out that, because of measurement error, scattered data points are not necessarily a truer indication of the shape of the boundary than the best-fit curve. In reality, a subducted plate does not descend in a perfectly straight line.

Possible Hypothesis

The longitudes suggest that the Tonga Trench is farther from the East Pacific Rise than the Peru-Chile Trench. Therefore, the East Pacific Rise material at the Tonga Trench is older than that at the Peru-Chile Trench.

PROCEDURE

- Point out that because earthquakes generally originate at the surface of the subducting plate in a subduction zone, a study of the depth of the epicenters of many earthquakes can reveal the shape of the subduction zone.
- The possible hypothesis will be confirmed if the profile of the Tonga Trench is steeper than that of the Peru-Chile Trench, showing that the material is denser and cooler.

DATA AND OBSERVATIONS

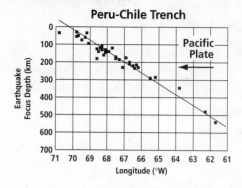

Peru-Chile Trench

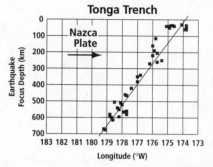

Tonga Trench

ANALYZE

1. 6500 km; about 200 million years
2. 675 km; 0.34 cm/year
3. The distance between the East Pacific Rise and the Peru-Chile Trench is ~4500 km, so it took 150 million years for the material to reach the trench if the rate of spreading was 3 cm/year. 540 km deep ÷ 150 million years = 0.39 cm/year.
4. The South American Plate is on the right. The Nazca Plate is on the left and is moving toward the right.
5. The Australian Plate is on the left. The Pacific Plate is on the right and is moving toward the left.

CHECK YOUR HYPOTHESIS

Answers will vary depending on students' hypotheses.

CONCLUDE AND APPLY

1. The Tonga Trench has a steeper profile and therefore contains denser, older material.
2. Answers will vary. Sample answer: A subduction profile and the rate of seafloor spreading indicate that the Tonga Trench contains older East Pacific Rise material than the Peru-Chile Trench does. However, Tonga material appears to sink more slowly. This may indicate that the South American Plate and the Australian Plate are different in composition or that the earthquake data are not comprehensive. Our hypothesis is supported, but could be strengthened by dating the rocks with an independent method.

18.1 ▪ Design Your Own
Modeling Lava Flow

OBJECTIVES
- Model the geologic processes associated with lava flows.
- Collect data on the structure of a model lava flow.

PROCESS SKILLS
observe, recognize and use spatial relationships, measure, experiment, interpret data, formulate models

TIME ALLOTMENT
2–3 class periods

POSSIBLE MATERIALS

dry cake mix (6 boxes)	plastic wrap (1 large roll)
water	wooden shims and
buckets with pouring	wedges (24 of each;
spouts (6)	4 sets for each group)
wire whisks (6)	protractors (6)
coffee tins with a 2-cm	plumb lines (6)
circular hole in the	stopwatches (6)
bottom (6)	metric rulers (6)
large spatulas (6)	toothpicks (1 large box)
wooden boards,	masking tape (1 large roll)
1 m × 2 m (6)	aprons (30)
paper (30 sheets; 1 sheet	safety goggles (30)
for each student)	

SAFETY PRECAUTIONS
- Have students wipe up spills immediately.
- Inform students that the hole in the bottom of the coffee tin may have sharp edges that can cut skin.

DISPOSAL
Do not pour used cake mix down the drain. Collect it in buckets and dispose of it in the trash.

PREPARATION
Students should work in groups of four.

Possible Hypothesis

A flow on a steep slope is faster, longer, thinner, and shallower than a flow on a gentle slope. A less viscous medium has an effect like that of a steeper slope. Structures are likely to develop more complexity and relief in slower flows.

PLAN THE EXPERIMENT
Troubleshooting
- The width measurements should be taken as close as possible to the moment that the head of the flow passes one of the 10-cm lines on the board.
- The viscosity of the "lava" should be the same for each slope. It may be necessary to add a little water and to remix the material between runs.

Possible Procedures

Tape paper to a board and draw a 10-cm grid on it. The first horizontal line will be the starting line. Cover the board with plastic wrap. Whip up a fairly smooth cake batter in a bucket. Use a plumb line, protractor, and wedges to prop the board at an angle of 15°. Block the hole in a coffee can and fill it nearly to the top with cake mix. Start the stopwatch as the flow passes the zero line. As the flow passes the 10-cm and 20-cm lines, record the time, the width of the flow at the 10-cm line, and the center depth at the 10-cm line.

Repeat these measurements as the flow passes each subsequent 10-cm line. Adjust the angle of the board to 25° and to 35°, repeating the process. To check the effects of viscosity, run again at the same angles, using thicker or thinner batter.

DATA AND OBSERVATIONS
Students should collect data in tables for width and time and for depth and time at each flow distance. They will collect data for three angles at a constant viscosity and for one or more of the same angles with different viscosities. Diagrams should show cross sections and details of the flow structures.

ANALYZE
1. The flow grew longer. The width of the flow increased at each point behind the head of the flow, getting wider with increasing distance from the head of the flow. The depth also increased.
2. A flow channel develops in the center. Levees are at the sides of the flow, starting some distance behind the head. Shear zones appear where a levee meets the main flow. Shear zones may give rise to ridges.
3. The flow is faster on a steeper slope and with less viscous lava. The rates of growth of the width and depth of the flow decrease with increasing slope. Pouring rate varied with viscosity, but was kept as constant as possible for different slopes.

CHECK YOUR HYPOTHESIS
Answers will vary depending on students' hypotheses.

CONCLUDE AND APPLY
1. Answers will vary. Sample answer: The slope of the model incline is like that of a volcano. Flow speed, viscosity of material, and shape of flow are similar, but differ in scale. The consistency, composition, and temperature of the medium are not represented.
2. Shield volcanoes have wider, deeper, shorter flows than cinder-cone and composite volcanoes if the total volume of lava is the same.

18.2 ▪ Investigation
Analyzing Volcanic-Disaster Risk

OBJECTIVES

- Assess the probability of a volcanic disaster.
- Investigate the feasibility of an insurance policy against volcanic disaster.

PROCESS SKILLS

classify, use numbers, interpret data, predict

TIME ALLOTMENT

1 class period

MATERIALS

Tables 1 and 2 (included in lab)
calculators (30)

PREPARATION

- Students should work individually.
- Spend some time reviewing probability.

PROCEDURE

Allow students to discuss the questions with one another.

DATA AND OBSERVATIONS

All questions should be answered using the data provided in Tables 1 and 2.

ANALYZE

1. 16 eruptions/10 000 years = 1.6×10^{-3}
2. 8 eruptions/10 000 years = 8×10^{-4}
3. 1 eruption/100 000 years = 1×10^{-5}
4. 80 eruptions
5. 80 eruptions/10 000 years = 8×10^{-3}
6. 49 eruptions/10 000 years = 4.9×10^{-3}; annual cost = \$490 000
7. 20 eruptions/10 000 years = 2×10^{-3}; annual cost = \$2 million
8. 10 eruptions/10 000 years = 1×10^{-3}; annual cost = \$10 million
9. 8 eruptions/100 000 years = 8×10^{-5}; annual cost = \$8 million
10. Total annual cost is about \$20 million. The adjusted cost is \$2 billion.

CONCLUDE AND APPLY

1. The statistics may be incomplete, leading one to underestimate the annual probability, or there may be more eruptions than average.
2. adjusted annual cost = \$6 billion; premium = \$6 billion/\$2 million = \$3000
3. 90% (\$6 billion = \$5.4 billion; 10% × 2 million people = 200 000 people; \$5.4 billion/200 000 people = \$2.7 million/person)
4. Volcanic disasters are rare, and their timing is very uncertain. When they do happen, they are very expensive. The costs are dominated by large eruptions that may occur only once every 1000 years. Overall, premiums would be too costly to be a practical investment.

19.1 ▪ Investigation
Predicting Earthquakes

OBJECTIVES
- Analyze the locations, magnitudes, and depths of recent earthquakes.
- Predict where earthquakes are most likely to occur next few weeks.

PROCESS SKILLS
classify, communicate, recognize and use spatial relationships, predict, use numbers, interpret data

TIME ALLOTMENT
2 class periods, separated by a week

MATERIALS
computer with Internet access
fine-point pens, 6 different colors (90; 15 of each color)

PREPARATION
- Students should work in pairs.
- If computer access is restricted, print the lists before class and photocopy them for each pair of students.

PROCEDURE
The more points that are plotted, the more statistically significant students' predictions will be. The web site typically has data for several hundred earthquakes, however, so you probably will need to limit the number of plotted points. It is recommended that students plot at least 150 points.

DATA AND OBSERVATIONS
Students' data should be similar to those given here. The location of students' 5° × 5° area is likely to be in the Pacific Ring of Fire.

Table 1

	Actual Earthquakes		Predicted Earthquakes in the 5° x 5° Area	
	Number of Earthquakes	Percentage of Earthquakes	Predicted Earthquakes	Actual Earthquakes
Richter Magnitude				
<4	0	0	0	0
4–4.9	72	24	0.5	1
5–5.9	41	14	0.3	1
6–6.9	3	1	0	0
7–7.9	0	0	0	0
>8	0	0	0	0
No data	182	61	1.2	1
Depth (km)				
0–50	221	74	1.5	2
51–100	22	7	0.2	0
101–150	21	7	0.2	1
151–200	8	3	0	0
>200	21	7	0.2	0
No data	5	2	0	0

ANALYZE
1. Sample answer: 15.4 days; 298 earthquakes ÷ 15.4 days = 19.4 earthquakes/day.
2. Sample answer: 5 earthquakes in the 5° × 5° area ÷ 15.4 days = 0.3 earthquakes/day.
3. Sample answer: 2 earthquakes; this prediction is based on the earthquake rate: 0.3 earthquakes/day × 7 days = 2.1 earthquakes.
4. See Table 1.

CONCLUDE AND APPLY
1. Most earthquakes occur near tectonic plate boundaries.
2. Answers will vary. In the sample data, the predictions are statistically accurate.

19.2 ▪ Design Your Own
Earthquake News Report

OBJECTIVES

- Address the issues involved in communicating technical ideas to a popular audience.
- Make a team presentation about earthquakes.
- Critique technical presentations in a constructive way.

PROCESS SKILLS

communicate, interpret scientific information

TIME ALLOTMENT

3–5 class periods

POSSIBLE MATERIALS

research resources about earthquakes
overhead projector
poster boards
drawing supplies
printer paper

PREPARATION

Students should work in groups of five.

Possible Hypotheses

Important concerns might include three of these objectives: Make the presentation interesting. Explicitly state premises for an argument. Make logical deductions clear and simple. Draw clear analogies to everyday experience. Illustrate abstract ideas with relevant examples. Convey how well-founded a concept or numerical value is. Use appropriate emphasis for the conclusion. Use clear graphics to illustrate difficult ideas.

PLAN THE EXPERIMENT

- Have students watch an earthquake documentary or assign them to read a magazine article about earthquakes. Discuss the material, focusing on structure of the article or documentary, communication techniques, and depth of technical treatment.
- Suggest possible research resources.
- Set a time limit for presentations, at least 10–15 minutes. Schedule (at least) one class meeting for presentations. If you have the equipment, videotape the presentations.

Possible Procedures

The team sets the task, assigns roles, and discusses individual research responsibilities. Each person will write his or her part of the script, incorporating research results. The members of the team organize the presentation, deciding who speaks in what order. They organize the script, cutting or expanding it to fit the time limit. They agree on visual aids and then produce them. They rehearse the presentation, and they all show up on the day of the event.

DATA AND OBSERVATIONS

Each presentation should demonstrate that the teams researched various aspects and characteristics of earthquakes. Each student's role within a presentation should vary, indicating individual understanding of earthquakes.

ANALYZE

Students' notes will vary, but should cover all the other teams' presentations. Students should include comments on content, emphasis, and clarity.

CHECK YOUR HYPOTHESIS

Answers will vary depending on students' hypotheses.

CONCLUDE AND APPLY

1. Transcripts and illustrations will vary, but each should accurately reflect the dialogue and visual aids used in that student's presentation.
2. Students' reviews will vary, but each review should offer a critical appraisal of each presentation, using constructive language.
3. Answers will vary, but should reflect the lessons learned about scientific communication.

20.1 ▪ Investigation
Plate Tectonics of North America

OBJECTIVES
- Identify the major plates associated with North America and their movements.
- Describe the locations and orientations of major mountain chains of North America.
- Explain how geologic evidence supports the theory of plate tectonics.
- Predict how future tectonic processes might affect the North American continent.

PROCESS SKILLS
infer, communicate, recognize and use spatial relationships, predict, interpret data

TIME ALLOTMENT
3 class periods

MATERIALS
red, blue, and orange markers (30 of each color)

PREPARATION
- Students should work individually to complete their maps.
- Review map-reading skills and the basic processes involved with tectonism.

PROCEDURE
Have students work in small groups to discuss the questions and present a brief tectonic history.

DATA AND OBSERVATIONS
Answers to Procedure questions:

1–3.

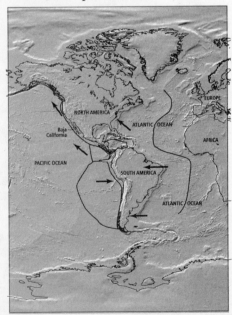

5. The North American Plate's leading edge is the northwest coast; its trailing edge is the southeast coast.
6. subsea faults
7. Examples of boundaries associated with North America include the convergent boundary along the west coast of North America; the divergent boundary east of North America; and the transform boundary called the San Andreas Fault.

ANALYZE
1. Answers will vary. Sample answer: The Mid-Atlantic Ridge is associated with seafloor spreading and the westward movement of the North American plate. Trenches along the western coasts of the Americas form as the result of subduction of the Pacific Plate.
2. northwest
3. The major mountain systems are along the eastern and western margins of the continent and are generally oriented in a north-south direction.
4. In the past, tectonic plates interacted with the North American Plate to produce the major mountain ranges present on the continent.
5. Forces were from the south-southeast.
6. Answers will vary. Sample answer: the Pacific Plate, the San Andreas Fault, volcanoes, earthquakes, and subsea faults
7. The peninsula might break off from the continent.

CONCLUDE AND APPLY
1. Answers will vary. Sample answer: The North American Plate is moving to the northwest relative to the Pacific Plate. The North American Plate and the African Plate are moving away from each other. The Pacific Plate is moving northwest against the western margin of North America and forms a transform boundary—the San Andreas Fault. The Appalachians formed when the North American Plate converged with the African Plate. Convergence between the North American Plate and the Pacific Plate played an important role in the formation of the Rocky Mountains. The deep-sea trenches along the western coast of North America result from the Pacific Plate being subducted beneath the North American Plate. The volcanic mountains of the Cascade Range (including Mount Rainier, Mount Shasta, and Mount Saint Helens) and of the Sierra Nevada were produced in part by volcanic activity associated with the subduction of an oceanic plate under the continental plate. Earthquakes are produced by friction as descending plates scrape beneath overriding slabs.

20.2 ▪ Mapping
Analysis of Geologic Maps

OBJECTIVES

- Identify structural elements of the North American continent by rock age and type.
- Describe the tectonic forces that have shaped the mountain ranges of North America.
- Describe some of the geologic characteristics of the Appalachian and Rocky Mountain systems.
- Compare the tectonic history of some of the major mountain chains of North America.

PROCESS SKILLS

classify, infer, recognize and use spatial relationships, interpret scientific illustrations

TIME ALLOTMENT

2 class periods

MATERIALS

map D from Lab 20.1 on page 155
markers, 8 different colors (30 of each color)

PREPARATION

- Students should work individually to complete their maps.
- Review map-reading skills and legend interpretation.
- Provide students with copies of the geologic time scale.

PROCEDURE

- Students may work in small groups for interpretation and discussion purposes.
- Have groups present their conclusions to the class. Then analyze and discuss them as a class.

DATA AND OBSERVATIONS

Plate movements that are associated with the tectonic history of the North American continent include the convergence of the African and North American plates 350 million years before present, which crumpled sediments to produce the Appalachian Mountain system; the separation of the North American and African plates 180 million years before present, which produced the North Atlantic Ocean; and the ongoing subduction of the Pacific and Juan de Fuca plates under the North American plate, which produced the Rocky Mountain system.

ANALYZE

1. sedimentary deposits
2. The shield areas are pink and green. Arrows should follow the direction of the curves.

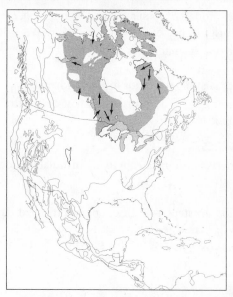

3. The central craton and the Atlantic and Gulf coastal plains are composed of large areas of undeformed sedimentary deposits, which are called platform deposits. The Appalachian and Rocky Mountain ranges are the result of complex tectonic activity.
4. Arrows should run in a northwesterly direction.

CONCLUDE AND APPLY

1. The Appalachian system was produced by the collision of North America and Northern Africa, which resulted in some volcanic activity, faulting, and the folding of flat-lying beds of sedimentary rocks. The formation of the Rocky Mountains is the result of the subduction of the Pacific and Juan de Fuca plates under the continental plate and the faulting, uplift, and volcanic activity associated with those movements.

2. Answers will vary. Sample answer: In general, the Appalachians are older; they were formed as the result of convergence. Extensive folding and faulting of rocks resulted. A Paleozoic basement with sedimentary deposits formed on the southeast margin of the Appalachians. The Rocky Mountains are still active. The Rockies include large areas of volcanic and plutonic rocks. Sedimentary deposits are in structurally negative areas and mildly folded. The chain of volcanoes along the western margin of North America is associated with current tectonic plate activity. The Basin and Range system, the Tetons, and the Sierra Nevada Mountains were produced by faulting.

21.1 ▪ Investigation
Fossilization and Earth's History

OBJECTIVES

- Construct models of fossils formed by molding, casting, and original preservation.
- Compare the characteristics of different types of fossils.
- Construct possible scenarios for fossil formation.
- Evaluate the quality of information that comes from the fossil record.

PROCESS SKILLS

observe, infer, communicate, predict, formulate models

TIME ALLOTMENT

1 class period for steps 1–3; 1 class period the next day for steps 4–7; 1 class period the next day for steps 8–10; and 1 class period 4 days later for step 11 and the lab questions

MATERIALS

seashells (10)
petroleum jelly (1 large jar)
plaster of Paris (1 bag)
water (2 gallons)
plastic spoons (20)
food coloring (1 bottle)
paper cups (40)
grapes (20)
marking pens (10)
freezer

dead, unsquashed, hard-bodied insect (such as beetles or ants) (10)
waxed paper, about 10-cm square (10 pieces)
liquid glue (1 large bottle)
gloves (30 pairs)
aprons (30)
safety goggles (30)

SAFETY PRECAUTIONS

Make sure you have a Material Safety Data Sheet (MSDS) for the glue and plaster of Paris.

PREPARATION

- Students should work in groups of three.
- Put some grapes in the freezer 1 week before beginning the lab and look at them on the first day. Then the lab could be done in 3 days.
- Arrange for access to a freezer for the grapes part of the lab.

Alternative Materials
Use clear resin instead of liquid glue.

PROCEDURE

Have students collect enough hard-shelled insects for each group to have one.

DATA AND OBSERVATIONS

The first diagram should show an impression of the shell in the plaster of Paris. The second should show the colored block of plaster with a shell-shaped bump on it.

ANALYZE

1. The plaster is hard and rocklike.
2. sediments that were deposited after the shell dissolved
3. The first (white plaster) is a mold; the second is a cast.
4. an impression of both sides of the complete shell
5. Answers will vary. Sample answer: Sticky sap traps an insect, which is covered with additional sap. The sap hardens around the insect, preserving it from decomposition.
6. The frozen grape looks about the same. The grape that was left out will probably be shriveled and may have mold on it.

CONCLUDE AND APPLY

1. Casts and molds show only the surface characteristics of life-forms. Original preservation can provide information about internal as well as external characteristics, and both hard and soft tissue.
2. quick burial and the formation of sedimentary layers of rock
3. Very low temperatures preserve substances such as fruit and meat because they slow down or prevent the growth of decay organisms. Thus the low temperature of frozen mud preserves dead organisms. Mud may also form a protective coating around the remains of an organism and discourage scavengers and decomposers.
4. Except for exceptional cases such as freezing and mummification, most of the time only bones and teeth are preserved. Soft tissues, such as skin, hair, and internal organs, would be missing. Pictures will vary but should show only half a skeleton.
5. quickly covered by sediments that harden into rock; trapped in tar, amber, ice, or freezing mud; or buried in dry sand or caves
6. Answers will vary. Sample answer: Fossil formation is uncommon for some organisms, and most fossils would be formed in dry, sandy regions, in sediments on the ocean floor, in polar ice, or in tar pits or other oxygen-free environments. These places would not provide a representative sample of the world's population.

21.2 ▪ Design Your Own
Analysis of a Climate-Change Time Line Using Planktonic Foraminifera

OBJECTIVES

- Identify right-coiling and left-coiling *Neogloboquadrina pachyderma*.
- Plan and carry out a study of climatic change using *N. pachyderma* as an indicator of temperature change.
- Gather microfossil data and plot them on a graph.
- Interpret the climatic history of Earth during the last 160 000 years.

PROCESS SKILLS

observe, classify, infer, use numbers, interpret data, form hypotheses

TIME ALLOTMENT

2 class periods

POSSIBLE MATERIALS

representations of microfossil samples, from the present to 160 000 years ago (10 sets)
calculators (30)

PREPARATION

- Students should work in groups of three.
- Enlarge, copy, and laminate Figure 1 on the next page, and cut the pictures apart to represent a collection of microfossils. You could also download the pictures from a web site.
- For each group, prepare 16 sample envelopes, labeled 0–9 999, 10 000–19 999, etc., of microfossil samples representing one of the time periods—at 10 000-year intervals—from the present to 160 000 years ago.

Possible Hypothesis

The percentage of right-coiling *N. pachyderma* in each sample can be calculated and plotted on a graph. This graph will indicate any climate changes from 160 000 years ago to the present. To determine if a sample is left-coiling or right-coiling, begin at the smallest part of the shell, farthest from the opening, and follow the shell's direction to the outermost part.

PLAN THE EXPERIMENT

- Review the concept of microfossils as indicator organisms, the method of calculating percentage, and identification of the right-coiling and left-coiling *N. pachyderma*.
- The students are only looking for left- and right-coiling *N. pachyderma*. The other forams in the samples are included to simulate what might be found in a real sample.
- Tell students that each picture of a microfossil represents five microfossils for the purpose of the chart. For

example, envelope 1 might contain 46 right-coiling, 10 left-coiling, and random quantities of miscellaneous microfossils. Entries in the chart would be five times those numbers, or 230 right-coiling and 50 left-coiling.

- The sample envelopes should contain the numbers of right- and left-coiling *N. pachyderma*, as listed in the table in Data and Observations, for each time period (divided by 5), with random quantities of other fossils. The correct percentages are given in the table in Data and Observations under the heading "% Right-Coiling."

Possible Procedures

Order the samples chronologically from 0 to 160 000 years ago. Separate the *N. pachyderma* from each sample, count the number of right-coiling and left-coiling shells, and record these numbers in a table. Calculate and record the total number of *N. pachyderma* and the percentage of right-coiling shells. Make a line graph of the data. Interpret the graph in terms of climate change.

DATA AND OBSERVATIONS

Left-coiling *N. pachyderma*: samples 7, 8, 11
Right-coiling *N. pachyderma*: samples 9, 10, 21, 22

Sample Table

Age (years ago)	# Right-Coiling *N. pachyderma*	# Left-Coiling *N. pachyderma*	Total *N. pachyderma*	% Right-Coiling *N. pachyderma*
0–9 999	230	50	280	82
10 000–19 999	220	75	295	75
20 000–29 999	70	230	300	23
30 000–39 999	45	300	345	13
40 000–49 999	50	300	350	14
50 000–59 999	65	390	455	14
60 000–69 999	20	140	160	13
70 000–79 999	55	285	340	16
80 000–89 999	60	265	325	18
90 000–99 999	210	55	265	79
100 000–109 999	120	20	140	89
110 000–119 999	85	45	130	65
120 000–129 999	205	70	275	75
130 000–139 999	55	205	260	21
140 000–149 999	45	330	375	12
150 000–160 000	90	1352	225	40

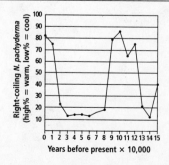

Lab 21.2, *continued*

ANALYZE

1. The percentage of right-coiling and left-coiling *N. pachyderma* provides evidence of the variable temperature of the ocean.

2. No; the temperature changes are inferences based on traits of the foraminifera in the samples.

3. The cycles are not even, but the temperature falls and rises consistently, with one time span of fairly level readings.

4. Answers will vary. The intervals on each axis should be equal.

5. The visual display of data helps show the variation in climate.

CHECK YOUR HYPOTHESIS

Answers will vary depending on students' hypotheses.

CONCLUDE AND APPLY

1. Answers will vary but should include statements about the wide fluctuations in climate, based on the microfossil evidence.

2. The differing percentages of right-coiling and left-coiling *N. pachyderma*

3. no

4. in a warming phase

5. Answers will vary. Sample answer: Droughts in some places are caused by a decrease in meltwater from smaller amounts of mountain and glacial snow. Older people remember deeper snow cover and longer winters during their childhood.

6. Answers will vary. Sample answer: The climate will continue to warm for thousands of years, rising at least to the highest previous estimate of the average temperature. This rise would continue the pattern shown in the graph for the last 160 000 years.

Figure 1

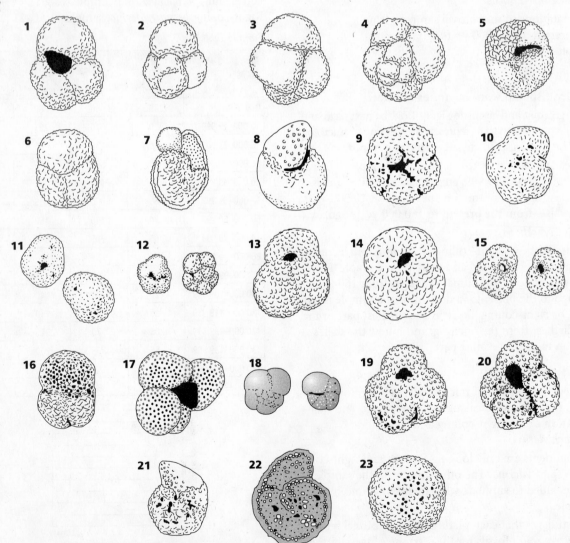

22.1 ▪ Investigation
Sequencing Time

OBJECTIVES

- Compare the proportionate length of a human life to that of Earth.
- Calculate the scale at which Earth's history can be graphically compared to a human lifetime.
- Analyze the timing and scope of the evolution and diversification of life on Earth.

PROCESS SKILLS

use numbers, interpret data, infer, communicate

TIME ALLOTMENT

1 class period

MATERIALS

pencils (30)
2.5-m long rolls of paper (30)
calculators (30)
metersticks (30)

PREPARATION

- Students should work individually.
- Review the geologic time scale with students. Point out that in most versions, the Precambrian is graphically collapsed. Ask students why this is common.

PROCEDURE

Monitor students' progress as they are completing the time scales. Create your own personal time scale on the chalkboard, displaying your calculations to help students understand the process.

DATA AND OBSERVATIONS

Students will develop an accurate geologic time scale showing a full-scale representation of the Precambrian. Students will develop a parallel and proportionate personal time scale that will allow them to better conceptualize the age of Earth and the timing of the evolution of various living things.

ANALYZE

1. About 88 percent of Earth's existence occurred during the Precambrian.
2. Answers will vary; for a student who is 15 years, 8 months old, nearly 14 years of his or her life is proportional to length of the Precambrian.
3. Bacteria have been alive for about 85 percent of Earth's existence.

CONCLUDE AND APPLY

1. No; life arose relatively early, but diversification recorded in this fossil record occurred in the latter part of Earth's total history.
2. Answers will vary. For the typical 15.75-year-old, the length of time humans have been alive is proportional to 2.5 days.

22.2 ▪ Mapping
What came first?

OBJECTIVES

- Represent life-forms that appeared during different periods of Earth's history, beginning with the Precambrian.
- Relate time to the number and complexity of organisms on Earth.
- Describe how information about the Precambrian can be used to analyze planetary materials in the search for life elsewhere in the universe.

PROCESS SKILLS

observe, classify, infer, communicate, predict, interpret data

TIME ALLOTMENT

1 class period

MATERIALS

geologic time scale
event cards (30)

PREPARATION

- Students should work individually.
- Make a geologic time scale from adding-machine tape or strips of vinyl or card stock glued or stapled together. You will need a length of 25.5 yards. Prepare the time scale using a scale of 1 inch = 5 million years. The time scale begins 4.6 billion years ago (b.y.b.p.). Mark this at the left end of the time scale. Place the following information at the distances indicated: 120″ from the left end, 4 b.y.b.p.: 240″, 3 b.y.b.p.; 480″, 2 b.y.b.p.; 720″, 1 b.y.b.p.; 802″, 590 million years before present (m.y.b.p.); 872″, 240 m.y.b.p.; 907″, 65 m.y.b.p.; 920″, Recent.
- Prepare 8.5″ × 12″ event cards, using enlargements of the illustrations on the next page. On three cards, write "Permian Mass Extinction Event," "Drastic Geographic and Climatic Changes," and "Cretaceous-Paleogene Mass Extinction Event." You could label the cards with the ages listed in Table 1 or have students refer to the table to find their own times.
- If you have more than 24 students, either create more event cards or plan to have students announce geologic time or check correct event placement on the time scale.

PROCEDURE

- Hang the time scale around the room. Discuss the time periods, and have students identify and label the Precambrian, Paleozoic, Mesozoic, and Cenozoic.
- Have each student pick an event card. Explain that each card represents the first evidence of an organism in the fossil record or the occurrence of a particular event during Earth's history. As each approximate geologic time (beginning with 3 b.y.b.p.) is announced, the student representing that organism or event should stand in front of the time scale at the place that represents that age.

DATA AND OBSERVATIONS

Precambrian time lasted from 4.6 b.y.b.p. to 540 m.y.b.p. (last event in the table is ediacara organisms). The Paleozoic era lasted until 250 m.y.b.p. (last event is the Permian Mass Extinction Event). The Mesozoic Era lasted until 66 m.y.b.p. (last event is ants). We are currently living in the Cenozoic Era (last event is *Australopithecus afarensis* "Lucy").

ANALYZE

1. Proterozoic Eon, Paleozoic Era, Mesozoic Era, Cenozoic Era
2. Beginning of the scale to ~802″ = Proterozoic Eon (including the Precambrian); ~802″ to ~872″ = Paleozoic Era; ~872″ to ~907″ = Mesozoic Era; ~907″ to ~920″ = Cenozoic Era
3. The Precambrian is the longest and oldest period. The Cenozoic Era is the shortest and most recent.
4. Answers will vary. Sample answer: The Precambrian is the oldest period and contains very few life-forms and long periods when nothing happened, while the Cenozoic Era is the most recent period and contains many life-forms. The Precambrian began with an atmosphere without oxygen and without oceans; it ended with minimal life. The Cenozoic Era is the result of 4.6 billion years of evolution, during which the addition of oxygen to the atmosphere and other geologic and climatic changes provided an environment for the development of many diverse life-forms.

CONCLUDE AND APPLY

1. It made life possible for oxygen-breathing animals and produced the ozone layer that filters ultraviolet radiation.
2. Answers will vary and may include observations about the vastness of time that makes up the Precambrian, differences in the presence of life throughout Earth's history, and the steady buildup (with extinctions) in number and complexity of living things.
3. Answers will vary and may include the notion that the discovery of organisms similar to cyanobacteria and green algae might indicate the presence of early life-forms similar to those of Earth, and of oxygen in the atmosphere.

Lab 22.2, *continued*

Illustrations for Event Cards

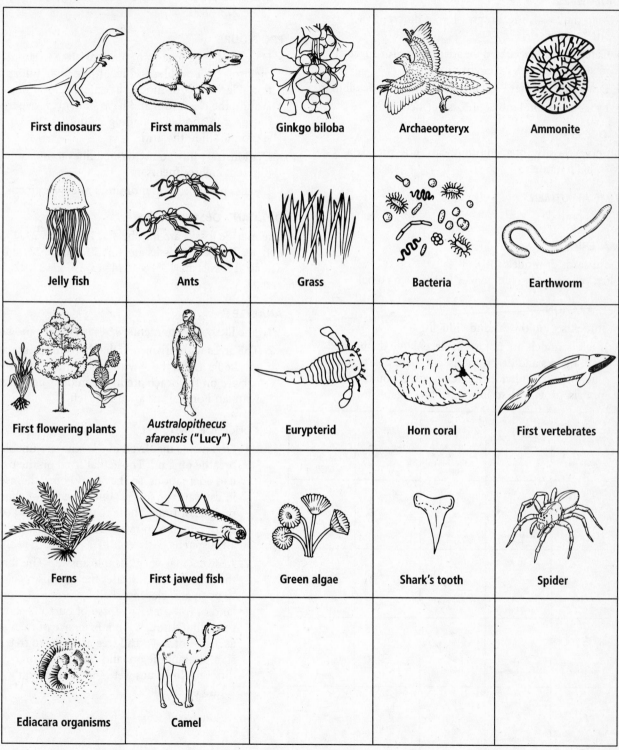

First dinosaurs	First mammals	Ginkgo biloba	Archaeopteryx	Ammonite
Jelly fish	Ants	Grass	Bacteria	Earthworm
First flowering plants	*Australopithecus afarensis* ("Lucy")	Eurypterid	Horn coral	First vertebrates
Ferns	First jawed fish	Green algae	Shark's tooth	Spider
Ediacara organisms	Camel			

23.1 ▪ Mapping
Water to Land

OBJECTIVES

- Map the fossils in a progression of different environments.
- Categorize fossils based on adaptations for survival in sea, beach, or land environments.
- Draw the boundaries of environments on a fossil map.
- Defend interpretations of fossil evidence.

PROCESS SKILLS

observe, classify, infer, communicate, interpret data, formulate models

TIME ALLOTMENT

1 class period

MATERIALS

fossil cards or models (30)
blue, yellow, and green pencils (30 of each color)

PREPARATION

- Students should work individually.
- If fossil models are not available, enlarge the printed fossil figures and descriptions, cut them apart, and glue them on individual index cards. If you use fossil models, provide descriptions of the organisms.

- Hands-on fossil kits available for loan can be obtained from Library GEO Center, U.S. Geological Survey, Denver, CO, (303) 236-1015, or the Geology Museum at the Colorado School of Mines, Golden, CO, (303) 273-3823.

PROCEDURE

- Have students move from place to place to simulate the process of finding and recording fossil information. Place cards or models at different locations around the classroom and have students move from one desk to another, spending 2 minutes at each station to fill in the grid.
- Demonstrate how to use dashed lines to indicate different environments.
- Discuss possible fossil indicators of environment.

DATA AND OBSERVATIONS

The marine fossils are numbers 5, 10, 15, 20, 24, 25, 29, and 30. The beach fossils are 4, 9, 14, 18, 19, 23, and 28. The land fossils are 1–3, 6–8, 11–13, 16, 17, 21, 22, 26, and 27.

ANALYZE

1. The likely environments were sea, beach, and land.
2. The areas with organisms that lived in the sea are on the far right, those with organisms that could survive on the beach are in the middle, and those with land organisms are on the left.

CONCLUDE AND APPLY

1. Organisms that lived in the sea were unable to breathe on land. Those that lived on the beach had adaptations, so they could bury themselves in wet sand or survive out of water for short periods of time. Those that lived on land could carry out all respiratory functions in Earth's atmosphere.
2. Answers may vary. Sample answer: The shape of the clam fossils indicates the organism's ability to open and close its shell for protection on land or in water. The fossil of burrows shows a tunneling through land. Evidence of trees such as fossils of the cycad tree and gingko tree is a sign of plant life on land. The footprint of a dinosaur indicates wet sand as commonly found on beaches.

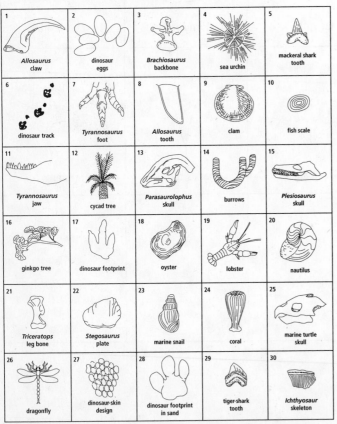

23.2 ▪ Investigation
Searching for Oil with Microfossils

OBJECTIVES

- Identify eight species of fossil benthic foraminifera and their preferred ocean habitats.
- Analyze diagrams of foraminifera samples for water-depth range.
- Infer water depths in the basin.
- Use water depth to predict where to find potential source rock and reservoir rock.

PROCESS SKILLS

classify, infer, recognize and use spatial relationships, predict, interpret data

TIME ALLOTMENT

1 class period

MATERIALS

colored pencils (60)

PREPARATION

- Students may work in groups of two or three but should complete their own maps.
- Briefly review the concepts of preferred habitat and sampling locations.

PROCEDURE

Go over the idea of downslope transportation and identification of the deepest-dwelling forms to represent the true water depth.

DATA AND OBSERVATIONS

Figure 2

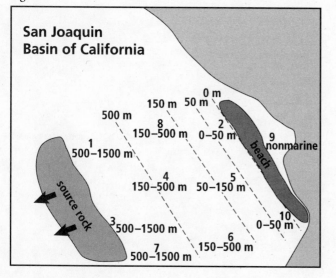

ANALYZE

1. Answers may vary. Sample answer: Sample 9 may have been a beach during the geologic past; therefore, benthic organisms would not have lived there.
2. Samples 1, 3, 4, 5, 6, 7, 8

CONCLUDE AND APPLY

1. Zero water depth and the absence of fossil foraminifera indicate that this location was probably dry sand, a beach.
2. samples 2 and 10
3. Answers may vary. Sample answer: Water depths at the locations of sample 9 (0 m depth) and samples 2 and 10 (0–50 m depth) indicate a slope from dry land to 50 m. This is characteristic of a shoreline or beach. The beach line runs southeast and includes the area between samples 2, 10, and 9.
4. See map in Data and Observations.
5. west/southwest of the site of sample 3 because the water depth is greater than 1000 m
6. See map in Data and Observations.
7. Answers may vary, but should point out that the beach contains the kind of permeable material that is associated with reservoir rock. The nearby ancient water depth of more than 1000 m probably covered abundant organic material and silt and clay sediments, which are associated with source rock.

24.1 ▪ Mapping
Cenozoic Ice Sheets and Plant Distribution

OBJECTIVES

- Describe the distribution of different plant groups in North America at different times during the last ice age.
- Explain the relationship between changes in plant distribution and the extent of the Laurentian ice sheet.
- Make inferences about the relationship between plant distribution and climate change.

PROCESS SKILLS

observe, infer, recognize and use spatial relationships, measure, predict, form hypotheses

TIME ALLOTMENT

2 class periods

MATERIALS

fine-point colored markers or colored pencils
(30 of each of 10 colors; 300 total)
political map of North America

PREPARATION

- Students may work in groups of three, but should complete their own maps.
- Review map-reading skills and the concepts of pollen analysis and plant succession.

PROCEDURE

Encourage discussion about the relationship between the extent of the ice sheet and the distributions of the various types of plants and of the predictions for the western part of the United States

DATA AND OBSERVATIONS

Students' maps should accurately reflect the colors provided in the legend. The legend lists groups of plants starting with those that grow in the coldest climates and ending with the warmest weather plants.

ANALYZE

1. a. 18 ka
   b. 5; Tundra, Forest Tundra, Boreal Forest, Mixed Forest, Deciduous Forest
   c. 6 ka
   d. same as (b) plus Aspen Park, Prairie, and Southeast Forest
   e. As the climate got warmer, the ice sheet retreated and the number and type of plant groups increased.

2. a. Mixed Forest and Deciduous Forest
   b. The climate in the midwestern area had become warmer.
3. a. It is a subarctic climate, extremely cold and windy with much snow.
   b. Illinois, Iowa, and Missouri
   c. the North Atlantic and Central states

CONCLUDE AND APPLY

1. Answers will vary, but in general, students should place plant groups at the approximate distance from the ice sheet as they are in the eastern portion of North America. Students may explain that since the ice sheet did not extend as far south in the western portion of the continent as it did in the east, plant groups that were found in the southern portion of the continent at that time would be found farther north in the western portion.

24.2 ▪ Investigation
Index Fossils and Dinosaur Bones

OBJECTIVES

• Develop a hypothesis about a correlation between rock layers in Montana and western Canada.

• Identify rock layers that contain index fossils.

• Predict which rock layers in western Canada will contain the same kind of fossils as those in Montana.

PROCESS SKILLS

infer, predict, interpret data, form hypotheses

TIME ALLOTMENT

1 class period

MATERIALS

colored pencils (60)
index-fossil chart

PREPARATION

• Students may work in groups of three, but should complete their own correlations.

• Copy the chart of index fossils for each student.

• You might make a transparency of the answer chart to use in a class discussion at the end of the lab.

PROCEDURE

Teaching Strategies

Point out to students that since some fossils are few and far between, rock types are also used to correlate strata. Though knowing in which rocks certain fossils are found will help students, they will still need to make decisions, inferences, and predictions when correlating the strata.

Troubleshooting

Briefly review the concept of fossilization in sedimentary rock layers and the formulation of hypotheses.

DATA AND OBSERVATIONS

Students' hypotheses may vary. They should assign the dinosaur bone to the Canadian layer that they correlated with layer D.

ANALYZE

1. Answers will vary. Sample answer: Layers **g** and **j** do not correlate with other layers in Figure 2; in Figure 1, they correlated to **n** and **c**. So, the correlations for **f** through **c** all moved down a layer in Figure 2.

2. The correlations in Figure 2 because they are based on the occurrence of index fossils as well as rock characteristics.

CONCLUDE AND APPLY

1. Layer **l** because it has the same index fossils as layer **d** in Montana.

2. Layer **g** is younger. Layer **n** in western Canada correlates with layer **f** in Montana, and layer **f** is older than layer **g**.

3. No; layer **h** has no dinosaur index fossils. It shows only trilobites, which are found in layers that are much older than those in which dinosaurs are found.

Type of Rock	Montana		Western Canada	Type of Rock
	Bivalve (mussel)	g	n Gastropod	
	Gastropod	f	m Bivalve	
	Bivalve	e	l Cycad and dinosaur bone	
	Cycad and dinosaur bone	d	k Brachiopod	
	Brachiopod	c	j Nautiloid	
	Graptolite	b	i Graptolite	
	Trilobite	a	h Trilobite	

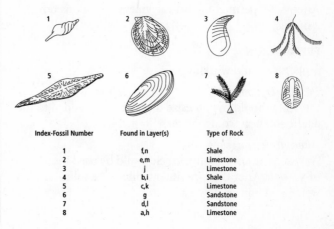

Index-Fossil Number	Found in Layer(s)	Type of Rock
1	f,n	Shale
2	e,m	Limestone
3	j	Limestone
4	b,i	Shale
5	c,k	Limestone
6	g	Sandstone
7	d,l	Sandstone
8	a,h	Limestone

25.1 ▪ Design Your Own
Neutralizing Acid Precipitation

OBJECTIVES

- Design an experiment to test the pH levels of two solutions.
- Determine how to neutralize an acidic solution.
- Compare and contrast an acidic solution and a neutralized solution.

PROCESS SKILLS

infer, communicate, interpret data, form hypotheses, separate and control variables

TIME ALLOTMENT

1 class period to set up the experiment; 15 minutes each day for 5 days to neutralize the acidic solution and to test and record the pH levels; 1 class period to plot data and analyze results

POSSIBLE MATERIALS

distilled water (8 liters)
powdered limestone (1 large bottle)
white vinegar (1 bottle)
baking soda (1 box)
250-mL glass beakers (30)
stirring rods (30)
measuring spoons (30)

droppers (15)
marking pens (15)
plastic wrap (1 roll)
pH paper (75 strips)
pH color charts (15)
gloves (30 pairs)
aprons (30)
safety goggles (30)

SAFETY PRECAUTIONS

- If any glassware breaks, have students notify you instead of cleaning up the glass themselves.
- Make sure all solutions have labels with content names and caution statements.
- Secure a Material Safety Data Sheet (MSDS) for hazardous chemicals.

DISPOSAL

After the experiment, pour the vinegar solutions down a drain.

PREPARATION

Students should work in pairs.

Possible Hypothesis
Students should hypothesize that limestone added to the acidic solution would decrease its acidity.

Alternative Materials
A weak solution of sulfuric acid could be used instead of vinegar. After the experiment, dilute the solution with water, and pour it down a drain.

PLAN THE EXPERIMENT

Troubleshooting
- Make sure that students use clean, dry stirring rods when they mix the solutions.
- Students will need to test the pH levels of the solutions 4 or more hours after they add the limestone to obtain accurate measurements.

Possible Procedures

Add a teaspoon of vinegar to the distilled water, stir the solution, and use the pH paper to test the acidity of the solution. If the pH level is below 4, add pinches of baking soda to the solution. If the pH level is above 4, add a drop or two of vinegar. When the pH level is properly adjusted, pour the solution into two beakers. Add the powdered limestone to one of the beakers, stir, and record the pH levels of both solutions. Label the beaker with the limestone in it. Cover the beakers with plastic wrap to prevent evaporation. Each day for 5 days, stir the solutions, and test and record the pH levels.

DATA AND OBSERVATIONS

Students should find that the acidity of the solution containing limestone steadily decreases over the course of the experiment, perhaps to as much as 6.0 pH, while the acidity of the control remains the same.

ANALYZE

1. The control was the solution with no limestone added. The independent variable was the limestone.
2. The addition of limestone decreased the acidity of the solution. It was effective because limestone is a basic substance with a high pH level—the limestone neutralized the acidic vinegar solution.
3. Answers will vary, but the pH level of the limestone/vinegar solution should steadily increase, while the pH level of the control remains the same.
4. The control should have the same pH level as a tomato. The pH level of the limestone/vinegar solution may be as high as 6, which is between the pH levels of unpolluted rain and milk.

CHECK YOUR HYPOTHESIS

Answers will vary depending on students' hypotheses.

CONCLUDE AND APPLY

1. The rainfall with the higher pH would not adversely affect vegetation and aquatic organisms because it has nearly the same pH as unpolluted rain. The acidic rainfall would likely affect functions in both the vegetation and the aquatic organisms.
2. Limestone can be added to the bodies of water to neutralize the acid rain.
3. It would be temporary. If more acid precipitation fell into the lake or pond, the acidity of the water would have to be readjusted.

25.2 ▪ Investigation
Water Usage

OBJECTIVES

- Analyze changing trends in water usage over a 40-year period.
- Determine which categories use the most water per day.
- Discuss conservation methods that might decrease water use.

PROCESS SKILLS

infer, use numbers, communicate, interpret data

TIME ALLOTMENT

1 class period

MATERIALS

calculators (30)

PREPARATION

- Students should work individually.
- Make sure that students understand that the category "Public supply" refers to county and city water departments, which serve local businesses and homes.

PROCEDURE

Have students keep a daily log of their water usage for a week. Have them review their logs and discuss ways to reduce their water use.

DATA AND OBSERVATIONS

Category	1950	1955	1960	1965	1970	1975	1980	1985	1990
Electricity	151	272	378	491	643	756	794	707	737
Irrigation	336	416	416	454	491	529	567	518	518
Industry	140	147	144	174	178	170	170	117	113
Public supply	53	64	79	91	102	110	129	140	147
Rural/ livestock	14	14	14	15	17	19	21	29	30

ANALYZE

1. Approximately 1542 billion liters of water were used each day in 1990. In 1950, around 680 billion liters of water were used daily.

2. Electricity increased water use the most. The increases are likely caused by a growing human population, which uses more electricity.

3. Industry showed a decrease in water usage. Students may reason that improved technology and tighter industry standards have contributed to the decrease. Accept all reasonable answers.

4. Water usage peaked in 1980. The categories of public supply and rural livestock have increased since then. These increases are likely caused by increased populations of people and livestock.

5. Electricity and irrigation consistently account for most water usage in the United States. In 1980, these two categories used approximately 1361 billion liters of water per day.

6. Answers will vary. Sample answer: Electricity: water used to generate power; irrigation: water used for plants; public supply: water used to drink and bathe; rural/livestock: water used for cattle; industry: water used to cool equipment. Accept all reasonable answers.

CONCLUDE AND APPLY

1. 1520 billion liters/day divided by 252 million people = 448 L/day/person

2. Answers may vary, but should closely match the data shown on the graph. Overall water usage has decreased slightly since 1980; however, it still remains much higher than pre-1970 water usage.

3. Answers will vary. Sample answers: As individuals, students could use less water to wash cars or water lawns, take shorter showers, and turn the water off when brushing their teeth. Governments could give incentives for industry to develop more efficient ways of using water to generate power or to manufacture products. Accept all reasonable answers.

26.1 ▪ Design Your Own
Solar Water-Heater

OBJECTIVES

See SE lab page 201.

PROCESS SKILLS

observe, infer, communicate, formulate models, form hypotheses, interpret data

TIME ALLOTMENT

2 class periods

POSSIBLE MATERIALS

water
black tubing (18 m)
shallow cardboard boxes,
   about 30 cm × 40 cm (6)
black construction paper
   (50 sheets)
clear plastic wrap (1 roll)
insulating materials
   (cotton, newspaper, cloth, etc.)

tape (6 rolls)
scissors (6 pairs)
alcohol-based
   thermometers (6)
clothespins (6)
clean plastic 2-L
   bottles (12)
safety goggles (30)

SAFETY PRECAUTIONS

- If a thermometer breaks, students should notify you instead of cleaning up the broken glass.
- Avoid using mercury-based thermometers. Mercury is toxic.
- Instruct students to use caution when handling sharp objects such as scissors.

DISPOSAL

Drain any remaining water in the tubing into the bottles and use it to water plants if possible.

PREPARATION

- Students should work in groups of five.
- Have students bring in empty plastic bottles and insulating materials, such as newspapers and cotton, the week before the activity.

Possible Hypothesis

The efficiency of the solar water-heater depends largely on the soundness of the design and the availability of sunlight.

PLAN THE EXPERIMENT

- Students should build the solar water-heaters near bright, sunny windows or outside in the Sun. If the sky is overcast, reschedule the activity.
- Fill up bottles with water and allow the water to reach room temperature before the lab starts.

Troubleshooting

For a steady flow of water, the empty container must be lower than the solar heater.

Possible Procedures

Students designs should resemble the figure below. If necessary, help students by suggesting this setup.

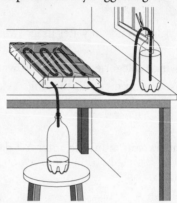

DATA AND OBSERVATIONS

Students should find that water temperature increases after the water passes through the black tubing in the solar heater, somewhere around 15°C after 30 minutes if conditions are good.

ANALYZE

1. Answers will vary. Water temperature should increase after the water goes through the heater.
2. Answers will vary. A line graph might show a steady increase in temperature throughout the test period.
3. Answers will vary. Students should describe how the solar heater malfunctioned or functioned.
4. Answers will vary. Designs that received a good deal of sunlight probably performed well. A slow, steady flow of water through the tubing could improve the performance of the design. Accept all reasonable suggestions for improving efficiency.

CHECK YOUR HYPOTHESIS

Answers will vary depending on students' hypotheses.

CONCLUDE AND APPLY

1. Answers will vary. Sample answer: Solar energy reaches Earth, strikes the first bottle and the tubing, flows with the water through the solar heater, and empties into the second bottle.
2. Answers will vary. Sample answer: The amount of sunlight, thickness of the insulation, and beginning temperature of the water affected the performance of the solar heater.
3. Answers will vary. Sample answer: Solar energy is nonpolluting and renewable, but it is dependent on receiving plenty of sunlight and is difficult to store.

26.2 ▪ Investigation
Assessing Wind Energy

OBJECTIVES

- Construct a tool to measure wind speed.
- Observe and record wind speeds at different locations.
- Determine if local wind speeds are high enough to generate electricity.
- Consider the advantages and disadvantages of wind energy.

PROCESS SKILLS

formulate models, communicate, observe, infer, interpret data

TIME ALLOTMENT

1 class period to make the protractor and take the first data; 20 minutes each day for 4 days to observe and record data; 1 class period to analyze results

MATERIALS

small plastic balls (30)
white paper (30 sheets)
tape (1 roll)
cardboard (5 large, flat pieces)
scissors (30 pairs)
marking pens (30)

heavy-duty sewing needles (30)
heavy thread (2 spools)
calculators (30)
safety goggles (30)

SAFETY PRECAUTIONS

- Caution students to be careful when punching holes with the needle. Tell them to be careful when handling sharp objects such as scissors.
- Instruct students to wear safety goggles during the lab procedure.

PREPARATION

- Students should work individually.
- Make a list of suitable sites before beginning the activity. This will encourage students to choose sites that are not sheltered by buildings or trees.
- Get several table-tennis balls or other small plastic balls from sporting goods stores or toy departments.

Alternative Materials

A ready-made protractor can be used instead of the handmade protractor.

PROCEDURE

- If wind energy is used in your area, arrange a field trip to a wind farm or to a house that relies on wind energy. Have students prepare questions beforehand to ask the wind-farm supervisor or the home owner. Students should focus on the pros and cons of using wind energy.
- If wind energy is not common in your area, show students photographs of wind farms. Discuss why wind farms require a large amount of land. Make sure that students understand that there are advantages and disadvantages associated with the use of all energy resources.

Troubleshooting

Students must hold the protractor steady and level to record accurate results. Have students work with partners so that one student holds the protractor while the other student records the angle.

DATA AND OBSERVATIONS

Students will record and measure wind speeds in their areas and compare their data to the minimum wind speed required to produce electricity.

ANALYZE

1. Answers will vary. If students chose open sites, average wind speeds among groups should be relatively constant, particularly if the groups took their measurements at the same time each day.
2. Answers will vary. Students should find that the greatest wind speeds were recorded in open, relatively flat areas.
3. Answers will vary. Students should note that winds do not blow steadily every day and that this negatively affects the reliability of wind as an energy resource.
4. Answers will vary. Check students' calculations of average wind speeds.

CONCLUDE AND APPLY

1. An increase in wind speed of around 2.6 km/h would double the output.
2. Wind turbines could be damaged by very strong winds.
3. Answers will vary. Sample answer: The average wind speed was 25 km/h, which is greater than 21 km/h, the minimum effective wind speed.

27.1 ▪ Design Your Own
Cleaning Up Oil Spills

OBJECTIVES

- Develop criteria to determine the effectiveness of different materials in cleaning up oil spills.
- Model a cleanup of an oil spill.
- Compare and contrast the effectiveness of different materials as cleaning agents for oil spills.

PROCESS SKILLS

formulate models, observe, communicate, separate and control variables, interpret data

TIME ALLOTMENT

1 class period

POSSIBLE MATERIALS

olive oil (2 large bottles)
shallow pans (10)
paper towels (1 large roll)
water
toothpicks (1 large box)
feathers (60)
string (1 large spool)
cotton balls (90)
cardboard (10 small pieces)

droppers (10)
liquid detergent
  (1 large bottle)
gravel (1 large bag)
sponges (10)
gloves (30 pairs)
aprons (30)
safety goggles (30)

DISPOSAL

Have garbage bags available for disposing of oily materials. Dilute oily water with liquid detergent before pouring the water down the drain. Consult your own regulations about proper disposal techniques.

PREPARATION

Students should work in groups of three.

Possible Hypothesis

Students may predict that cotton balls and paper towels will prove most effective in cleaning up the oil spill, or that the cardboard and string can effectively skim the oil off the water's surface.

Alternative Materials

Sand can be substituted for gravel, vegetable oil for olive oil, and wooden ice-cream sticks or pencils for toothpicks.

PLAN THE EXPERIMENT

Suggest that students develop a scale to rank the effectiveness of the cleaning materials.

Troubleshooting

Make sure that students test each material separately in order to accurately judge its effectiveness.

Possible Procedures

Spread the gravel along one short edge of the pan, then carefully pour water into the pan until it is two-thirds full. Test each material separately, to control variables. Use toothpicks, cardboard, and string to skim oil off the water's surface. The sponge, paper towels, cotton balls, and feathers can absorb the oil. The dropper can suction the oil from the water, and the liquid soap can break the oil down. **CAUTION:** *Oil on the floor can be hazardous, and may cause slips or falls. Wipe up any spills immediately.*

DATA AND OBSERVATIONS

Students should find that the cotton balls and paper towels are the most effective cleaning agents, particularly on the "rocky shore." A combination of cleaning methods is the most effective strategy, for example, using string to corral the oil, then the dropper to remove it.

ANALYZE

1. Answers will vary. The cotton balls and the paper towels are probably the most effective cleaning agents. The least effective cleaning materials are probably the toothpicks, cardboard, and string.

2. Answers will vary. Students may have developed a scale to rank the material or simply have observed the amount of oil removed from the water.

3. Answers will vary. Sample answer: The skimming materials, such as cardboard and string, and the dropper aren't as effective at cleaning oil from the rocky beach as the absorbing materials, such as the cotton balls and paper towels. These absorbing materials can reach into nooks and crannies. They are particularly effective when combined with the liquid detergent.

4. Answers will vary. Sample answer: Although the detergent does break down oil, it might also prove dangerous to wildlife. All the cleaning materials present disposal problems.

5. Answers will vary. Students should find that a combination of methods works best. Their explanations should be based on their recorded observations.

CHECK YOUR HYPOTHESIS

Answers will vary depending on students' hypotheses.

CONCLUDE AND APPLY

1. The feathers were thickly coated with oil. An actual oil spill would affect a bird's ability to stay warm, fly, swim, and find food.

2. Winds cause ocean waves. Large waves would likely hinder efforts to clean up an oil spill.

27.2 ▪ Investigation
Algal Blooms

OBJECTIVES
- Observe the growth of algae in two controlled experiments.
- Discover what makes algae thrive.
- Recognize that excessive growth of algae may be linked to human activities.

PROCESS SKILLS
observe, infer, communicate, separate and control variables, formulate models

TIME ALLOTMENT
1 class period to set up the experiment; 10 minutes each day for 10 days to observe the jars; 1 class period to analyze results

MATERIALS
distilled water (30 L)
liquid fertilizer (150 mL)
pond water (15 L)
1-L glass jars with lids (60)
100-mL graduated cylinders (15)
marking pens (15)
microscopes (3)
microscope slides (60)
coverslips (60)
droppers (15)
gloves (30 pairs)
aprons (30)
splash-resistant safety goggles (30)

SAFETY PRECAUTIONS
- If any glassware breaks, have students notify you instead of cleaning up the glass themselves.
- Label all jars.
- Make sure you have a Material Safety Data Sheet (MSDS) for fertilizer while doing this lab.

DISPOSAL
After the lab, pour the solutions down a drain and wash the glass jars.

PREPARATION
- Students should work in pairs.
- Get liquid fertilizer from a greenhouse, a hardware store, or the gardening section of a department store.

Alternative Materials

Aquarium water can be substituted for pond water. A hand lens can be used instead of a microscope.

PROCEDURE
Have students interview a specialist in water pollution. They could contact the local branch of the Environmental Protection Agency (EPA) or their municipal water department. Students should ask the specialist how he or she tests for eutrophication, which occurs when excessive fertilizer enters a body of water and triggers a population explosion of algae and plants, and how the situation can be remedied.

DATA AND OBSERVATIONS
The water in jar 2 should exhibit the greatest algal growth. Jar 3, which received no fertilizer and no sunlight, should exhibit the least growth.

ANALYZE
1. The fertilizer was the independent variable in both experiments. The jars without fertilizer were the controls. Sunlight was the distinguishing factor between experiments.
2. Answers will vary. Students should have observed a pronounced green color in jar 2, which is evidence of algal growth. The color should have changed very little in the other jars. Under a microscope or hand lens, students should easily have seen algae in the water from jar 2.
3. Jar 2 should have exhibited the greatest change in color, that is, the most algal growth. Jar 3 should have exhibited the least. Jar 2 showed the most change because it had fertilizer and ample sunlight. Jar 3 had neither fertilizer nor sunlight.
4. An initial population of algae was needed to model an algal bloom; the algae were in the pond water.
5. Algae appear to grow best when they have a steady source of food and exposure to sunlight.

CONCLUDE AND APPLY
1. Fish and other aquatic life need oxygen to survive. If the oxygen in a pond was depleted, the aquatic life would suffocate.
2. Answers will vary. Sample answer: Farmers could use less fertilizer, rotate crops, or leave fields fallow so that the soils are not depleted of nutrients. Accept all reasonable answers.
3. Answers will vary. Sample answer: Algae thrive in warm conditions, as in sunlight. So heated water might contribute to an algal bloom.

28.1 ▪ Investigation
Make Your Own Telescope

OBJECTIVES

- Measure the diameter and focal length of lenses.
- Find the ideal telescope length, given a pair of lenses whose focal lengths are known.
- Examine the magnification properties of various pairs of lenses.
- Construct a telescope.

PROCESS SKILLS

observe, interpret data, define operationally

TIME ALLOTMENT

1 or 2 class periods

MATERIALS

set of 3 lenses with long focal lengths
　(set A: A1 has the shortest focal length of the set;
　A3 has the longest; and A2 is in between) (10 sets)
set of 3 lenses with short focal lengths
　(set B: B1 has the shortest focal length of the set;
　B3 has the longest; and B2 is in between) (10 sets)
set of 3 lenses of identical focal length
　and different diameters (set C) (10 sets)
ring stands (10)
burette clamps (10)
metersticks (10)
lens holders (20)
screens (10)
screen holders (10)
nested cardboard tubes (20)
foam lens holders (20)
safety goggles (30)

SAFETY PRECAUTIONS

- Warn students never to look at the Sun through a telescope. Tell them to choose a distant object other than the Sun to project through their lenses. Remind students that wearing goggles can help reduce any glare.
- Caution students about handling glass lenses. Tell them that any sharp edges may cut their skin.

PREPARATION

Students should work in groups of three.

PROCEDURE

Strictly speaking, the focal length of a lens is the image distance for an object that is infinitely far away so that rays of light from the object are parallel. However, students are instructed to find the image distance of an object that is merely distant and to regard that as the focal length. The resulting error should not interfere with the usefulness of the lab.

DATA AND OBSERVATIONS

Table 1

Lens ID	A1	A2	A3	B1	B2	B3	C1	C2	C3
Diameter (cm)	3.3	3.3	3.3	1.8	1.8	1.8	2.0	3.2	4.3
Focal length (cm)	10	20	30	2.5	5.0	10	40	40	40

In each case, the telescope length should be close to the sum of the focal lengths, and the magnification should be close to the ratio of the focal lengths (objective/eyepiece).

ANALYZE

Note: References to lens IDs in both of the following sections should be based on the figures used in Table 1 above. Answers will vary depending on the lenses used, but all answers should be derived from Table 1 data.

1. The length of the telescope is equal to the sum of the focal lengths.
2. The magnification of the telescope is equal to the ratio of the focal lengths.
3. C2/B2 would have a magnification of 8.
4. more than A3/B2, which has a magnification of 6

CONCLUDE AND APPLY

1. A larger objective lens gives a clearer, brighter image.
2. C3 objective and B1 eyepiece would make the best telescope because that arrangement gives the greatest magnification and has the largest objective lens.

28.2 ▪ Design Your Own
Observing the Moon

OBJECTIVES

- Measure the transit time of the Moon for 1 week.
- Predict the times of the next full moon and quarter moon.
- Determine the exact length of the month.

PROCESS SKILLS

observe, recognize and use spatial relationships, predict, use numbers, interpret data

TIME ALLOTMENT

1 class period for preparing the observing apparatus; about half an hour a day for 4–5 consecutive days; and 1 class period to analyze the data

POSSIBLE MATERIALS

accurate watch
plumb lines (2 or 3 m) with weights (2)
stepladders (2)
simple ladder
rope
map compass with crosshairs
calculators (30)
safety goggles (30)

SAFETY PRECAUTIONS

- Warn students never to look at the Sun through a telescope or binoculars. Remind students that wearing goggles can help reduce any glare.
- Caution students against climbing on ladders. Make sure the horizontal ladder is secured to the step ladders with rope in order to prevent the ladder from falling over or falling to the ground.

PREPARATION

Students should work together as a class.

Possible Hypothesis

The correct hypothesis is that the Moon is orbiting Earth counterclockwise when viewed from above the north pole. Therefore, the Moon will transit later each day.

Alternative Materials

Other plumb line supports might be playground equipment or other school apparatuses.

PLAN THE EXPERIMENT

- Have students draw the Sun and Earth, indicating the daytime and nighttime sides of Earth, an arrow to show the counterclockwise spin of Earth, and a person looking east at dawn.
- Transits of the Sun always occur near midday; those of the Moon occur at any time of day. The best time of

the month for this investigation would be near first quarter, when the Moon transits in the early evening. Note also that the Moon transits about 50 minutes later each day.

Possible Procedures

Set up two stepladders with a ladder secured horizontally across the top with rope. Suspend plumb lines from the ladder, as far apart as possible. Line the plumb lines up with the southern horizon to indicate the local meridian. Move the lines closer together if necessary so that the observer can sight the meridian at the expected elevation for transit of the Moon. Measure the transit time of the leading and trailing edges of the Sun and the Moon on 4–5 consecutive days. Average the two measurements to determine the exact transit time.

DATA AND OBSERVATIONS

Date	Transit Time of Sun Leading Edge	Transit Time of Sun Trailing Edge	Transit Time for Sun	Transit Time of Moon Leading Edge	Transit Time of Moon Trailing Edge	Transit Time for Moon
Monday	12:18:24	12:20:20	12:19:22	17:52:36	17:54:41	17:53:39
Tuesday			12:19:16			18:41:36
Wednesday						19:29:40

ANALYZE

1. later, by 48–52 minutes
2. The Moon orbits counterclockwise.
3.

Date	Time of Sun Transit (s)	Time of Moon Transit (s)	Phase (= difference between previous two columns) (s)	Phase (degrees)
Monday	44 362	64 419	20 057	83.57
Tuesday	44 356	67 296	22 940	95.58
Wednesday	44 370	70 180	25 810	107.54

4. drawing of circle that has points corresponding to the data for phase in degrees

CHECK YOUR HYPOTHESIS

Answers will vary depending on students' hypotheses.

CONCLUDE AND APPLY

1. Answers will vary. Sample answer: 70 180 s + (2 × 86 400 s) − 64 419 s = 178 562 s (if there are 2 intervening days)
2. 107.54° − 83.57° = 23.97°
3. 178 562 s ÷ 23.97° = 7449 s per degree
4. 2 681 640 s; 31 days, 0 hours, 54 minutes, 0 seconds
5. Answers will vary. Predictions should typically be good to within a day.

29.1 ▪ Investigation
Your Age and Weight on Other Planets

OBJECTIVES
- Calculate your age on the other eight planets of the solar system.
- Calculate your weight on each planet.

PROCESS SKILLS
use numbers, interpret data

TIME ALLOTMENT
1 class period

MATERIALS
calculators (30)
scale

PREPARATION
- Students should work individually.
- Students must understand the distinction between mass and weight. The mass of a body is a fixed property, whereas the weight of a body is the gravitational force experienced by that body.

PROCEDURE
- Lead the class through the algebraic arguments to help students understand them.
- Extend the lab by asking about moving about on the surface of various planets. Recall how easily astronauts moved about on the Moon.

Troubleshooting
The following formulas will help students convert measurements into different units as required. Explain to students how the unit lb is based on mass and Earth's gravitational pull on that mass.

Pound (lb) /Kilogram (kg)
1 lb = .455 kg
1 kg = 2.2 lb

DATA AND OBSERVATIONS
Table 2

Planet	Your Age in Planet Years	Planet Mass/ Earth Mass (kg)	Earth Radius/ Planet Radius (km)	Square of Radius Ratio (km)	Your Weight on Planet (N)
Mercury	4.154	0.0553	2.6151	6.8386	168 N
Venus	1.627	0.8150	1.0542	1.1114	403 N
Earth	1.000	1.0000	1.0000	1.0000	445 N
Mars	0.532	0.1074	1.8781	3.5274	169 N
Jupiter	0.084	317.83	0.0892	0.0080	1125 N
Saturn	0.034	95.162	0.1059	0.0112	472 N
Uranus	0.012	14.536	0.2496	0.0623	403 N
Neptune	0.006	17.147	0.2576	0.0664	503 N
Pluto	0.004	0.0021	5.3389	28.504	26.5 N

ANALYZE
1. Oldest in Mercury years, youngest in Pluto years; this is not surprising because the period of Mercury is shortest, being closest to the Sun.
2. Jupiter

CONCLUDE AND APPLY
1. Sample answer: I can lift about 445 Newtons, which is approximately 45.5 kg or 100 pounds.
   445 N × (445 N/1125 N) = 176 N

   A 175-N backpack (approximately 18 kg or 40 lb) is the heaviest I could lift.
2. Sample answer: I could lift a car on Pluto.
   445 N × (445 N/26.5 N) = 7473 N

29.2 ▪ Design Your Own
Relating Gravitational Force and Orbits

OBJECTIVES

- Construct a simple model of planetary motion.
- Check the model to see how well it follows Kepler's third law.
- Use the model to find out if orbital period depends on the mass of the central body.
- Estimate the mass of Earth.

PROCESS SKILLS

predict, form hypotheses, separate and control variables, formulate models

TIME ALLOTMENT

2 class periods

POSSIBLE MATERIALS

glass tubes, 15 cm, fire
  polished and taped (10)
scissors (10)
duct tape (3 rolls)
fishing line
plastic-foam balls, 10 cm (10)
paper clips (1 package)

metal washers (400)
metric rulers (10)
stopwatches (10)
marking pens (10)
calculators (10)
safety goggles (30)

PREPARATION

Students should work in groups of three.

Possible Hypothesis

If the model is simulating the solar system well and following Kepler's third law, then the quantity P^2/a^3 should be constant.

PLAN THE EXPERIMENT

You may need to guide students to see the inverse relationship of P^2 to weight.

Troubleshooting

It takes considerable skill to swing the ball in an orbit of fixed radius. Students may have to practice this for a while before recording data.

Possible Procedures

Cut 60 cm of fishing line, and thread it through the tube. Tape one end of the line securely to the ball. Make a small paper clip into a hook, and secure it to the other end of the fishing line. Thread 20 washers onto a second paper clip, and suspend this weight from the hook. Mark the fishing line so that, when the mark is at the bottom of the glass rod, the

distance from the top of the glass rod to the center of the ball is 40 cm. Swing the ball at a steady radius of 40 cm. Simultaneously start the stopwatch and start counting complete revolutions. After about a minute, stop the stopwatch and record the number of swings and the time. Repeat for radii of 35 cm, 30 cm, and so on. To vary the central mass, change the number of washers on the hook instead of changing the radius for each run. Start with 40 washers, then use 35, then 30, and so on.

DATA AND OBSERVATIONS

The following tables give sample values.

Radius (cm)	Swings	Total Time (s)	Period (s)	P^2/a^3 (× 10^{-5})
40	41	61.9	1.51	3.52
35	49	60.3	1.23	3.51
30	62	60.1	0.97	3.53
25	⋮	⋮	0.74	3.47
20	⋮	⋮	0.53	3.51

Weights	Swings	Total Time (s)	Period (s)	P^2
40	87	60.0	0.69	0.476
35	83	60.6	0.73	0.533
30	76	60.0	0.79	0.624
25	69	60.0	0.87	0.757
20	62	60.1	0.97	0.941
15	54	60.5	1.12	1.254

ANALYZE

1. The period increases with increasing radius.
2. The period decreases with increasing weight.
3. Answers may vary, but the results should reflect Kepler's third law.

CHECK YOUR HYPOTHESIS

Answers will vary depending on students' hypotheses.

CONCLUDE AND APPLY

1. Answers may vary, but should address how constant P^2/a^3 is.
2. P^2 halved as weights doubled.
3. The year would be 0.707 (or $1/\sqrt{2}$) of its present value.

30.1 ▪ Investigation
Diameter and Rotation of the Sun

OBJECTIVES
- Measure the diameter of the Sun.
- Measure the rotational rate of the Sun.
- Estimate the size of sunspots.

PROCESS SKILLS
observe, infer, use numbers, interpret data

TIME ALLOTMENT
15 minutes per class period on 4 or 5 consecutive days; 1 class period to analyze data and answer questions

MATERIALS
metersticks (10)
index cards (20)
scissors (10 pairs)
tape (10 rolls)
aluminum foil, 4 cm squares (10)
straight pins (10)
single-edge razor blades (10)
unlined white paper (10 sheets)
clipboards (10)
small telescopes (10)
small telescopes stands (10)
safety goggles (30)

SAFETY PRECAUTIONS
- Permanent eye damage or blindness may result from looking at the Sun through an optical instrument. Make sure that students are aware of this and that they wear goggles at all times during the lab procedure.
- Instruct students to use caution when handling pins, scissors, or razor blades. Warn them that such objects may puncture or cut their skin.

PREPARATION
- Students should work in groups of three.
- Pick a week that is forecast to have sunny weather.
- Drawings should be made at the same time of day, to within 5 minutes or so. Otherwise the Sun's orientation will have changed.

Alternative Materials
Binoculars could be used instead of a telescope.

PROCEDURE
- Point out that the movement of the sunspots holds the key to estimating the rotation of the Sun.
- Students may note that clouds appear to drift across the image in a direction opposite that in which they drift across the Sun. The Sun's image is inverted by the telescope.
- To use their sunspot drawings, students should plot the daily positions of the sunspot on the diameter of a semicircle, project points onto the semicircle to indicate position on the Sun, and measure the angle.

DATA AND OBSERVATIONS

Diameter of the Sun's Image (cm)	Distance Between Pinhole and Screen (cm)
0.8	86.3

If the sunspot drawings are made at the same time of day, the Sun will have roughly the same orientation in each drawing.

ANALYZE
1. Diameter of Sun = (0.8 cm × [1.5 × 10^8] km)/ (86.3 cm) = 1 390 000 km. This is close to the accepted figure, 1 392 000 km.
2. The patterns of sunspots should show that the Sun is similarly oriented in each drawing. If a drawing is made a little later in the day because of clouds, it should be apparent that the Sun's image for this drawing has rotated.
3. Answers will vary, but the ratio should be less than 1:100.
4. The largest sunspots are typically 15 000 km across. The diameter of Earth is 12 756 km.

CONCLUDE AND APPLY
1. Sunspots would move in straight lines if viewed from above the equator and in circles if viewed from above the poles.
2. The sunspots should move in straight lines parallel to the equator. The viewpoint is above the Sun's equator.
3. Answers will vary. The Sun rotates in about 28 days at its equator.

30.2 ▪ Mapping
Constellations and the Seasons

OBJECTIVES

- Identify several stars and constellations in the night sky.
- Understand how stars move during a night.
- Understand why different constellations are visible during a year.
- Measure the latitude of your city or town.

PROCESS SKILLS

observe, recognize and use spatial relationships, interpret data

TIME ALLOTMENT

1 class period to prepare; three or four 15-minute sessions outdoors on a clear evening, spaced 2 hours apart; 1 class period the next day

MATERIALS

protractors with hole at origin (10)
stiff, thin wire (10 pieces, each measuring 10 cm)
small weights (10)
tracing paper (10 sheets)
binoculars (10 pairs)
safety goggles (30)

SAFETY PRECAUTIONS

- Instruct students to use caution when handling wire. Warn them that wire can be sharp and may puncture or cut their skin.
- Have students wear safety goggles during the lab procedure.

PREPARATION

- Students should work in groups of three.
- This investigation is designed for the northern hemisphere during autumn or winter.

PROCEDURE

In class, have students prepare the protractor apparatus and read the lab. In the early evening, assemble the entire class to make the first observation of Polaris and the Pointers. The subsequent observations of Polaris and the Pointers can be performed as homework.

DATA AND OBSERVATIONS

Polaris remains at the same altitude and above the same feature on the horizon. It does not move at all. The position angle of the Pointers advances about 30° counterclockwise every 2 hours. The initial orientation of the Pointers will depend on the time of year and the observation time.

Table 2

Constellation	Autumn	Winter	Spring	Summer
Bootes	not visible	not visible	overhead	west
Lyra	northwest	not visible	east	west
Orion	east	south	not visible	not visible
Pegasus	south	northwest	not visible	east

ANALYZE

1. Polaris does not move.
2. The Big Dipper and all stars rotate counterclockwise around Polaris.
3. 4 minutes/degree
4. 24 hours/360°; the stars' apparent motion is due to Earth's spinning once in 24 hours.
5. Seasonally, Gemini moves east to west.

CONCLUDE AND APPLY

1. Latitude on Earth = altitude of Polaris
2. Gemini is below the horizon at night in summer because the Sun is in Gemini.
3. The summer triangle rises in spring, moves east to west, and sets in autumn.
4. 18 hours later, at noon

31.1 ▪ Investigation
Modeling Spiral Galaxies

OBJECTIVES
- Model spiral galaxies.
- Compare and contrast scientific theories about the formation of spiral arms.
- Describe the characteristics of spiral galaxies.

PROCESS SKILLS
model, communicate, observe, infer, compare and contrast

TIME ALLOTMENT
1 class period

MATERIALS
water (3 L)
oil (1 bottle)
teaspoons (15)
nondairy powdered creamer (1 container)
250-mL beakers (15)
small rocks (15)
bucket (15)
aprons (30)
safety goggles (30)

SAFETY PRECAUTIONS
Tell students to notify you if a spill or breakage occurs. Students should always wear safety goggles in the lab.

PREPARATION
- Students should work in pairs.
- Nondairy powdered creamer and vegetable oil can be found in most grocery stores.

Alternative Materials

Hot coffee and cream can be substituted for the water, oil, and creamer. Caution students to take care if hot coffee is used.

PROCEDURE
Teaching Strategies
- Have students work in pairs to conduct the experiment.
- Show students digitally enhanced images of barred spiral, normal spiral, irregular, and elliptical galaxies. Have students compare and contrast the different shapes and colors of the images. Ask students if they think the colors are true colors or colorization. Most digitally enhanced images will be colorized.

Troubleshooting

The experiment can be conducted with water and oil alone; however, the spiral arms formed by the oil may be difficult to see. The powdered creamer essentially makes the oily spiral arms more visible. Also, the creamer will clump slightly, and thus model interstellar matter. Make sure students add the creamer after the oil, or the creamer will dissolve in the water.

DATA AND OBSERVATIONS
When stirring the mixture, students will observe the formation of spiral arms. When stirring stops, the spiral arms break apart. In a similar manner, the spiral arms of some galaxies are maintained by disturbances in space. Following the disturbance, broken patterns may appear in the arms. Students will also observe the formation of waves when the rock is dropped into the bucket of water. The waves model the shockwaves formed by a supernovae.

ANALYZE
1. The creamer formed spiral arms in the mixture. The arms broke apart when stirring ceased.
2. Waves formed on the surface of the water. The rock modeled a supernovae.
3. Answers will vary. Students may note that, after stirring the mixture, they observed a spiral shape caused by some disturbance. This observation may be compared to a spiral galaxy. Students' observations may differ from a spiral galaxy in a number of ways, including scale, length of disturbance, and the nature of the disturbance itself.
4. The nuclear bulge is located in the center of the galactic disk. The disk and bulge are surrounded by a spherical region called the halo. Globular clusters are located in the halo.

CONCLUDE AND APPLY
1. Observations should support the theory that spiral arms are continually changing features that form and re-form in response to disturbances in space.
2. The shockwaves would sweep up the dust and gas.
3. Most young stars would be located in the spiral arms of the disk. Most old stars would be located in the nuclear bulge or in globular clusters in the halo.
4. Answers will vary. Students may say that they could repeat the experiment and stir the mixture rapidly with no organized stirring pattern to model an irregular galaxy.

31.2 ▪ Mapping
Three-Dimensional Map of the Local Group

OBJECTIVES
- Map the Local Group from three viewpoints.
- Construct a scale model showing the locations of the galaxies of the Local Group.

PROCESS SKILLS
classify, recognize and use spatial relationships, measure, use numbers, formulate models

TIME ALLOTMENT
2–3 class periods

MATERIALS
cardboard, 30 cm × 20 cm (10 pieces)
fishing line or thread (40 meters)
metric rulers (10)
scissors (10)
heavy needles (10)
modeling clay (10 containers)

SAFETY PRECAUTIONS
Instruct students to be careful when using sharp objects to make holes in the cardboard. Warn them that pointed objects can puncture skin.

PREPARATION
- Students should work in groups of three.
- Each group needs enough modeling clay for 31 little galaxies.
- M31 is just about visible to the naked eye from a dark site.

PROCEDURE
Check each group's work after step 2 of the procedure.

DATA AND OBSERVATIONS
See the tables below.

ANALYZE
1. 9 million ly × 7 million ly × 6 million ly
2. Volume = 3.78×10^{20} ly^3.
3. There are 11 galaxies within 1 million ly of the Milky Way and 9 within 1 million ly of M31.

CONCLUDE AND APPLY
1. 5×10^{15} ly$^3 \div 3.78 \times 10^{20}$ ly$^3 \times 100\% = 0.0013\%$. Galaxies fill about one-thousandth of a percent of space.
2. 15×10^9 ly $\div 2 \times 10^6$ ly $= 7500$.
3. 2×10^6 ly $\times 10^{13}$ km/light year $\div 100$ km/s $= 2 \times 10^{17}$ s; 2×10^{17} s $\div (60 \times 60 \times 24 \times 365)$s/year $= 6$ billion years.

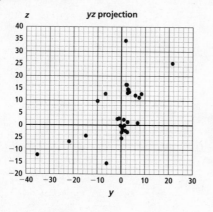

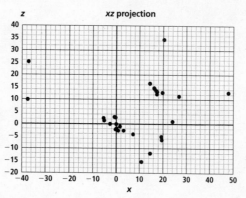

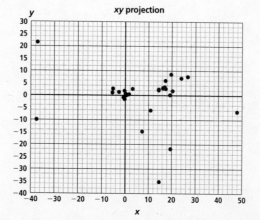

Credits

ART CREDITS

Glencoe: **x, xi, xii**; Navta Associates: **1, 2, 33, 45, 51, 63, 64, 67, 75, 83, 190, 191, 193, 206, 247, 266, 268, 270, 272, 283, 291, 313**; MacArt Design: **12, 23, 38, 39, 51, 53, 54, 57, 58, 60, 61, 65, 66, 67, 73, 97, 105, 109, 114, 122, 125, 129, 133, 158, 165, 181, 182, 183, 186, 188, 197, 206, 218, 221, 233, 235, 238, 282, 292, 295, 296, 297, 299, 302**; MapQuest.com: **16**; Mapping Specialists: **146, 154, 155, 288, 289**

PHOTO CREDITS

16 (c)United States Geological Survey; 69 United States Geological Survey; **241** (tl)TSADO/ESO/Tom Stack & Associates, (tr)Jean-Charles Cuillandre/Canada-France-Hawaii Telescope/Science Photo Library